1968

F

TOPICS FROM THE
THEORY OF NUMBERS

A mathematics text edited by
Carl B. Allendoerfen

TOPICS FROM THE THEORY OF NUMBERS

EMIL GROSSWALD

University of Pennsylvania

The Macmillan Company, New York

Collier - Macmillan Limited, London

First Printing

Library of Congress catalog card number: 66-19711

THE MACMILLAN COMPANY, NEW YORK
COLLIER-MACMILLAN CANADA, LTD., TORONTO, ONTARIO

PRINTED IN THE UNITED STATES OF AMERICA

To the memory of my father
Paul Grosswald

PREFACE

In 1962 I gave a course in number theory for undergraduates at the University of Pennsylvania. To my pleasant surprise, the group of students turned out to be exceptionally eager and well prepared and contained not only undergraduates, but also a sprinkling of graduate students. This led me to supplement the excellent text of Niven and Zuckerman with some notes of my own. These included, among other topics, a self-contained proof of the Prime Number Theorem. In the obvious references during the lectures to the discoverers of the first proofs of this theorem, I spoke of the then almost centenary Hadamard and of de la Vallée-Poussin as illustrious contemporary mathematicians; I may even have quoted a joke (first heard from P. Erdös) to the effect that proving such an important result seems to confer immortality. Between the time of those lectures and completion of the manuscript, both Hadamard and de la Vallée-Poussin have joined the ranks of the immortal mathematicians of the past. May this book help to keep alive the memory of their imperishable work!

Those first notes were rewritten and expanded as I had further opportunities to lecture on number theory; yet it was only with considerable doubt that I gave in to the insistence of some of my students and colleagues (and editors) and decided to "polish" those notes in order to write the present volume. Indeed, there existed in English several excellent books on number theory on a comparable level, and I was not convinced that there was a need for still another one, or that I could improve on those previous presentations. However, with the "finished product" in front of me, it seems that there is rather little overlap with any other text I know of, except, of course, for the most fundamental topics which are common to all books in this field. Also the style seems to be different from that of most other books because of both the emphasis given to the historical point of view and the inclusion of references to a large amount of source material (books and papers) quoted in the text and the bibliographies.

The book consists of three parts and two appendices. *Part I* is an introductory, mainly historic part, consisting of two chapters (Introduction, Notations). Most of my students have reacted extremely well to the classroom presentation of this part, which I would never omit. However, if the students (or their instructor) are not interested in the historic development, this part can be skipped without inconvenience, except, perhaps, for a few pages in which symbols and notations are explained. In case the class *is* interested in the historic aspect but has little time available, Part I may be given as a supplementary reading assignment, and the instructor may begin with Part II.

Part II consists of four chapters on elementary number theory (Divisibility, Congruences, Quadratic Residues, Arithmetic Functions). While much of this material is standard fare, some of it is developed well beyond minimal requirements (for instance, intervals between consecutive primes, the number of solutions of higher congruences modulo prime powers, perfect numbers, Ramanujan function, and so on).

Part III consists of three divisions, which may be studied independently of each other and in any desired order. In a standard one-semester course on the junior–senior level, I was never able to cover more than three of the six chapters—that is, at most two of the three divisions. These are:

(A) The Riemann Zeta Function (Chapter 7) and the Prime Number Theorem (Chapter 8);

(B) Diophantine Equations and Fermat's Conjecture (Chapter 9), Ideal Theory (Chapter 10), and the Proof of Fermat's Conjecture for Regular Primes (Chapter 11);

(C) The Theory of Partitions (Chapter 12).

In view of the title of this book it does not seem to me that any special explanation is due concerning the topics covered or any apology necessary for those topics which have been omitted. In order to make this book as self-contained as possible (consistent with a reasonable size), two appendices have been added, one on topics from advanced calculus and general analysis, the other on topics from algebra. Needless to say, these appendices are here mainly for reference purposes and are not meant to replace regular courses in their respective fields.

Throughout the book more difficult sections and problems are marked with a star (*) and a few particularly difficult ones by a double star (**). Within each chapter, the definitions, lemmas, theorems, and remarks have separate consecutive numbers; the same is true for the numbered formulas. The corollaries carry the number of the theorem from which they are derived, followed by a number of their own. Thus, the second corollary of Theorem 6 is called Corollary 6.2. References to definitions, lemmas, theorems, corollaries, or remarks of the same chapter carry only the corresponding number; however, if reference is made to one of them in another chapter, then the number of the statement is preceded by that of the chapter where it is stated. If a theorem, corollary, or definition contains several statements, these are numbered (1), (2), and so on. If one wants to refer to statement (3) of the first corollary to Theorem 1 of Chapter 12, one speaks of Corollary 1.1(3) in Chapter 12 and of Corollary 12.1.1.(3) in any other chapter. Sections within a chapter are numbered in a similar way. Section 3 of Chapter 7 and Section 5 of Chapter 9 contain miscellaneous definitions and theorems which are listed consecutively. Statement 12 of Section 3 in Chapter 7 will be quoted as 3.12 in Chapter 7 and as 7.3.12 in any other chapter, with similar notations for the statements of Section 5 in Chapter 9.

Each chapter in Parts II and III is followed by a number of problems. Some of these are simple exercises, others (occasionally marked by a star) are actually theorems of independent interest that did not fit into the main text; still others will require the student to supply complete proofs for statements accepted in the text as " obvious " or which have been dismissed there because they follow by "trivial arguments." I sincerely hope that the students will agree with me and prove the "obviousness" to themselves by dashing off the needed arguments in no time at all! Should I be wrong, then I shall be glad to hear from irate students and instructors, in order to supply the not-so-obvious arguments in some future edition. But, on this subject of textbook problems, as well as on another, related one, I cannot express my own feelings better than by quoting from Ahlfors' *Complex Analysis*, "... the author has not had the inclination to relieve the teacher from making up more and better exercises ..." and, in particular, "... it is to be hoped that no teacher will follow this book page by page, for nothing could be more deadening." This, of course, holds true even for the author of a text and I myself could never use my own book without considerable (and each time different) modifications, suggested by the abilities and interests of the students.

Finally, a word of acknowledgment is in order. My interest in number theory was awakened by my revered teacher, Professor H. Rademacher. It is through him that I became aware of the classical works of Fermat, Euler, Gauss, Riemann, Hadamard, and de la Vallée-Poussin. Furthermore, within my generation, no student of number theory could fail to be influenced by the works of Landau, Hardy, Littlewood, Ramanujan, Hilbert, and Hecke. Also, some of the excellent textbooks by contemporary mathematicians such as those by Niven and Zuckerman, LeVeque, Vinogradov, or Harvey Cohn may have influenced my presentation of some of the topics. I owe, however, a special debt of gratitude to Professors M. Kac, P. Bateman, and R. Dixon.

Without the strong encouragement of Professor Kac I might never have written this book. Professor Bateman read part of the manuscript and Professor Dixon, after an incredibly careful reading, made numerous and most pertinent suggestions for corrections of errors, improvements in presentation, and even for changes in the formulation of some problems. Also my students, Dr. D. Goldsmith and Dr. R. Alter, were helpful in the early stages of the preparation of the manuscript, and Mrs. S. Goldsmith did the excellent typing of its final version. I also am grateful to the University of Pennsylvania, which gave me the opportunity both to study and to teach the theory of numbers. The manuscript was completed during the first few weeks of a sabbatical leave, with support from the University of Pennsylvania and the National Science Foundation (Under Grant GP 3137).

E. G.

Paris

CONTENTS

xi

Contents

TOPICS FROM THE
THEORY OF NUMBERS

PART ONE

Introduction,
Historical Background
and Notations

CHAPTER 1

Introduction and
Historical Background

1. NUMBER THEORY THE QUEEN OF MATHEMATICS

Numbers have exerted a fascination on the human mind since the beginnings of recorded history. Among the treasures of the Egyptian antiquity we find the famous Rhind papyrus [6], that tells us about the mathematics practiced in Egypt almost 2000 years B.C. Still older cuneiform tablets (see [5]) show us that arithmetic, at least, was already quite sophisticated in Mesopotamia at the end of the third millenium B.C.

Of all the branches of mathematics the one that seems to appeal most to our esthetic feelings is number theory, considered by many (by Euler (1707–1783), for instance) as the queen of mathematics. Why is that so? Some people believe that this strong esthetic appeal is due to the very limited practical usefulness of number theory. However, there might be a better reason. In hardly any other branch of mathematics is it possible to ask really significant, non-trivial questions, without preceding them by an annoyingly long list of definitions. In number theory, on the other hand, one can ask many questions in such simple terms, that the famous " man in the street " can immediately understand—but generally not answer them! In fact, the answers to some of these " simple to ask " questions are so difficult, that nobody has yet found them. Other questions, of course, have been answered already by the ingenious mathematicians of antiquity, or of medieval and modern times. In most cases (excepting, of course, the trivial questions) the answers *can not* be formulated quite so easily as the questions themselves. In some other cases it is utterly impossible to convince the "man in the street" of the correctness of a certain answer, laboriously arrived at, and which does not strike one as plausible at first sight. Indeed, it might be necessary first to teach him a considerable amount of mathematics and then to present him with a formal proof of the answer.

2. A PROBLEM

In order to illustrate these situations, consider, for instance, the following problem: A man has a debt of \$10. He wants to repay it in bills of \$1, \$5, or \$10. In how many ways can he pay his debt? Here the answer is clear. He may pay by

- (i)   one \$10 bill;
- (ii)   two \$5 bills;
- (iii)   one \$5 bill and five \$1 bills;
- (iv)   ten \$1 bills.

In other words, there are four solutions to this problem. If we denote by x, y, and z the number of \$10, \$5, and \$1, bills, respectively, used in the payment, then our problem may be formulated as follows: find the solution of the equation

$$10x + 5y + z = 10 \tag{1}$$

in non-negative integers x, y, and z.

Let us observe first, that here the situation is different from that usually encountered in elementary algebra. Indeed, we are supposed to determine *three* quantities x, y, z and dispose of only *one* equation. Clearly, without additional conditions, the problem is not very interesting, as one may choose arbitrary values for two of the quantities, say, x and y, and then solve (1) for z, obtaining $z = 10 - 10x - 5y$. Here, however, we are *not* free to select *arbitrary* values for x and y, but must choose non-negative integers. (We cannot use a negative number of bills to pay a debt, nor can we tear up a bill and use part of it.) It is this added restriction that makes the problem more difficult—and at the same time more interesting and meaningful. Such equations, that have to be solved in integers, sometimes with added side conditions (such as here that x, y, $z \geq 0$), were known already in antiquity and are called Diophantine equations, after Diophantus of Alexandria (who lived in the third or fourth century A.D.). So far, presumably, every person of normal intelligence, will have understood both the problem and its solution. Let us now consider briefly the formal solution of (1). From $y \geq 0$, $z \geq 0$ it follows that $10 = 10x + 5y + z \geq 10x$. Hence, $x \leq 1$; as we also have $x \geq 0$, there are, clearly, only two possibilities:

(i) either $x = 1$, and (1) becomes $5y + z = 0$, so that (remembering $y \geq 0, z \geq 0$) $y = z = 0$; or else

(ii) $x = 0$ and (1) becomes $5y + z = 10$.

If $y = 0$, then $z = 10$; if $y = 1$, then $z = 5$; if $y = 2$, then $z = 0$; finally, if $y > 2$, then $z < 0$, contrary to our condition $z \geq 0$. These are precisely the answers already obtained informally. It seems likely that whoever understood the question in the first place, will have no trouble understanding also the four possible solutions

(i) $x = 1, y = 0, z = 0$;

(ii) $x = 0, y = 0, z = 10$;

(iii) $x = 0, y = 1, z = 5$;

(iv) $x = 0, y = 2, z = 0$,

even if the formal proof given is not clear to him in every detail. Let us now, however, consider once more equation (1), ignoring the original problem and, while still requiring that x, y, z be integers, drop the condition of non-negativity.

Let us assume that x_0, y_0, z_0 are some integral values that satisfy (1) (e.g., 0, 2, 0) and consider the expressions

$$x = x_0 + a_1 t + b_1 u,$$
$$y = y_0 + a_2 t + b_2 u,$$
$$z = z_0 + a_3 t + b_3 u.$$

Substituting these in (1), we obtain

$$10x_0 + 5y_0 + z_0 + (10a_1 + 5a_2 + a_3)t + (10b_1 + 5b_2 + b_3)u = 10,$$

or, because $10x_0 + 5y_0 + z_0 = 10$,

$$(10a_1 + 5a_2 + a_3)t + (10b_1 + 5b_2 + b_3)u = 0.$$

This equality will be satisfied for all values of t and u, provided that we select for (a_1, a_2, a_3) and for (b_1, b_2, b_3) sets of solutions (not necessarily the same) of the equation

$$10x + 5y + z = 0, \tag{1'}$$

obtained from (1) by dropping the "second member." Equation (1') is usually referred to as "the homogeneous equation corresponding to (1)." We may choose, for instance, $a_1 = 0$, $a_2 = 1$, $a_3 = -5$ and $b_1 = -1$, $b_2 = 1$, $b_3 = 5$; then, with above values $x_0 = 0$, $y_0 = 2$, $z_0 = 0$, we obtain

$$x = -u,$$
$$y = 2 + t + u, \tag{2}$$
$$z = -5t + 5u.$$

From the way in which the expressions (2) have been obtained, it is clear that if we substitute for u and t any integer, we obtain an integer valued solution of (1). Actually, it may be shown that, at proper choice of a_1, a_2, a_3 and of b_1, b_2, b_3, we obtain in this way *all* integral valued solutions of (1); here, however, we shall only verify that if we now insist that x, y, z be non-negative, we obtain once more the well-known solutions of the original problem. First, $x \geq 0$ requires that $u \leq 0$. Next, $y \geq 0$ requires that $t + u \geq -2$, and $z \geq 0$ requires that $-t + u \geq 0$. Adding the last two shows that $2u \geq -2$ or $u \geq -1$. Hence, in view of $u \leq 0$, we only may have $u = -1$ or $u = 0$. In the first case, $x = 1$, $y = 1 + t$, $z = -5t - 5$. From $0 \leq y = 1 + t$ and $0 \leq z = -5t - 5$ we obtain that $0 \leq 1 + t \leq 0$, so that $t = -1$ and $y = z = 0$. If $u = 0$, then $x = 0$ and $y = 2 + t \geq 0$, $z = -5t \geq 0$. The last two inequalities require $-2 \leq t \leq 0$, so that $t = -2$, -1, or 0, leading to the solutions $x = 0$, $y = 0$, $z = 10$; $x = 0$, $y = 1$, $z = 5$; and $x = 0$, $y = 2$, $z = 0$, respectively. Adjoining to these three solutions corresponding to $u = 0$ also the single solution obtained with $u = -1$, we have indeed the four already known, non-negative, integral valued solutions of (1). It would not be too surprising, if the meaning of (2) as general solution of (1) could not be grasped without some effort by every person who understands perfectly the *problem* of solving equation (1) in integers.

3. SOMETHING ABOUT THE CONTENTS OF THIS BOOK

Often the simple sounding problems asked within the context of number theory turned out to be too difficult even for the most powerful mathematicians who attacked them. But their efforts were not spent in vain. As a matter of fact, many flourishing branches of mathematics owe their very existence or their development to unsuccessful attempts to solve problems in number theory. In what follows, we shall mention a few instances and describe a few number theoretic problems, some solved, some still open, all of which have greatly stimulated the development of mathematics as a whole. Incidentally, this description should prove more helpful in telling what number theory is than a formal definition of the term, which will not be given here. Next, we shall try to acquire some of the technical tools used in the attack on these problems and indicate in detail the solutions of some of them. For many other problems, however, the techniques needed are of a highly specialized nature and we shall have to forego their detailed discussion in the present book. This is particularly true of problems requiring a thorough acquaintance with the theory of functions of a complex variable, or of more algebra than is customarily presented at undergraduate level. In fact, this book attempts to be reasonably self-contained and while some acquaintance with functions of a complex variable is desirable (especially for Chapters 7 and 8) no more previous knowledge is actually required than can be expected after having attended good undergraduate courses in advanced calculus and modern algebra (the latter needed for Chapters 9, 10, and 11 only).

4. NUMBER THEORY AND OTHER BRANCHES OF MATHEMATICS

Among the many problems in the theory of numbers, that had a great impact upon the development of entire branches of mathematics, we quote, as examples, the following:

(a) The study of the distribution of primes sparked the development of the *theory of functions of a complex variable* and, in particular, that of the *theory of entire functions*. With the help of these theories, the original problem has been essentially solved—but in the process of finding the solution new problems arose, some of which are still wide open.

(b) The so-called "last theorem of Fermat" led to the creation of the *theory of algebraic numbers*, one of the most important and flourishing branches of modern number theory—and through it to that of much of modern algebra. Fermat's "last theorem" still has not been proven, but one is almost inclined to forget this fact as a rather irrelevant detail, because the successes of the theory of algebraic numbers completely overshadow the not terribly important statement of Fermat.

(c) The Theory of Partitions gave a strong impetus to the study (by Euler) of *generating functions*. Many of the original problems of Euler have been solved, but the theory of partitions continues to lead to new developments in such diverse fields as modular functions, saddle-point method of integration, and combinatorial analysis.

We shall consider these problems in greater detail.

5. THE DISTRIBUTION OF PRIME NUMBERS

Among the oldest and most fascinating problems in number theory is that of *the distribution of prime numbers*. In order to discuss it, we need the following:

Definition 1. An integer $p > 1$, that is not the product of two other positive integers, both smaller than p, is called a *prime number*; an integer $a > 1$ that is not a prime is called *composite*.

The integer 11 is a prime, because there are no integers a, b such that $a \cdot b = 11$, $1 \leq a \leq b < 11$. But 42 is not a prime; it is a composite number, because $6 \cdot 7 = 42$ and $1 \leq 6 \leq 7 < 42$ holds. Similarly, $25 = 5 \cdot 5$ is not a prime, and so on. It is convenient to agree that 1 is not a prime. If we list the primes in increasing order, the first few are:

$$2, 3, 5, 7, 11, 13, \ldots.$$

It is easy to write up all primes less than say, 100 or 200, but to make a complete list of primes up to say, 10^7 is rather time consuming. Nevertheless, reliable lists of primes exist up to 10^7 (see [3], or [1]) and (apparently less reliable ones (see [2])) even up to 10^8. If we study these lists in some detail we observe two contrasting features:

(i) A great irregularity in detail; for instance we observe again and again the occurrence of " twin primes, " that is, of primes p and q, with $q = p + 2$; at the same time we meet with arbitrarily large "isolated primes," that is, primes preceded and followed by a large number of composite numbers. But we also find

(ii) a certain regularity in the distribution of primes, in the sense that on the average the prime numbers seem to thin out steadily. This means, more precisely, that the number of primes out of, say, 1000 consecutive integers, seems to decrease with a certain regularity. For instance, in the ten blocks of 1000 consecutive integers between 1 and 10,000 (i.e., in 1–1000, 1001–2000, ..., 9001–10,000) one finds as number of primes per block 168, 135, 127, 120, 119, 114, 117, 107, 110, and 112, respectively, and there are only 53 primes in the block of 1000 integers from 9,999,001 to 10,000,000. This observation may lead one to suspect that from some point on perhaps all numbers will turn out to be composite; or, in other words, that the total number of primes might be finite (even if, presumably, very large). That this is not so was known already in antiquity (Euclid, ca. 300 B.C.) and we shall soon see a very short proof of the fact that there are infinitely many primes (see Theorem 3.9). We shall denote by $\pi(x)$ the number of primes up to, but not larger than some given quantity, x, or, in symbols, set $\pi(x) = \sum_{p \le x} 1$.

It has already been mentioned that if x increases, $\pi(x)$ also increases beyond any preassigned bound. In fact, on the basis of counting the primes, one may be led to suspect that $\pi(x)$ increases somewhat like $x/(\log x)$. Actually, Legendre (1752–1833) and Gauss (1777–1855; the corresponding statement is found in a notebook published only posthumously) stated the conjecture that the ratio between $\pi(x)$ and $x/(\log x)$ approaches unity, as $x \to \infty$. This may be expressed symbolically by $\pi(x) \sim x/(\log x)$. An equivalent formulation is

$$\lim_{x \to \infty} \pi(x) \cdot (\log x)/x = L \qquad \text{exists, and} \quad L = 1. \tag{3}$$

Tchebycheff (1821–1894), in an attempt to prove (3), showed that there exist two positive constants c and C, such that $c \le 1 \le C$ and

$$c \frac{x}{\log x} < \pi(x) < C \frac{x}{\log x}$$

holds for all $x \ge 2$. He also showed that if the limit L exists at all, then $L = 1$ follows. Hence, if one could "only" show that the limit in (3) exists, the Gauss-Legendre conjecture would be completely proven. However, it turned out that to prove the existence of the limit in (3) is very hard and no direct approach seemed to work. In 1859 Riemann (1826–1866) undertook the study of this problem in a famous memoir, by a very different, indirect approach. Following an idea that occurs already in Euler's work, he connected the problem of prime numbers with the properties of the function $\zeta(s) = \sum_{n=1}^{\infty} n^{-s}$. While Euler considered $\zeta(s)$ only for real values of s, Riemann let s take complex values. Riemann is one of the founders of the theory of functions of a complex variable and a case can be (and has been) made for the assertion that it was his interest in the study of primes that prompted him to investigate the general theory of functions of a complex variable.

In spite of his brilliant achievements, Riemann was not completely successful. His sketch of a proof of (3) had serious gaps. The most important of these could not be filled until properties of the class of functions, called *entire functions* had been established. During the last decade of the 19th century, J. Hadamard (1865–1963) became interested in the problem of the primes. Realizing the nature of the tool needed for its solution, he set out to systematize and complete the work previously done by Laguerre

(1834–1886), Poincaré (1854–1912), Borel (1871–1956), Picard (1856–1941), and others. The result was his celebrated theory of entire functions. Using this theory, Hadamard and, simultaneously, de la Vallée Poussin (1866–1962), succeeded in proving (3), which, since then, is known as *the prime number theorem*. Several gaps in Riemann's memoir still remained. Part of these were taken care of by the work of von Mangoldt (1854–1925), Landau (1877–1938), and others. But at least one conjecture, very important for a more precise formulation of the prime number theorem, has so far stubbornly defied all attempts of a proof (or of a refutation). This famous *Riemann hypothesis* states that $\zeta(s) \neq 0$ in the half plane Re $s > \frac{1}{2}$. The attempts to prove it, while, so far, unsuccessful, led to such beautiful developments as, among others, the theory of almost periodic functions (Bohr, 1887–1951)—and the end of this story is not yet in sight.

It should be added that in 1947, Selberg and Erdös succeeded in finding an elementary (but by no means easy) proof of (3), thus dispensing altogether with the use of the theory of functions, largely created in order to cope with this problem.

6. FERMAT'S "LAST THEOREM"

In 1637, Fermat (1601–1665) stated that the diophantine equation $x^n + y^n = z^n$, with integral $n > 2$, has no solutions in positive integers x, y, z. For $n = 2$, such solutions of course exist, for instance, $3^2 + 4^2 = 5^2$. Fermat asserted to have a "truly marvelous proof" of his statement, but today it is generally believed that his argument (which apparently was never revealed) must have been incomplete (see, however, Mordell, [4]). A proof of Fermat's statement for the particular case $n = 4$ is known and is quite easy. It is also comparatively simple to prove the statement for $n = 3$ (Euler, ca. 1760). In fact, the statement has been proven at least up to $n = 4002$ (see [7]). But, trying to adapt the method of proof that works for $n = 3$ to the general case, Kummer (1810–1893) ran into a completely unexpected difficulty. We know (and shall prove it formally) that any integer can be factored into primes in essentially (i.e., except for the order of the factors) one way only. Most people feel that the uniqueness of factorization into primes is so obvious, that a formal proof is almost a waste of time. Yet Kummer (and Dirichlet even before him) found that in an only slightly more general setting, the statement (of essential uniqueness of factorization) is actually false. This, of course, points out once more that even the seemingly most obvious statements have to be proven (starting from some system of axioms) before they can be accepted. Kummer overcame the difficulty by introducing "ideal numbers"; these led, through Kummer's own work, Dedekind's (1831–1916) and that of their followers, to the development of the theory of algebraic numbers and much of modern algebra.

The study of other diophantine equations led to the development of algebraic geometry, one of the most active branches of contemporary mathematics.

7. THE THEORY OF PARTITIONS

If an integer $n > 0$ is given, we may represent it, in general, in many ways, as a sum of positive integers. Taking for instance $n = 5$, we observe that

$$5 = 4 + 1 = 3 + 2 = 3 + 1 + 1 = 2 + 2 + 1$$
$$= 2 + 1 + 1 + 1 = 1 + 1 + 1 + 1 + 1.$$

Each such representation by a sum (involving, possibly, only a single summand, namely, n itself) is called a partition of n. Partitions that differ only by the order of the summands are not considered distinct. From the above example we see that $n = 5$ has seven distinct partitions, or, in symbols, $p(5) = 7$. The series $F(x) = \sum_{n=0}^{\infty} p(n)x^n$, which has as coefficient of x^n precisely $p(n)$, is called a *generating function* of the $p(n)$. It is easy to show (and was known already to Euler) that if we agree to set $p(0) = 1$ (so far $p(0)$ had not been defined), then $F(x) = \prod_{n=1}^{\infty} (1 - x^n)^{-1}$. Here, and in general in work with generating functions, the actual convergence is unimportant; incidentally, one may show that both representations of $F(x)$ actually do converge for $|x| < 1$. Equating these two different expressions of $F(x)$ and transforming either one, or the other, or both sides of the equality, one obtains by elementary reasonings such results as

$$p(n) = p(n - 1) + p(n - 2) - p(n - 5) - p(n - 7) + \cdots$$
$$+ (-1)^{j+1} p(n - m_j) + \cdots; \quad (4)$$

here $m_j = \frac{1}{2}j(3j \pm 1)$ and the sum obviously breaks off when $3j^2 - j > 2n$. Formula (4) permits one to compute $p(n)$ "by recurrence," if one already knows $p(1), p(2), ..., p(r)$, for all $r \leq n - 1$. As a matter of fact, however, $p(n)$ increases very rapidly with n and (4) soon becomes unmanageable. An approximate value of $p(n)$ can easily be obtained by rather simple, combinatorial considerations, with the result that $e^{An} < p(n) < e^{Bn}$ holds, with some appropriate positive constants $A < B$. More than that is true.

Hardy (1877–1947) and Ramanujan (1887–1920) proved that actually $p(n) \sim \dfrac{1}{4\sqrt{3}\,n}\, e^{\pi\sqrt{2/3}\,\sqrt{n}}$. This result required the use of a "Tauberian Theorem," that is, of a rather sophisticated reasoning, whereby one draws conclusions concerning summands, from a knowledge of the behavior of their sum. Finally, the work of Hardy, Ramanujan and Rademacher (1892–   ) led to an *exact* formula for $p(n)$. In order to obtain it, use had to be made of the theory of functions of a complex variable, of the theory of modular functions and of many other analytical devices. The theories involved have been materially stimulated by the investigation of the partition function. In 1943 Erdös obtained by elementary (but not easy) reasoning, the above quoted asymptotic formula of Hardy and Ramanujan for $p(n)$ (except for the proof that the outside constant is $1/4\sqrt{3}$; the latter was supplied by D. J. Newman in 1951).

8. ELEMENTARY NUMBER THEORY

In the preceding sections we discussed some classical problems of number theory which have sparked the development of advanced branches of mathematics and whose treatment required the tools furnished by these advanced theories. However, it would be a great mistake to believe that number theory cannot be studied profitably unless, say, complex variables and abstract algebra have been mastered. On the contrary, it might be argued, that the study of number theory should precede that of those theories—in agreement with the actual historic sequence of events. Be that as it may, it is a fact that many interesting and challenging problems can be handled by very simple methods.

These form the so-called *elementary number theory*. Many questions concerning primes, or partitions can be handled by elementary methods. If it happens that a seemingly difficult and deep problem yields to a particularly simple, elementary reasoning, then we experience that striking sensation of elegance, already alluded to in Section 1. Such is, for instance, Euclid's proof that there are infinitely many primes. It also happens that some of the most fundamental concepts of modern algebra (actually, of all of modern mathematics) such as groups, rings, fields, modules, ideals, to name just a few, are obtained by the processes of abstraction and generalization from situations we meet in elementary number theory. Finally, the prerequisites needed for an understanding of this elementary theory are minimal. All this adds up to making elementary number theory an ideal starting point.

Therefore, in what follows some elementary number theory (divisibility, linear and quadratic congruences, number theoretic functions) will be presented first; this, together with some rudiments of the theory of functions of a complex variable and some algebra (recalled for the convenience of the reader in Chapter 7, Section 3, and Chapter 9, Section 5, respectively; see also Appendices A and B) should enable us to study in some detail the three problems mentioned earlier in the present chapter. Our aim will be to obtain in each case, as simply as possible, the most important and characteristic results, rather than the strongest known formulation of the corresponding theorems. While we shall keep in mind the ultimate aim, it is hoped that many results obtained on the way will prove interesting and rewarding by themselves.

BIBLIOGRAPHY

1. C. L. Baker and F. J. Gruenberger, *The First Six Million Prime Numbers*. Microcard Foundation, West Salem, Wisconsin, 1959.
2. J. P. Kulik (Vienna), Manuscript list of primes up to 10^8 (not sufficiently reliable).
3. D. H. Lehmer, *List of Prime Numbers from 1 to* 10,006,721. Washington: Carnegie Institute of Washington, Publication No. **165**, 1914.
4. L. J. Mordell, *Three Lectures on Fermat's Last Theorem*. Cambridge: Cambridge University Press, 1921.
5. O. Neugebauer, *Vorgriechische Mathematik—Die Grundlehren der Mathematischen Wissenschaften in Einzeldarstellungen*, Vol. **13**. Berlin: Springer, 1937.
6. *Rhind (or Ahmes) Papyrus*, written presumably 1700–1600 B.C., now in the British Museum.
7. J. L. Selfridge, C. A. Nicol, H. S. Vandiver, *Proceedings of the National Academy of Sciences*, Vol. **41**, 1955, pp. 970–973.

CHAPTER 2

Introductory Remarks and Notations

The theory of numbers is concerned primarily with the properties of the *natural numbers* 1, 2, 3, ... and, more generally, with those of the *rational integers* ..., -2, -1, 0, 1, 2, 3, ... Throughout this book, rational integers will be denoted by lower case latin letters. The set of all rational integers will be denoted by **Z**. In general, sets of numbers will be denoted by boldface capitals.

The sum, difference, and product of two rational integers are again rational integers, that is, they are again elements of the set **Z**. We recall the

Definition 1. Whenever an operation defined on the elements of a set **A** is such that it can be performed unrestrictedly and has as a result again an element of **A**, we say that the set **A** is *closed* under that operation.

According to Definition 1, the set **Z** is closed under addition, multiplication and subtraction. However, there are many other operations that we may want to perform on numbers, such as division, extraction of roots, solving of equations (with, say, coefficients in **Z**), and so on. Unfortunately, **Z** is not closed even under division, because if a and b are rational integers, it is usually impossible to find a third rational integer c such that $a \div b = c$. Attempts to construct sets that permit the unrestricted performance of the desired operations lead to successive generalizations of the concept of "number" and we shall have to consider *rational numbers* (that is, fractions a/b, where a and b are rational integers, $b \neq 0$), *irrational real numbers* (such as

$\sqrt{2}$, e, or π) and even *complex numbers* ($z = x + iy$, x, y real, $i^2 + 1 = 0$). The set of all rational numbers will be denoted by **Q**, that of all real numbers by **R** and that of all complex numbers by **C**. The reader is assumed to be familiar with these concepts, as well as with the operations of addition, subtraction, multiplication, division, taking powers, extraction of roots, exponentiation, and taking of logarithms.

Current symbols, such as = (equal to), $\neq$ (not equal to), > (greater than), $\geq$ (greater than or equal to), < (less than), $\leq$ (less than, or equal to), $a \mid b$ (a divides b), $a \nmid b$ (a does not divide b), $\sum_{n=1}^{N} f(n)$ (summation symbol), and so on, will be used without further explanations. As a matter of fact, we already did use them without explanation, comment, or apology, in Chapter 1.

Whenever convenient, we shall make use also of a few symbols from set theory and from logic. We list here the most common symbols.

1. The braces { }; these are used to enclose the elements of a given set. For instance, if **P** stands for the set of all prime numbers, we may write **P** = {2, 3, 5, 7, ...}.

2. The symbol $\in$; it is used to show that an element belongs to a given set, thus $b \in \mathbf{B}$ means that b is an element of the set **B**. For example $12 \in \mathbf{Z}$, $7 \in \mathbf{P}$. One uses $\notin$ to show that some element does not belong to a given set, for instance $6 \notin \mathbf{P}$.

3. The symbols of inclusion, $\supset$ and $\subset$; $\mathbf{A} \supset \mathbf{B}$ means that every element of the set **B** is also an element of the set **A**, or, in symbols: $\alpha \in \mathbf{B}$ implies that $\alpha \in \mathbf{A}$. By definition, $\mathbf{A} \subset \mathbf{B}$ means the same as $\mathbf{B} \supset \mathbf{A}$. For instance, $\mathbf{Z} \subset \mathbf{Q} \subset \mathbf{R} \subset \mathbf{C}$. Observe that $\mathbf{A} \subset \mathbf{B}$ and $\mathbf{A} \supset \mathbf{B}$ imply $\mathbf{A} = \mathbf{B}$.

4. The symbols $\cup$ (union) and $\cap$ (intersection); $\mathbf{A} = \mathbf{B} \cup \mathbf{C}$ (read: **A** equals the union of **B** and **C**) means that the set **A** consists of all (and only) those elements that belong to either **B** or **C**. For instance, if **B** = {3, 5, 6, 7} and **C** = {3, 6, 8, 9}, then **A** = {3, 5, 6, 7, 8, 9,}. $\mathbf{D} = \mathbf{B} \cap \mathbf{C}$ (read: **D** equals the intersection of **B** and **C**) means that the set **D** consists of exactly those elements, that belong to both sets, **B** *and* **C**. In above example, **D** = {3, 6}.

5. The quantifier $\exists$ (read: there exists); for instance, to state the fact that there exists a prime between 14 and 18 we may write, $\exists\, p$, $p \in P$, $14 \leq p \leq 18$.

6. The symbols of implication: $\Rightarrow$ (implies), $\Leftarrow$ (is implied by); $\Leftrightarrow$ (implies and is implied by); the latter one means that the statement preceding the symbol $\Leftrightarrow$ is equivalent to the statement following it. Occasionally we use this symbol to define a new concept; in that case the symbols preceding (or

following) $\Leftrightarrow$ are defined to mean the same thing as the (already known) symbols following (or preceding) $\Leftrightarrow$. In order to avoid any possible misunderstanding, we shall write "def" under a double arrow used in a definition: $\underset{\text{def}}{\Leftrightarrow}$.

7. The symbol $\ni$ (read: such that); sometimes $\ni$ is replaced by |, if there is no danger of confusion with the symbol for "is divisible by." This is particularly useful in the definition of sets, characterized by complicated conditions satisfied by their elements.

More symbols will be introduced as needed, often to be used only in a single chapter, or even a single section.

Finally, a few words concerning the proofs. A bewildering variety of methods are used in number theory. Sometimes the same theorem can be proven by several methods (so, it seems, according to Professor M. Gerstenhaber ([1], p. 397) that there are 152 different proofs for the quadratic reciprocity formula (see Theorem 5.3)); on the other hand, for some important theorems, there exists essentially only one proof—which occasionally (while correct; hence fully convincing) is not even really satisfactory. As an example consider the following theorem. If $d - 3$ is divisible by 4 and $(-d/n)$ is the symbol of quadratic residuacy defined in Chapter 5, then $d^{-1} \sum_{n=1}^{d-1} n(-d/n)$ is always a negative integer; I wish I could see arithmetically why! Also, as already mentioned, until recently the proof of the Prime Number Theorem (PNT) required the use of complex variables, although the statement of the Theorem has nothing to do with complex quantities.

Everything else being equal, we shall give preference to direct proofs, using concepts germane to the substance of the theorem; however, we shall not be dogmatic about it. If a proof by induction, or an indirect proof (that is, a proof by *reductio ad absurdum*, or by contradiction) is simpler, we shall not hesitate to use it, even if a direct proof is available. It is assumed, of course, that the reader is familiar with all these types of proofs. Similarly, if a proof, using concepts not occurring in the statement of a theorem, is easier, or more transparent than one that avoids them, we shall present the more transparent one. For instance the PNT will be proven by a simple analytic argument (using complex variables), in preference to the (technically) elementary, but rather difficult, proof which is now available. In the following chapters of Part II, we shall discuss some topics of elementary number theory; these are of independent interest and some of them will be needed in order to study the Riemann Zeta function, the PNT, Fermat's Conjecture, and the Theory of Partitions, which follow in Part III. Occasionally, topics of elementary number theory, of intrinsic interest, are developed far beyond the point actually needed in Part III. The reader who is in a hurry and whose curiosity about one of the three main problems treated in Part III cannot wait, may, therefore, start by reading only the definitions and statements of theorems in Part II (with special emphasis on Chapter 3 on Divisibility and Chapter 6 on Arithmetic Functions); he may then go to the chapters that interest him most in Part III. Whenever he feels the need for some specific theorem of Part II, he may go back and try to master it.

For the reader, however, interested in getting thoroughly acquainted with the subject matter, it is recommended that he study carefully this elementary Part II. He should not omit to work out the problems of each chapter—all of them, if possible—before proceeding to the next chapter. Part III consists of three units (Chapters 7 and 8; Chapters 9, 10, and 11; Chapter 12). Once Part II is mastered, it matters little in what order the reader takes up the individual units of Part III, nor does he have to study all of them, because these units are completely independent of each other.

BIBLIOGRAPHY

1. M. Gerstenhaber, *Am. Math. Monthly*, **70**, 1963, pp. 397–398.

PART TWO

Elementary
Number Theory

CHAPTER **3**

Divisibility

1. GENERALITIES AND FUNDAMENTAL THEOREM

As already mentioned, we assume that the reader is familiar with the properties of the natural integers (defined, for instance, by Peano's axioms) and those of the rational integers, as well as with the elementary operations. Given any two rational integers, one can always add, subtract, or multiply them and one obtains as result again an integer. We already observed in Chapter 2 that in general this is no longer the case with the operation of division; hence, the following definition is non-trivial.

Definition 1. An integer a is said to be divisible by an integer $b \neq 0$, if the equation $a = bx$ has a solution with x an integer. If a is divisible by b, we say also that b divides a, or, in symbols, $b \mid a$.

We note some immediate consequences of this definition and formulate them in the following

Theorem 1. *If $a, b, c \in \mathbf{Z}$, then*
(1) $a \mid 0, 1 \mid a, a \mid a$;
(2) $a \mid b \Rightarrow a \mid b \cdot c$;
(3) $a \mid b, b \mid c \Rightarrow a \mid c$;
(4) $a \mid b \Rightarrow ac \mid bc$;
(5) $a \mid b_i \, (i = 1, 2, ..., r) \Rightarrow a \mid m_1 b_1 + m_2 b_2 + \cdots + m_r b_r$ *for all* $m_i \in \mathbf{Z}$;

21

(6) $a > 0, b > 0, a \mid b \Rightarrow a \leq b$;

(7) $ab > 0, a \mid b, b \mid a \Rightarrow a = b$.

At this point the reader should convince himself that he thoroughly under-stands the meaning of each symbol used, by translating the hypotheses, as well as each of the seven statements of Theorem 1 into words. The proof of this theorem is left as an exercise to the reader.

In Part I, Definition 1 we have defined the concept of a prime; now our first aim is to prove what is often called the Fundamental Theorem of Arithmetic, stating that the factorization of an integer into primes is essenti-ally unique. However, before we can do this, we must first show that every integer larger than one can be factored into primes at least in *some* way. We state this fact as

Theorem 2. $1 < n \in \mathbf{Z} \Rightarrow n = p_1 p_2 \cdots p_r$.

REMARK 1. Theorem 2 does *not* assert that the primes $p_1, p_2, \ldots, p_r$ are all distinct.

PROOF (by induction). The statement is trivially true for $n = 2$, $n = 3$, $n = 5$ and, in general, for any n that is itself a prime; it also is easily verified for $n = 4 = 2^2$, $n = 6 = 2 \cdot 3$, and so on. Assume that Theorem 2 has already been found to hold for $k = 2, 3, \ldots, n$; then we shall show that the Theorem holds also for $k = n + 1$ and, hence, by induction, for all integers. Indeed, either $n + 1$ is a prime p and then $n + 1 = p$, so that the Theorem holds with $r = 1$; or else $n + 1 = a \cdot b$, with a and b both less than $n + 1$. Hence, $a \leq n, b \leq n$ and, by the induction hypothesis $a = p_1 p_2 \cdots p_t$; $b = p'_1 \cdots p'_s$, so that $n + 1 = a \cdot b = p_1 \cdots p_t \cdot p'_1 \cdots p'_s$, with $p_1, \ldots, p_t, p'_1, \ldots, p'_s$ all primes and the theorem is proven.

The commutativity of multiplication permits us to rearrange the prime factors so that they should be nondecreasing. The product $2 \cdot 5 \cdot 3 \cdot 5 \cdot 2$ ($= 300$), for instance, may be rearranged to read $2 \cdot 2 \cdot 3 \cdot 5 \cdot 5 = 2^2 \cdot 3 \cdot 5^2$. This is called a *standard* or *canonical* factorization of $n = 300$.

Definition 2. $n = p_1^{s_1} p_2^{s_2} \cdots p_r^{s_r}$ is a *standard*, or *canonical* factorization of n if and only if $p_1 < p_2 < \cdots < p_r$ and all exponents are positive integers.

Now we are able to state

Theorem 3.   (Fundamental Theorem of Arithmetic). *The standard factor-ization of a natural integer n is unique.*

The proof of Theorem 3 is easy, if we assume for a moment the validity of

Theorem 4. $p \mid a \cdot b, p \nmid a \Rightarrow p \mid b$.

Indeed, Theorem 4 may be generalized almost trivially to

Corollary 4.1. $p \mid a_1 a_2 \cdots a_r \Rightarrow \exists\, i (1 \le i \le r) \ni p \mid a_i$.
In words: if a prime divides a product of integers, then it divides at least one of them.

PROOF OF COROLLARY 4.1 (by induction on r).   The statement is trivially true for $r = 1$; for $r = 2$ it is precisely the statement of Theorem 4, which we accept provisionally. We complete the proof, by showing that if the Corollary holds for $r - 1$ factors, then it also holds for r factors. Indeed, set $a_1 a_2 \cdots a_{r-1} = n$, so that $a_1 a_2 \cdots a_r = n a_r$. Then, by Theorem 4, $p \mid n a_r \Rightarrow p \mid a_r$ or $p \mid n$. In the first alternative, the Corollary holds with $i = r$; in the second, $p \mid n \Rightarrow p \mid a_1 a_2 \cdots a_{r-1}$ and the Corollary holds, by the induction hypothesis, for some i, $1 \le i \le r - 1$.

The proof of Theorem 3, as well as many other proofs to come, becomes neater if we keep in mind the following, almost obvious

REMARK 2.   Every non-empty set of positive integers contains a smallest element.
Indeed, denote the set by **A** and let $a \in$ **A**; such an a exists by the assumption that **A** is non-empty. Next, consider the finite set of positive integers $1, 2, \cdots, a$ and cross out all (finitely many) integers of this set, not belonging to **A**. Then some integers will be left standing (a itself, for instance) and the first among those integers that were left is precisely the smallest element of **A**.
It may be mentioned that if in the above considerations the set of positive integers with the *order relation* $\le$ is replaced by some other, more complicated sets and order relations, it is not always easy (or even possible) to verify that every subset has a smallest element. A set having this property is called *well ordered*. We are now ready to prove Theorem 3 (always assuming the validity of the, as yet unproven, Theorem 4).

PROOF OF THEOREM 3 (by contradiction).   If we deny the statement of Theorem 3, then there exists a non-empty set **A** of positive integers, for which the standard factorization is not unique. By Remark 2, there exists a smallest integer in **A**, let it be n. Then, by assumption, $n = p_1 p_2 \cdots p_r = p'_1 p'_2 \cdots p'_s$, where $p_1 \le p_2 \le \cdots \le p_r$ are primes and $p'_1, p'_2, \cdots, p'_s$ are also primes (some, possibly, repeated; we do *not* require the factorization $p'_1 \cdots p'_s$ to be canonical. From $p_1 \mid n = p'_1 \cdots p'_s$ and Corollary 4.1 it follows that $p_1 \mid p'_j (1 \le j \le s)$, whence, by the definition of primes, $p_1 = p'_j$. Hence, dividing out this common factor and setting $n_1 = n/p_1$, it follows that $n_1 = p_2 p_3 \cdots p_r = p'_1 p'_2 \cdots p'_{s-1} p'_{s+1} \cdots p'_j$ (the slight modification needed in case $j = 1$ or $j = s$ should be written out in detail by the reader). The factorization $p_2 p_3 \cdots p_r$ is canonical and we may also rearrange the primes $p'_k (k \ne j)$ in nondecreasing order, relabeling them, say, as $q_1 \le q_2 \le \cdots \le q_{s-1}$; the unordered set of primes

$\{p'_k\}, 1 \leq k \leq s, k \neq j$ is, of course, identical to the set $\{q_l\} (1 \leq l \leq s - 1)$. We have obtained so far that $n_1 = p_2 p_3 \cdots p_r = q_1 q_2 \cdots q_{s-1}$. These two canonical factorizations of n_1 cannot be the same, because if they were, they would lead to a unique factorization for $n = p_1 n_1 = p'_j n_1$, contrary to our assumption. Hence, n_1 is an integer with at least two distinct factorizations, $n_1 \in A$. But $n_1 < n$, contrary to the definition of n as *smallest* integer in A. This contradiction shows that the set A is actually empty, that is, there are *no* positive integers with two distinct canonical factorizations.

In order to complete the proof of Theorem 3, it still remains to prove the key Theorem 4. However, in order to avoid a circular reasoning (*petitio principii*), we *may not* use, in this proof of Theorem 4, any results like Corollary 4.1 or Theorem 3, which were obtained precisely by *assuming* Theorem 4. We may, of course, use Theorem 1 and Theorem 2.

In the proof we shall need the concepts of *greatest common divisor* and of a *module*, which we now proceed to define.

Definition 3. Let a, b, $d \in Z$; if $d \mid a$, then d is called a *divisor of a*; if $d \mid a$ and $d \mid b$, then d is called a *common divisor of a and b*. The largest positive common divisor of a and b is called their *greatest common divisor* (g.c.d.) and is denoted by $d = (a, b)$. Two integers a and b, whose greatest common divisor $d = 1$ are called *relatively prime*, or *coprime*; in symbols: $(a, b) = 1 \underset{\text{def}}{\Leftrightarrow} a, b$ are coprime.

Having defined divisors and common divisors, we shall give here also the definition of multiples and common multiples, although these will not be needed immediately.

Definition 4. Let $a, b \, m \in Z$; if $a \mid m$, then m is called a *multiple of a*; if $a \mid m$ and $b \mid m$, then m is called a *common multiple of a and b*. The smallest positive common multiple of a and b is called their *least common multiple* (l.c.m.) and is denoted by $m = [a, b]$.

For many purposes it is more convenient to define $d = (a, b)$ as follows:

Definition 3*. $d = (a, b) \underset{\text{def}}{\Leftrightarrow} d \in Z, d > 0, d \mid a, d \mid b$, and $c \in Z, c \mid a, c \mid b$ $\Rightarrow c \mid d$.

The concepts of g.c.d. and l.c.m. may be generalized as follows:

Definition 3'. d is called the g.c.d. of the integers $a_1, a_2, \ldots, a_r$, in symbols $d = (a_1, a_2, \ldots, a_r)$, provided that
   (i) $d \mid a_i (i = 1, 2, \ldots, r)$;
   (ii) $d > 0$; and
   (iii) $c \mid a_i (i = 1, 2, \ldots, r) \Rightarrow c \mid d$.

One may observe that Definition 3′ is the direct generalization of Definition 3* rather than of Definition 3.

Definition 4′. m is called the l.c.m. of the integers $a_1, a_2, \ldots, a_r$, in symbols $m = [a_1, a_2, \ldots, a_r]$, provided that

  (i) $a_i \mid m (i = 1, 2, \ldots, r)$;
  (ii) $m > 0$; and
  (iii) $a_i \mid m_1 (i = 1, 2, \ldots, r) \Rightarrow m_1 \geq m$.

Before we proceed further, we have to show, first, that, given any two rational integers a and b, there exists an integer d with the properties required by Definition 3*; and next, that this integer is the same as $d = (a, b)$ of Definition 3. In order to do that, we shall introduce one more concept, namely, that of a *module*. This is not strictly indispensable in the present case, yet the proofs, based on this concept, are at least as easy as any other available ones and have the added advantage that they generalize most readily to more difficult situations—including some, where even the concept of g.c.d. does not exist (see Section 3). Until we prove the identity of Definitions 3 and 3*, it will be understood that $d = (a, b)$ is the g.c.d. according to Definition 3.

Definition 5. A *module* S is a set of numbers such that with any two elements of S, also their difference belongs to S.

REMARK 3. Although the elements of a module need not be integers, in what follows we shall be concerned exclusively with modules† consisting of rational integers.

REMARK 4. The set S consisting of zero alone, in symbols: $S = \{0\}$, satisfies the definition of a module. In what follows we shall ignore this trivial module without mentioning it explicitly every time. Hence, whenever we speak of a module, we shall assume that it contains at least one element $a \neq 0$.

From the assumptions $0 \neq a \in S$ and the defining property of a module it follows that $0 = a - a \in S$; hence,

$$a \in S \Rightarrow -a = 0 - a \in S.$$

Therefore,

$$a \in S, \qquad b \in S \Rightarrow -b \in S \Rightarrow a + b = a - (-b) \in S,$$

and not only the difference, but also the sum of any two elements of S belongs to S. Furthermore, $a \in S \Rightarrow 2a = a + a \in S$ and, by induction, $a \in S \Rightarrow na \in S \Rightarrow -na \in S$ for every natural integer n. This suggests the following

---

† The correct plural is of course *moduli*; however, at least in the United States, this latin plural has acquired a rather pedantic ring. Therefore, we shall follow the common custom and use the plural *modules*. In Great Britain, most authors do write *moduli*.

Theorem 5.   *A (non-trivial) module* S *of rational integers consists precisely of the multiples of a fixed positive integer* d, *that is,*

$$S = \{nd\}.$$

PROOF.   By assumption $\exists a \ni 0 \neq a \in S$; as seen, also $-a \in S$; but $a \neq 0 \Rightarrow a \neq -a$ and either a, or $-a$ is positive. It is only a matter of notation to say that $a > 0$. Hence, the set of positive integers belonging to S is not empty and, by Remark 2, there exists a smallest positive integer in S; let us denote it by d. We already know that with d also every integer of the form nd (n any rational integer) belongs to S, so that $\{nd\} \subset S$. We now want to prove the opposite inclusion $S \subset \{nd\}$; that is, we want to show that if $m \in S$, then there exists a rational integer n, such that $m = nd$. Because $m \in S \Leftrightarrow -m \in S$, it is sufficient to consider only the case $m > 0$ (hence, $n > 0$). If $m \neq nd$ for all n, then there exists an integer k, such that $kd < m < (k + 1)d$, or $0 < m - kd < d$. The positive integer $r = m - kd$ belongs to S, being the difference of the two elements m and kd of S. However, $r = m - kd < d$, contradicting the definition of d as *smallest* positive integer in S. This contradiction proves that $m = nd$; hence, $S \subset \{nd\}$ and $S = \{nd\}$ as asserted.

REMARK 5.   It might be worthwhile to remark that in the proof of Theorem 5 we have made use of the "Archimedean Axiom": Given any two positive numbers m (arbitrarily large) and d (arbitrarily small), it is always possible to find a positive integer k, such that $m < (k + 1)d$.

Theorem 6.   *Let a and b be two given rational integers and let m and n run independently through the set* Z *of rational integers; then* S = {am + bn} *is a module; actually* S = {kd}, *where* d = (a, b).

We recall that here $d = (a, b)$ is the g.c.d. of a and b according to Definition 3.

PROOF OF THEOREM 6.   It is trivial to verify that S is a module; it remains to prove the second statement of the Theorem. By Theorem 5, $S = \{kf\}$ for some positive integer f. Now, by its definition, $d \mid a$ and $d \mid b$; hence, by Theorem 1(5), $d \mid am + bn$ and every element kf of S is divisible by d. In particular, $d \mid f$, whence, by Theorem 1(6), $d \leq f$. Selecting now $m = 1$, $n = 0$, it follows that $f \mid a$; similarly, taking $m = 0$, $n = 1$, it follows that $f \mid b$. Hence, f is a common divisor of a and b so that, by Definition 3, $f \leq d$. We already obtained the inequality $d \leq f$ so that $d = f$ and Theorem 6 is proven.

Corollary 6.1. $d = (a, b) \Rightarrow \exists\, m, n \ni ma + nb = d.$

Corollary 6.2. $(a, b) = 1 \Rightarrow S = Z.$

Corollary 6.3 $(a, b) = 1 \Leftrightarrow \exists \, m, n \ni ma + nb = 1.$

Corollary 6.4. $c \mid a, c \mid b \Rightarrow c \mid am + bn \Rightarrow c \mid d.$

The ambitious reader may want to prove these Corollaries by himself. It is suggested that he write out the proofs completely, and compare them afterwards with those given here.

PROOFS OF COROLLARIES. The sets $\{am + bn\}$ and $\{kd\}$ are identical by Theorem 6; hence, for every rational integer k, there exist rational integers m, n such that $ma + nb = kd$. Taking in particular $k = 1$ yields Corollary 6.1. Next, setting in Corollary 6.1 $d = 1$ reduces the module $\mathbf{S} = \{kd\}$ to $\{k\} = \mathbf{Z}$, proving Corollary 6.2. Corollary 6.3 follows from Corollary 6.1 with $d = 1$. The first implication of Corollary 6.4 follows from Theorem 1(5), the second from Corollary 6.1.

REMARK 6. From Theorem 6 it follows that $d = (a, b)$ could also be defined as the smallest positive element of the module $\mathbf{S} = \{am + bn\}$.

Corollary 6.4 shows that the g.c.d. of a and b, as defined by Definition 3, has the property that every common divisor c of a and b divides also d; from this and Theorem 1(6) immediately follows that every common divisor c of a and b satisfies $c \leq d$. This proves both the meaningfulness of Definition 3* and its identity with Definition 3. After this extended preparation the proof of our key Theorem 4 comes almost as an anticlimax.

PROOF OF THEOREM 4. Assume $p \mid a \cdot b$, $p \nmid a$. Then $(p, a) = 1$ and by Corollary 6.3, $\exists \, m, n \ni mp + na = 1$, or $mpb + nab = b$. Now $p \mid p \cdot b$ trivially and $p \mid a \cdot b$ by assumption; hence, by Theorem 1(5), $p \mid mpb + nab = b$, as we wanted to prove. At this point the reader may want to look back and verify that we were not guilty of any circular reasoning. Indeed, using only the definitions of the g.c.d. and of a module, the Archimedean Axiom and Remark 2 we proved Theorem 5; next, using Theorems 1 and 5 we proved Theorem 6. From Theorem 6 and Theorem 1 followed the Corollaries to Theorem 6, and Theorem 4 then followed from Corollary 6.3 and Theorem 1. Theorem 4 is easily generalized to any number of factors as Corollary 4.1; finally, using Corollary 4.1, Theorem 2, and Remark 2 we proved Theorem 3.

2. DISCUSSION OF TWO OBJECTIONS

Two objections might have arisen in the reader's mind:

(a)   Why was the material not arranged following the outline in the last paragraph?

(b)   Why waste so much time and effort in order to prove the "obvious" statement of Theorem 4?

Objection (*a*) may be answered as follows: The proof of the important Theorem 3 is indeed very easy, if one is prepared to accept the plausible—not to say obvious—statement of Theorem 4. This fact was borne out by actually proving Theorem 3 in a few lines, without stopping for a proof of Theorem 4. Still, on second thought, one may want to have a clear conscience and give also a formal proof of the simple statement of Theorem 4: surely, the proof of such an "obvious" fact could not be too hard! It may have come as something of a surprise to some readers, that it actually took us several definitions, two preparatory theorems (Theorems 5 and 6) and quite a few remarks and corollaries requiring no less than four pages, in order to prove Theorem 4. But this already leads us to discuss

Objection (*b*) The answer to this objection is that the apparently obvious statement of Theorem 4 is actually far from obvious. In fact, under assumptions only slightly different from those underlying Theorem 4 ($n \in \mathbf{Z}$ being replaced by $n \in \mathbf{A} \supset \mathbf{Z}$, where $\mathbf{A}$ is a set whose structure is only slightly more complicated than that of $\mathbf{Z}$—both are *rings* (see Chapter 9 and Appendix B, Section 2(a)), the statement becomes actually false. Hence, in order to have a chance to prove Theorem 4, we have to make use of every available information and exploit thoroughly the advantage of knowing that $n \in \mathbf{Z}$, by using the properties of the rational integers recorded in Theorem 1. This explains the length of the proof of Theorem 4. This consideration should also go a long way toward a justification of the effort spent in proving Theorem 4. Actually, one of the main difficulties in the study of *algebraic integers* (the set called $\mathbf{A}$ above) is due precisely to the absence of a theorem like our present Theorem 4 and, for reasons of just this kind, it has been impossible, so far, to prove, among others, Fermat's Conjecture. We shall learn more about this topic in Chapters 9–11; meanwhile, just to illustrate our point, let us consider here an example of a set of integers, where Theorem 3 *does not hold*. This example is due to Hilbert and, while it may be of only limited intrinsic interest, it has the merit of being easily understood. It is hoped that any reader, who will have given some thought to this example, will be ready to agree that even the most plausible looking statements (such as Theorem 4, for instance) should be proven formally, before they are accepted.

3. AN EXAMPLE OF HILBERT

Let us consider the set $\mathbf{H} = \{h\}$, consisting of precisely those positive rational integers, that are of the form $h = 4n + 1$, $0 \le n \in \mathbf{Z}$. When these integers are divided by 4, they leave a remainder equal to one. Such integers are said to be *congruent to one modulo 4*. In symbols this is usually written $h \equiv 1 \pmod 4$; hence $\mathbf{H} = \{h \in \mathbf{Z} \mid h \equiv 1 \pmod 4, h > 0\}$.

Writing out the first few elements, we have

$$\mathbf{H} = \{1, 5, 9, 13, 17, 21, 25, 29, 33\ 37, 41, 45, 49, 53, 57, \cdots\}.$$

We shall learn more about congruences in Chapter 4; however, we may observe already now that the set $\mathbf{H}$ is closed under multiplication. Indeed, $h_1, h_2 \in \mathbf{H} \Rightarrow h_1 = 4n_1 + 1$, $h_2 = 4n_2 + 1$, $n_1, n_2 \in \mathbf{Z} \Rightarrow h_1 h_2 = 4(4n_1 n_2 + n_1 + n_2) + 1 = 4n + 1 \in \mathbf{H}$, because $0 < n = 4n_1 n_2 + n_1 + n_2 \in \mathbf{Z}$; hence, multiplication is well defined on $\mathbf{H}$. We also observe that some elements h of $\mathbf{H}$ can be represented as products of other elements of $\mathbf{H}$, all smaller than h, while others cannot be so represented. For instance, $25 = 5 \cdot 5$, $5 \in \mathbf{H}$; but 5 cannot be split in this way. Nor can 9 because $3 \notin \mathbf{H}$, nor can 21 because $3 \notin \mathbf{H}$, $7 \notin \mathbf{H}$. Let us agree to call *(Hilbert)-primes* those elements $p > 1$ of $\mathbf{H}$, that cannot be represented as products of elements of $\mathbf{H}$, all smaller than p. Denoting (only in this section) the set of these p by $\mathbf{P}$, we have $\mathbf{P} = \{5, 9, 13, 17, 21, 29, 33, 37, 41, 49, 53, 57, 61, 69, 73, 77, \ldots\}$. The other elements $h > 1$ of $\mathbf{H}$ may be called *composite*. The first few composite elements of $\mathbf{H}$ are $\{25, 45, 65, 81, 85, 105, \ldots\}$. Looking at these numbers, we may check that $25 = 5 \cdot 5$, $45 = 5 \cdot 9$, $65 = 5 \cdot 13$, ... so that we are inclined to believe that Theorem 4 (hence, also Theorem 3) holds for $\mathbf{H}$ just as for $\mathbf{Z}$. Consider, however, $h = 693$. Clearly, $693 = 4 \cdot 173 + 1 \in \mathbf{H}$. Also, $693 = 21 \cdot 33 = 9 \cdot 77$ and we observe that all four factors 33, 21, 9, 77, not only belong to $\mathbf{H}$, but actually even to $\mathbf{P}$. They are all "primes" and both factorizations are canonical. This shows that Theorem 3 does not hold for $\mathbf{H}$; but then Theorem 4 cannot hold either, because otherwise Theorem 3 (which is an immediate consequence of Theorem 4) would also hold—and it does not.

It is not hard to find the origin of the difficulty: This is due to to fact that we refuse to admit as factors the integers 3, 7, and 11, because these do not belong to $\mathbf{H}$. Indeed if we could "adjoin" them in some way to $\mathbf{H}$, we would obtain $693 = 21 \cdot 33 = 3 \cdot 7 \cdot 3 \cdot 11 = 3 \cdot 3 \cdot 7 \cdot 11 = 9 \cdot 77$ and the essential uniqueness of the factorization would again be saved.

*One final word concerning a way to "adjoin" such "missing elements" to a given set of numbers†. One observes that these "missing elements," 3, 7, 3, 11 are precisely the g.c.d. (in $\mathbf{Z}$) of the pairs of the factors of 693 in the two factorizations: $3 = (21, 9)$, $7 = (21, 77)$, $3 = (33, 9)$, $11 = (33, 77)$. These g.c.d. do not belong to $\mathbf{H}$; but we remember that to any two integers

---

† The idea presented here will not be used anywhere in this book, except in Chapters 9, 10 and 11, but should prove helpful to readers who intend to continue the study of algebraic numbers and the theory of ideals.

a, b with $d = (a, b)$ corresponds a module $\mathbf{S} = \{ma + nb\}$, all of whose elements are multiples of d. Such modules can be defined also over $\mathbf{H}$ (now $m, n \in \mathbf{H}$) instead of over $\mathbf{Z}$ and one still may denote the module corresponding to, say, 33 and 9, by (33, 9), regardless of whether $d \in \mathbf{H}$ or $d \notin \mathbf{H}$. In fact, if $d = 3 \notin \mathbf{H}$, then the module (33, 9), all of whose elements *do* belong to $\mathbf{H}$, succeeds quite effectively to replace in $\mathbf{H}$ in some sense the "missing element" $d = 3$.

4. TWO FURTHER THEOREMS

Before we change our subject, we shall state and prove two further results that will be needed later.

Theorem 7. $c \mid ab, (c, a) = 1 \Rightarrow c \mid b$.

PROOF. Same as of Theorem 4.

Theorem 8. $a \mid n, b \mid n, m = [a, b] \Rightarrow m \mid n$.

PROOF. Consider the module $\mathbf{S} = \{km\}$. If $n \in \mathbf{S}$, then the Theorem is proven. Otherwise, by the Archimedean Axiom, $\exists\, k \ni km < n < (k + 1)m$, or $0 < n - km < m$. But $a \mid n, a \mid m \Rightarrow a \mid r = n - km$; similarly $b \mid r$. Hence, $r = n - km$ is a positive common multiple of a and b, less than m; but m is, by definition, the *least* positive common multiple. This contradiction shows that $n \in \mathbf{S}$; hence, indeed $m \mid n$.

5. SOME RESULTS CONCERNING THE DISTRIBUTION OF PRIME NUMBERS

We already saw in Part I that the problem of the distribution of primes has fascinated the minds of men at least since the Greek antiquity. As already mentioned, some of the deepest methods of analysis and algebra have been brought to bear upon problems arising in this connection— and not always with full success. On the other hand, some of the most important results can be obtained with surprisingly simple reasonings—and were actually known to Euclid. We shall finish this chapter by proving two theorems concerned with the theory of prime numbers and shall come back to this topic in Chapters 7 and 8, for a renewed attack, with more powerful weapons.

Theorem 9 (Euclid). *There exist infinitely many primes.*

The great importance and interest of this theorem could hardly escape the reader; therefore, we pass without futher comments to its surprisingly simple proof.

PROOF OF THEOREM 9 (by contradiction). Let us assume that the set $\mathbf{P} = \{p\}$ of primes† is finite. Let r be the exact number of its elements, and let us list them in increasing order so that $p_1 = 2$, $p_2 = 3$, $p_3 = 5$, ..., up to p_r, the last (and largest) prime. The set $\mathbf{P}$ of r primes is, once more, assumed to contain *all* existing prime numbers. Consider now the integer

$$n = p_1 p_2 \cdots p_r + 1 = 2 \cdot 3 \cdot 5 \cdots p_r + 1.$$

We know (see Theorem 2) that n can be factored into primes, $n = q_1 q_2 \cdots q_k$ ($q_j \in \mathbf{P}$, $1 \le j \le k$), say, with $k > 1$. (Actually, $k > 1$, because $k = 1 \Rightarrow n = q_1 > p_r$, contrary to the definition of p_r, as largest prime; but this side remark is irrelevant for the proof.) One has $q_1 \mid n$; also, q_1 being a prime, $q_1 \in \mathbf{P}$; hence, $q_1 = p_j$ for some j, $1 \le j \le r$. Consequently, $q_1 \mid p_1 p_2 \cdots p_r$, and hence, by Theorem 1(5), $q_1 \mid n - p_1 p_2 \cdots p_r = 1$, contrary to the definition of a prime. This contradiction proves that no finite set P can contain all prime numbers.

Theorem 10. *There exist arbitrarily large gaps between consecutive primes.*

PROOF. We denote the product of the first k consecutive integers $1 \cdot 2 \cdot 3 \cdot \cdots \cdot k$ by $k!$ (read: k factorial) and observe that $k! + 2$ is divisible by 2, $k! + 3$ is divisible by 3, and, in general, for $2 \le q \le k$, $k! + q$ is divisible by q. Hence, none of these $k - 1$ consecutive integers is a prime; k, however, may be taken arbitrarily large and the Theorem is proven.

We can do still better. Indeed, also the integers $k! - q(2 \le q \le k)$ are composite, for the same reason as $k! + q$, and, clearly, $k!$ is composite too. Concerning the two integers $k! \pm 1$, however, we can say nothing. Either one, or both, or neither may be a prime. If both are primes, we have an instance of the so-called "twin primes," mentioned in Section 5 of the Introduction. These primes occur very rarely, (there might even be only a finite number of them; see the end of this chapter.) If exactly one of the integers $k! \pm 1$ is a prime, then there is an unbroken sequence of at least $k - 1$ composite numbers, isolating this prime from the preceding prime, as well as from the following prime. Such primes with large gaps before and after them are the "isolated primes" mentioned in Section 5 of the Introduction. If $k! \pm 1$ are both composite, then we have an unbroken sequence of at least $2k + 1$ composite integers (from $k! - k$ to $k! + k$ inclusive), separating consecutive primes $p < k! < p'$.

Taking, for instance, $k = 6$, $k! = 720$, $k! - 1 = 719$ is a prime, while $k! + 1 = 721 = 7 \cdot 103$ is composite. The prime preceding 719 is 709, the

---

† It should hardly be necessary to recall that **P** stands here for the set of all rational primes, as defined in Chapter 1 (Definition 1.1) and should not be confused with the "Hilbert primes" of Section 3.

prime following 719 is 727 leading to the "prime-free" gaps $727 - 719 = 8$ and $719 - 709 = 10$, respectively, both larger than the minimal gap $k - 1 = 6 - 1 = 5$. Similarly, for $k = 7$, $k! - 1 = 7! - 1 = 5039$ is a prime, while $k! + 1 = 7! + 1 = 5041 = 71^2$ is composite and the primes nearest to 5039 are $5023 < 5039 < 5051$, with gaps of 16 and 12, respectively, both, of course, larger than $k - 1 = 6$. In the case $k = 3$, however, $k! + 1 = 7$ and $k! - 1 = 5$ are a pair of twin primes. Finally, for $k = 5$, $k! + 1 = 121 = 11^2$ and $k! - 1 = 119 = 7 \cdot 17$ are both composite; the nearest primes are 113 and 127 with a gap of $127 - 113 = 14 > 2k + 1 = 11$.

★Actually, much stronger theorems are known, but the methods needed for the proofs are no more elementary. Therefore, we shall only mention some results, without proofs, and refer the interested reader to the pertinent literature.

Given an arbitrary positive integer g let us count the number of primes less than some fixed integer x and isolated (on both sides) by gaps no less than g; the result is that "almost all" primes are so isolated. This means that the ratio between the number of primes $p \leq x$ with at least one of the two gaps less than g, to the total number of primes $p \leq x$, can be made arbitrarily small, if only x has been selected sufficiently large (see [7], p. 164).

Even this statement is only a particular case of a still more general one, where one counts sequences of $r + 1$ consecutive primes $p_i < p_{i+1} < \cdots < p_{i+r}$, so that all gaps between them should be $\geq g$. It can be shown that "almost all" sets of $r + 1$ consecutive primes less than some fixed x satisfy this condition; here "almost all" has the same meaning as in the preceding statement, which, clearly, is nothing but the particular case $r = 2$ of the present one. Still stronger results are known, but we shall not pursue the matter further (for literature see besides [7] also [2], [3], [6], [9], and [10]).

Having seen that there are arbitrarily large gaps between consecutive primes and that these occur infinitely often, one may ask also questions in the opposite direction. So, for instance, one may wonder how often the *smallest* possible difference between consecutive primes may occur. All primes $p > 2$ being odd, this difference is even; hence, $p_{i+1} - p_i = 2$ is the smallest possible difference and the problem may be rephrased as a question concerning the frequency of twin primes less than a given (large) x. This is a famous unsolved problem. As mentioned earlier, it is not even known, whether there are infinitely many, or only finitely many pairs of twin primes. In 1919 Viggo Brun showed (see [1]), using the "sieve method" he invented essentially for this purpose, that if there are infinitely many twin primes, the sum of their reciprocals converges. The relevance of this result comes from the fact that the series $\sum (1/p)$ formed with the reciprocals of all rational primes *diverges*, as we shall prove in Chapter 7 (Corollary 7.2.2.) Hence, in a sense, there cannot be "too many" twin primes—even if the set of twin primes *is* infinite. A heuristic argument of Hardy and Littlewood (see [4]; also [5] (Appendix) and [8]) actually leads to the conclusion that there are about $cx/(\log^2 x)$ pairs of twin primes $p, p + 2$, with $p \le x$ (and where $c = 2\prod_{p\ge 3} (1 - (p - 1)^{-2}) = 1.3203236...$). If this is correct, then there are indeed infinitely many twin primes, but, while the argument is highly plausible, it has not yet been possible to tighten it into a proof, and the problem is still open.

Accepting provisionally the infinity of twin primes, we have, on one hand, infinitely often primes that are crowded closely together, on the other hand isolated primes, strewn among the integers, as thinly as we want. This illustrates the irregularity in the distribution of primes. For a study of the regularities of this distribution, we shall have to reconsider the whole problem with analytic tools and shall do this in Chapters 7 and 8.

PROBLEMS

1. Prove in detail all statements of Theorem 1.

2. Prove that for any two integers a, b with $b > 0$, there exist integers q and r with $0 \le r < b$, such that $a = bq + r$.

3. (Euclidean algorithm). In order to find $d = (a, b)$, we may proceed as follows: We apply successively the result of Problem 2 and find a sequence of couples (q_k, r_k), $0 \le r_k < r_{k-1}$, starting with

$$a = bq_1 + r_1,$$
$$b = r_1 q_2 + r_2,$$
$$r_1 = r_2 q_3 + r_3, ...,$$
$$r_{k-1} = r_k q_{k+1} + r_{k+1}, ...$$

Prove that after a finite number of steps we obtain a remainder $r_m = 0$ and that $r_{m-1} = (a, b) = d$.

4. Prove that if $(a, b) = d$, then $(ka, kb) = kd$.

5. Prove that if $(a, b) = 1$ and $(b, c) = 1$, then $(ac, b) = 1$.

6. Let $m = [a, b]$ denote the least common multiple of a and b. Prove that if $(a, b) = 1$, then $m = a \cdot b$; more generally, if $(a, b) = d$, then $m = a \cdot b/d$.

7. Given $a, b \in \mathbf{Z}$ with $(a, b) = d$, suppose that for $m, n \in \mathbf{Z}$ one has $am + bn = f$; does it follow that $f = d$? (See Corollary 6.3; can you generalize it?)

8. Prove that the product of any three consecutive integers is divisible by 6 and if the first integer is even, then the product is divisible by 24.

9. Prove that if $d = (a, b, c)$, then there exist integers m, n, k, such that $ma + nb + kc = d$.

10. Let $a = p_1^{a_1}p_2^{a_2} \cdots p_r^{a_r}$, $b = p_1^{b_1}p_2^{b_2} \cdots p_r^{b_r}$ (p_i are primes that divide either a or b ,or both, $a_i \geq 0$, $b_i \geq 0$, $i = 1, 2, \cdots, r$) and set
    $$c_i = \min(a_i, b_i), \qquad d_i = \max(a_i, b_i).$$
    Prove that
    $$d = (a, b) = p_1^{c_1}p_2^{c_2} \cdots p_r^{c_r} \qquad \text{and} \qquad m = [a, b] = p_1^{d_1}p_2^{d_2} \cdots p_r^{d_r}.$$

11. Find the greatest common divisor and the least common multiple of 693 and 144.

12. Prove that the diophantine equation $ax + by = c$ has solutions in integers x, y if, and only if $d \mid c$, where $d = (a, b)$.

13. Consider the system $\mathbf{H} = \{h \in \mathbf{Z} \mid h \equiv 1 (\mathrm{mod}\ 4), h > 0\}$ described in Section 3.
    (a) Find the two smallest positive integers h, for which Theorem 3 fails.
    (b) Find $p, a, b \in \mathbf{H}$, $p \nmid a$, $p \nmid b$, but $p \mid a \cdot b$ (so that Theorem 4 fails; here p means a "Hilbert"-prime as defined in Section 3).

14. Give a formal proof of the fact that $k! \pm q$ is composite for $2 \leq q \leq k$.

15. Find a sequence of at least 20 consecutive composite integers.

BIBLIOGRAPHY

1. V. Brun, "La série $\dfrac{1}{5} + \dfrac{1}{7} + \dfrac{1}{11} + \dfrac{1}{13} + \ldots$ est convergente ou finie," *Bull. des Sciences Math.* (2) **43**, 1919, pp. 100–104; 124–128.

2. P. Erdös, "On the difference of consecutive primes," *Quarterly J. of Math.* (Oxford), **6**, 1935, pp. 124–128.

3. P. Erdös, "On some applications of Brun's method," *Acta Sci. Math. Szeged*, **13**, 1949, pp. 57–63.

4. G. H. Hardy and J. E. Littlewood, "Some Problems of Partitio Numerorum," *Acta Math.* **44**, 1923, pp. 1–70.

5. G. H. Hardy and E. M. Wright, *An Introduction to the Theory of Numbers*, 3rd ed. Oxford: Clarendon Press, 1954.

6. K. Prachar, Ueber ein Resultat von Walfisz, *Monatshefte für Mathem.*, **58**, 1954, pp. 114–116.

7. K. Prachar, *Primzahlverteilung, Die Grundlehren der Math. Wiss. in Einzeldarst.*, Vol. **91**. Berlin: Springer, 1957.

8. D. Shanks, *Solved and Unsolved Problems in Number Theory*. Washington, D.C.: Spartan Books, 1962.

9. W. Sierpinski, "Remarques sur la répartition des nombres premiers," *Colloqu. Math.*, **1**, 1948, pp. 193–194.

10. A. Walfisz, "Stark isolierte Primzahlen," *Doklady Akad. Nauk SSSR*, **90**, 1953, pp. 711–713.

CHAPTER 4

Congruences

1. CONGRUENCES AS EQUIVALENCE RELATIONS. GENERAL PROPERTIES

We already met with the concept of "congruence" in Section 3.3. In this section we are going to explore it more systematically.

Definition 1.

$$a \equiv b \,(\text{mod } m) \underset{\text{def}}{\Leftrightarrow} m \mid a - b \qquad (\text{read: } a \text{ congruent to } b \text{ modulo } m).$$

$$a \not\equiv b \,(\text{mod } m) \underset{\text{def}}{\Leftrightarrow} m \nmid a - b \qquad (\text{read: } a \text{ not congruent—or incongruent—}$$
$$\text{to } b \text{ modulo } m).$$

If the "modulus" m is known and there is no danger of confusion, then one may write simply $a \equiv b(m)$ or even $a \equiv b$ only, and similarly $a \not\equiv b(m)$, or simply $a \not\equiv b$.

Theorem 1. *Modulo any integer m, the following congruences are equivalent (that is, each implies and is implied by each one of the other three): $a \equiv b$, $b \equiv a$, $b - a \equiv 0$, $a - b \equiv 0$.*

PROOF. Left to the reader.

Definition 2. If x is an integer and $x \equiv b \,(\text{mod } m)$, then b is said to be a *residue of x mod m*. If $0 \le b < m$, then b is called a *least positive* residue† of x mod m; if $-m/2 < b \le m/2$, then b is called a *least* residue of x mod m.

† See footnote to Definition 7.

36

Definition 3. A set of integers is called a *complete set of residues* (*mod m*), if no two of them are congruent (mod *m*), and if every rational integer is congruent to one of them (mod *m*).

EXAMPLE

$\{7, 8, -5, 10, 18, 40, 48\}$ form a complete set of residues (mod 7).

Integers that have the same residue with respect to a given modulus stand in a simple relation to each other. While the reader is presumably familiar with the meaning of this sentence and, in general, with equivalence relations, we recall here for convenience, a few pertinent definitions, followed by some examples.

Definition 4. (i) Given a set **S** of elements (not necessarily integers), any set $\mathscr{R} = \{(\alpha, \beta)\}$ of ordered pairs, $\alpha \in \mathbf{S}$, $\beta \in \mathbf{S}$ is called a (binary) *relation*. If $\alpha \in \mathbf{S}$, $\beta \in \mathbf{S}$ and $(\alpha, \beta) \in \mathscr{R}$, we say that α is in relation $\mathscr{R}$ to β and write $\alpha \mathscr{R} \beta$. (ii) A relation $\mathscr{R}$ among the elements of a set **S** is said to be *reflexive* if $\alpha \in \mathbf{S} \Rightarrow \alpha \mathscr{R} \alpha$; $\mathscr{R}$ is said to be *symmetric* if $\alpha, \beta \in \mathbf{S}$, $\alpha \mathscr{R} \beta \Rightarrow \beta \mathscr{R} \alpha$; finally, $\mathscr{R}$ is said to be *transitive* if $\alpha, \beta, \gamma \in \mathbf{S}$, $\alpha \mathscr{R} \beta$, $\beta \mathscr{R} \gamma \Rightarrow \alpha \mathscr{R} \gamma$. (iii) A relation $\mathscr{R}$ which is reflexive, symmetric, and transitive is said to be an *equivalence relation*. (iv) If $\mathscr{R}$ is an equivalence relation and $\alpha \mathscr{R} \beta$ then α is said to be equivalent to β under $\mathscr{R}$.

EXAMPLES

1. Ordinary equality, $a = b$. We check that $a = a$, $a = b \Rightarrow b = a$, and $a = b$, $b = c \Rightarrow a = c$; hence, ordinary equality is reflexive, symmetric, and transitive. It is an equivalence relation. Actually, the general concept of an equivalence relation arises by abstracting these key properties of ordinary equality.

2. The relation "less than," $a < b$. Clearly, $a < b$, $b < c \Rightarrow a < c$ and the relation is transitive. However, $a < a$ is false and $a < b$ does not imply $b < a$; hence, this relation is neither reflexive, nor symmetric.

3. The relation "divides," $a \mid b$. By Theorem 3.1(1) and 3.1(3) $a \mid a$ and $a \mid b$, $b \mid c \Rightarrow a \mid c$; hence, this relation is reflexive and transitive. However, $a \mid b$ does *not* imply $b \mid a$; hence, this relation is not symmetric.

4. The relation "to be the brother of" is transitive, but not reflexive, nor is it symmetric. (The fact that John is the brother of Mary does not imply that Mary is the brother of John.)

5. The relation "to be the son of" is not reflexive; nor is it symmetric, or transitive.

6. The relation "to look exactly alike" is reflexive, symmetric, and transitive; hence, it is an equivalence relation. However,

7. the relation "to resemble (somewhat,)" while reflexive and symmetric, is not transitive: it is possible that Peter resembles John (somewhat) and John resembles (somewhat) Dick, but Peter does not appear to resemble Dick at all.

Theorem 2.   *For every integer m, the congruence modulo m is an equivalence relation.*

PROOF. By Definition 1 and Theorem 1, modulo any integer m, $a \equiv a$; and also $a \equiv b$ implies $b \equiv a$ so that it only remains to check the transitivity: if $a \equiv b$ and $b \equiv c$, then

$$a - b = km, b - c = lm;$$

hence,

$$a - c = (a - b) + (b - c) = (k + l)m \Rightarrow m \mid a - c \Leftrightarrow a \equiv c,$$

and the proof is complete.

Each equivalence relation among the elements of a given set S leads to a partition of these elements into "equivalence classes." Formally, we have

Definition 5.   Given a set S and a relation $\mathscr{R}$ defined on S, all elements equivalent under $\mathscr{R}$ to a given one are said to form† an equivalence class.

EXAMPLE

In a box there are 24 marbles, of which 10 are red, 5 green, and 9 yellow. The relation "to have the same color" is easily seen to be an equivalence relation (see Example 6 above). Under it the 24 marbles are partitioned into three equivalence classes: one consisting of 10 red marbles, another of 5 green marbles, and the last of 9 yellow marbles.

Definition 6.   The equivalence classes induced by the congruence modulo m are called *residue classes modulo m.*

Theorem 3.   *The sets $0 \le r \le m - 1$ and $-m/2 < r \le m/2$ form complete sets of residues.*

PROOF. Left as an exercise to the reader.

Definition 7.   The set $0 \le r \le m - 1$ is called a *complete set of least*

† See Problem 2, page 63.

positive† residues; the set $-m/2 < r \le m/2$ is called a *complete set of least residues*.

Theorem 4.   *The following statements hold, all congruences without indication of a modulus being understood* mod *m*:

(1) $a \equiv b \Rightarrow ca \equiv cb$;

(2) $a \equiv b, c \equiv d \Rightarrow a + c \equiv b + d$;

(3) $a \equiv b, c \equiv d \Rightarrow ar + cs \equiv br + ds$;

(4) $a \equiv b, c \equiv d \Rightarrow ac \equiv bd$;

(5) $a \equiv b \Rightarrow a^n \equiv b^n$;

(6) $a \equiv b \pmod{mn} \Rightarrow a \equiv b \pmod{m}$;

(7) $a \equiv b \pmod{m} \Leftrightarrow a \equiv b \pmod{-m}$.

All these statements are immediate consequences of Definition 1; their proofs are left to the reader.

Theorem 5.   *If* $p(x)$ *is a polynomial with integer coefficients and* $a \equiv b$ (mod *m*), *then* $p(a) \equiv p(b)$ (mod *m*).

PROOF follows from Theorem 4(5) and 4(3).

So far, the properties of congruences appeared to be almost identical with the corresponding properties of ordinary equality. This observation illustrates well the point, that to some extent the properties of an equivalence relation are due to the fact that *it is an equivalence relation*. Ordinary equality and congruence (mod *m*), being both equivalence relations, share, of course, all those properties due precisely to the fact that they *are* equivalence relations. It might, therefore, be appropriate to point out at least one difference between the two relations.

If $ca = cb$ and $c \ne 0$, then we may cancel the common factor c and infer that $a = b$; however, if $c \not\equiv 0 \pmod{m}$ and $ca \equiv cb \pmod{m}$, we *cannot*, in general, conclude that $a \equiv b \pmod{m}$. In other words, the converse of Theorem 4(4) is false. Consider, for instance, the

EXAMPLE

$a = 21$, $b = 16$, $c = 12$, $m = 10$. Then $c \equiv 2 \not\equiv 0 \pmod{10}$, $ca = 252 \equiv 2 \pmod{10}$, $cb = 192 \equiv 2 \pmod{10}$, so that $ca - cb = 252 - 192 = 60 \equiv 0 \pmod{10}$; but $a = 21 \equiv 1 \pmod{10}$, $b = 16 \equiv 6 \pmod{10}$ and clearly, $1 \not\equiv 6 \pmod{10}$.

In view of this situation, it is comforting to know that a common factor may be canceled in a congruence, provided that it is coprime to the modulus.

---

† This is the customary definition; it might be better to call these *non-negative*, rather than *positive* residues and to reserve the name of complete set of least positive residue for the set $1 \le r \le m$; occasionally, the distinction is relevant.

Indeed if $ca \equiv cb \pmod{m}$, then $m \mid c(a - b)$; hence, if also $(c, m) = 1$ then it follows from Theorem 3.7 that $m \mid a - b \Leftrightarrow a \equiv b \pmod{m}$, as asserted. More generally, the following cancellation rule holds.

Theorem 6. $ca \equiv cb \pmod{m} \Rightarrow a \equiv b \pmod{m/(m, c)}$.

REMARK 1. One observes that the condition $c \not\equiv 0 \pmod{m}$ *does not* appear as an assumption in Theorem 6. Indeed, if $c \equiv 0 \pmod{m}$, $(m, c) = |m|$ and the last congruence reduces to $a \equiv b \pmod{\pm 1}$ (see Theorem 4(7)), which holds trivially for all integers a and b.

PROOF OF THEOREM 6. Let $(c, m) = d$; then $c = dc_1$, $m = dm_1$ with $(c_1, m_1) = 1$. By Definition 1, $ca \equiv cb \pmod{m} \Leftrightarrow ca - cb = mk, k \in \mathbf{Z}$, or $c(a - b) = mk$, so that $dc_1(a - b) = dm_1 k \Rightarrow c_1(a - b) = m_1 k \Rightarrow m_1 \mid c_1(a - b) \Rightarrow m_1 \mid a - b$ by $(c_1, m_1) = 1$ and Theorem 3.7; hence, $a \equiv b \pmod{m_1}$ and the Theorem is proven, because $m_1 = m/d = m/(m, c)$.

By setting $d = (m, c) = 1$, we obtain as an immediate corollary from Theorem 6,

Corollary 6.1. $(c, m) = 1$, $ca \equiv cb \pmod{m} \Rightarrow a \equiv b \pmod{m}$,

a result we had already found directly.

In the study of congruences with a composite modulus, the following Theorem is useful.

Theorem 7. $a \equiv b \pmod{m_1}$, $a \equiv b \pmod{m_2} \Rightarrow a \equiv b \pmod{[m_1, m_2]}$

PROOF. The assumptions state that $a - b$ is a common multiple of m_1 and of m_2; hence, the result follows from Theorem 3.8.

Corollary 7.1. $(m_1, m_2) = 1$, $a \equiv b \pmod{m_1}$, $a \equiv b \pmod{m_2} \Rightarrow a \equiv b \pmod{m_1 m_2}$.

The easy proof is left to the reader.

2. OPERATIONS WITH RESIDUE CLASSES

Let us consider the set $\{0, 1, 2, \dots, m - 1\}$ of least positive residues modulo m. By Theorem 3, each of these integers belongs to exactly one residue class. All congruences being understood modulo m, let **A** be a residue class to which belongs the least positive residue r_1; then $\mathbf{A} = \{a \mid a \equiv r_1\}$. Similarly, let $\mathbf{B} = \{b \mid b \equiv r_2\}$. By Theorem 4, if $a \in \mathbf{A}$ and $b \in \mathbf{B}$, then $a + b \equiv r_1 + r_2$ and $a \cdot b \equiv r_1 \cdot r_2$. If r_3 and r_4 are least positive residues such that $r_1 + r_2 \equiv r_3$ and $r_1 \cdot r_2 \equiv r_4$, then for *every* element a of **A** and *every* element b of **B** one has $a + b \equiv r_3$ and $a \cdot b \equiv r_4$, respectively; it is important to observe here that r_3 and r_4 are independent of a and b and depend only on r_1 and

r_2. Moreover, if we define the residue classes $\mathbf{C} = \{c \mid c \equiv r_3\}$ and $\mathbf{D} = \{d \mid d \equiv r_4\}$ then $a + b \equiv c$ and $a \cdot b \equiv d$ hold, regardless of the particular choice of elements within their residue class. This shows that the residue class of a sum or of a product does not depend at all on the summands, and factors themselves, but only on their respective residue classes.

This fact permits us to define *addition* and *multiplication* of *residue classes.* We define $\mathbf{A} + \mathbf{B} = \mathbf{C}$ to mean that any element of the residue class $\mathbf{A}$ added to any element of the residue class $\mathbf{B}$ equals an element of the residue class $\mathbf{C}$ and previous considerations have shown that this operation is, indeed, well defined. The equality $\mathbf{A} \cdot \mathbf{B} = \mathbf{D}$ has to be interpreted in a similar way. The results of these reasonings may be formalized in

Theorem 8. *The operations of addition and multiplication of residue classes are well-defined; the set of residue classes is closed under both operations.*

The last statement means, of course, that the sum and the product of any two residue classes is again a residue class. The least positive residue of a residue class may be considered (and is sometimes called) the "representative" of that class, and $\mathbf{A} = \{a \mid a \equiv r\}$ is conveniently represented by the symbol (r). Practically, in order to add or multiply residue classes, it is sufficient to add, or multiply their representatives, always dropping multiples of the modulus, so as to stay within the range $0 \le r \le m - 1$. This is called addition, or multiplication modulo m. For instance, to the modulus 5, we have $(2) + (4) = (1)$ and $(2)(3) = (1)$. In this way we may construct addition and multiplication tables for these residue classes. The tables for $m = 5$ and $m = 6$ listed below should be self-explanatory.

$$m = 6$$

addition

multiplication

(A)

	0	1	2	3	4	5
0	0	1	2	3	4	5
1	1	2	3	4	5	0
2	2	3	4	5	0	1
3	3	4	5	0	1	2
4	4	5	0	1	2	3
5	5	0	1	2	3	4

(B)

	0	1	2	3	4	5
0	0	0	0	0	0	0
1	0	1	2	3	4	5
2	0	2	4	0	2	4
3	0	3	0	3	0	3
4	0	4	2	0	4	2
5	0	5	4	3	2	1

$$m = 5$$

addition   multiplication

(C)

	0	1	2	3	4
0	0	1	2	3	4
1	1	2	3	4	0
2	2	3	4	0	1
3	3	4	0	1	2
4	4	0	1	2	3

(D)

	0	1	2	3	4
0	0	0	0	0	0
1	0	1	2	3	4
2	0	2	4	1	3
3	0	3	1	4	2
4	0	4	3	2	1

A comparison of these tables shows that the addition tables for $m = 5$ and $m = 6$ are very similar: increasing integers succeed each other on successive parallels to one of the diagonals on which we find $m - 1$. Of more interest are the multiplication tables. From that for $m = 6$, we read off such results as $(2)(2) = (4)$, $(3)(1) = (3)$; more generally, $(a)(1) = (1)(a) = (a)$. These relations look very much like the corresponding ones among ordinary integers and they do not surprise us. The result $(4)(5) = (2)$ is also easily interpreted, because $4 \cdot 5 = 20 \equiv 2 \pmod 6$. However, we also find $(3)(2) = (0)$. This is, of course, correct, because $3 \cdot 2 = 6 \equiv 0 \pmod 6$, but we have to note the fact that we obtain "zero" as product of two factors, both different from zero. We observe that this situation does not occur in the multiplication table for $m = 5$, where the products of non-vanishing factors (inside the heavy frame) are all different from zero. The reason for this difference is that 5 is a prime, while 6 is not. Technically, the set of residue classes modulo a prime form a *field*, while those modulo a composite integer form a *commutative ring with divisors of zero* (see Appendix B, Section 2(b)). The simplest way to avoid these "divisors of zero" is to restrict our attention to residue classes that are relatively prime to the modulus; this motivates the following definitions.

Definition 8.   A residue class $\mathbf{A} = \{a \mid a \equiv r \pmod m\}$ is called a *prime residue class*, if $(r, m) = 1$.

Definition 9.   A *complete set of reduced (or prime) residues* is a set $\mathbf{S} = \{r_i\}$ satisfying the following condition:

    (i) $i \neq j \Rightarrow r_i \not\equiv r_j \pmod m$;

   (ii) $r \in S \Rightarrow (r, m) = 1$;

   (iii) $(a, m) = 1 \Rightarrow \exists r \in S \ni a \equiv r \,(\text{mod } m)$.

If, in addition, $0 < r \leq m$, then S is called a *reduced set of least positive residues*; if $-m/2 < r \leq m/2$, then S is *a reduced set of least residues*.

In words, a complete set of reduced residues consists of a set of mutually incongruent integers, all coprime to the modulus, and such that every integer coprime to the modulus is congruent to (exactly) one of them.

Theorem 9. *Let* $\mathbf{R}$ *be the set of prime residue classes* mod m. *If* $\mathbf{A}, \mathbf{B} \in \mathbf{R}$, *then the equation* $\mathbf{AX} = \mathbf{B}$ *has exactly one solution* $\mathbf{X} \in \mathbf{R}$.

Corollary 9.1. *Every prime residue class* $\mathbf{A}$ *has exactly one "inverse" class* $\mathbf{B} = \mathbf{A}^{-1}$, *such that* $\mathbf{A} \cdot \mathbf{A}^{-1} = \mathbf{I}$, *where* $\mathbf{I} = \{n \mid n \equiv 1 \,(\text{mod } m)\}$.

The statement of Theorem 9 may be reformulated as follows: If $(a, m) = (b, m) = 1$ then the congruence $ax \equiv b \,(\text{mod } m)$ has exactly one solution modulo m; if $x = c$ is that solution, then $(c, m) = 1$.

PROOF. Let $S = \{r_1, r_2, \ldots, r_k\}$ be a set of least positive reduced residues mod m, and let $\mathbf{A} = (a), a \in S$. Next, consider the set $ar_1, ar_2, \ldots, ar_k$. Clearly, $(ar_j, m) = 1$, because $(a, m) = (r_j, m) = 1$. Also if $i \neq j$, $ar_i \not\equiv ar_j \,(\text{mod } m)$, because otherwise $m \mid a(r_i - r_j)$ and $(m, a) = 1 \Rightarrow m \mid r_i - r_j$, which is impossible for $0 < r_i, r_j < m$. Hence, the k integers $ar_j \,(1 \leq j \leq k)$ form a complete set of reduced residues mod m and each of its elements is congruent to exactly one element of S. In particular, if $\mathbf{B} = (b), b \in S$, there is exactly one element ar_j satisfying $ar_j \equiv b \,(\text{mod } m)$. Hence, if $C = \{c \mid c \equiv r_j \,(\text{mod } m)\}$, $ax \equiv b \,(\text{mod } m)$ holds if, and only if, $x \in C$. The proof is completed by the remark that $c \in C \Rightarrow (c, m) = 1$.

*From Theorem 9 and Corollary 9.1, together with obvious remarks concerning closure and associativity follows (see Appendix B, Section 1(a)):

Corollary 9.2. *The set* $\mathbf{R}$ *of prime residue classes* mod m *form a group under residue class multiplication; the identity element of the group is the class* $\mathbf{I} = \{n \mid n \equiv 1 \,(\text{mod } m)\}$.

3. THEOREMS OF FERMAT, EULER, AND WILSON

Definition 10. The number of positive integers r, not exceeding m and coprime with m is denoted by $\phi(m)$. In symbols

$$\phi(m) = \sum_{\substack{(m, r) = 1 \\ 0 < r \leq m}} 1.$$

EXAMPLES

$$\phi(1) = 1, \quad \phi(2) = 1, \quad \phi(3) = 2, \quad \phi(4) = 2, \quad \phi(5) = 4,$$

$$\phi(p) = p - 1, \quad \phi(p^r) = p^r - p^{r-1} = p^r\left(1 - \frac{1}{p}\right).$$

This function $\phi(m)$ is usually called Euler's ϕ-function.

REMARK 2†. A complete set of reduced residues consists of exactly $\phi(m)$ integers.

Theorem 10 (Euler). $(a, m) = 1 \Rightarrow a^{\phi(m)} \equiv 1 \pmod{m}$.

FIRST PROOF. Let $r_1, r_2, \ldots, r_k$ be a reduced set of residues mod m. If $(a, m) = 1$, then as seen in the proof of Theorem 9, also $ar_1, ar_2, \ldots, ar_k$ form a reduced set of residues; hence, each element of the first set is congruent (mod m) to one and only one element of the second set. Multiplying all these congruences termwise (see Theorem 4) we obtain $r_1 r_2 \cdots r_k \equiv a^k r_1 r_2 \cdots r_k$ (mod m). But $(r_1 r_2 \cdots r_k, m) = 1$; hence, by Corollary 6.1 we may cancel the common factor $r_1 \cdots r_k$ and obtain $1 \equiv a^k \pmod{m}$. As already observed (Remark 2), $k = \phi(m)$ and the Theorem is proven.

SECOND PROOF. (Assumes familiarity with Lagrange's Theorem—see Appendix B, Section 1(b)). $k = \phi(m)$ is the order of the multiplicative group **R** of prime residues; $(a, m) = 1 \Rightarrow \mathbf{A} = (a) \in \mathbf{R}$; hence, by Lagrange's Theorem, $\mathbf{A}^k = \mathbf{I}$ or $a^k = a^{\phi(m)} \equiv 1 \pmod{m}$.

The brevity and simplicity of this argument illustrates again the advantage of the modern algebraic approach.

Theorem 11 (Fermat). $p \nmid a \Rightarrow a^{p-1} \equiv 1 \pmod{p}$.

PROOF. Take $m = p$ in Theorem 10 and use $\phi(p) = p - 1$ (see preceding examples).

EXAMPLES

Modulo 7 one has $5^1 = 5$, $5^2 = 25 \equiv 4$, $5^3 = 125 \equiv 6$, $5^4 = 625 \equiv 2$, $5^5 = 3125 \equiv 3$, $5^6 = 15625 \equiv 1$. On the other hand, modulo 6 one finds $5^1 = 5$, $5^2 = 25 \equiv 1$, and, indeed, $\phi(6) = 2$ (a complete set of reduced residues mod 6 is $\{1, 5\}$).

Theorem 12 (Wilson). $(n - 1)! + 1 \equiv 0 \pmod{n} \Leftrightarrow n = p$.

† See Problem 18, page 64.

In other words, said congruence holds if n is a prime and is false if n is a composite number. Hence, the verification of this congruence may be considered as a test (not necessarily a very practical one) of primality for n.

PROOF. (i) Theorem 12 holds trivially for $n = 2$ and $n = 3$; hence, let $n = p \geq 5$ and select an r satisfying $1 \leq r \leq p - 1$; then $(r, p) = 1$ and, by Corollary 9.1, there exists exactly one m such that $mr \equiv 1 \pmod{p}$ and $1 \leq m \leq p - 1$. In general, $m \neq r$. Indeed if $m = r$, $m^2 - 1 \equiv 0 \pmod{p}$ so that $p \mid (m + 1)(m - 1)$, possible only if $m = 1$ or $m = p - 1$. In particular all $p - 3$ integers $2 \leq r \leq p - 2$ fall into pairs (observe that $p - 3$ is even), such that the corresponding products are congruent to $1 \pmod{p}$. Hence, $2 \cdot 3 \cdot 4 \cdot \cdots \cdot (p - 2) \equiv 1 \pmod{p}$ so that $(p - 1)! \equiv (p - 1) \equiv -1 \pmod{p}$ and the implication $\Leftarrow$ of the Theorem is proven.

(ii) The other implication is rather trivial. Indeed, in case n is not a prime, $n = a \cdot b$, $1 < a < n$, so that $a \mid (n - 1)!$, $a \nmid ((n - 1)! + 1)$ and, a fortiori,

$$n \nmid ((n - 1)! + 1) \Leftrightarrow (n - 1)! + 1 \not\equiv 0 \pmod{n}$$

and the proof is complete.

*The preceding proof follows essentially Gauss [2] and is quite satisfactory. Theorem 12 was actually known long before Wilson, presumably already by Leibniz. It was first published by Waring (1734–1798) who ascribes it to Wilson (1741–1793). It may be of interest to indicate also a different proof, not because it is superior to Gauss' proof, but because it is of an entirely different character and illustrates the use that can be made of analysis in number theoretic problems. This second proof is due to M. A. Stern (see [5], p. 391). The first published proof of Theorem 12 is due to Lagrange (see Problem 15).

SECOND PROOF OF THEOREM 12. The well-known Maclaurin series

$$-\log(1 - x) = \log \frac{1}{1 - x} = x + \frac{x^2}{2} + \frac{x^3}{3} + \cdots$$

shows that

$$\exp\left(x + \frac{x^2}{2} + \frac{x^3}{3} + \cdots\right) = \frac{1}{1 - x} = 1 + x + x^2 + \cdots.$$

This may be written as

$$e^x e^{x^2/2} e^{x^3/3} \cdots = 1 + x + x^2 + x^3 + \cdots.$$

The left-hand side may be expanded in a power series, as follows:

$$\left(1 + \frac{x}{1!} + \frac{x^2}{2!} + \cdots\right)\left(1 + \frac{x^2/2}{1!} + \frac{(x^2/2)^2}{2!} + \cdots\right) \cdots$$

$$\left(1 + \frac{x^p/p}{1!} + \frac{(x^p/p)^2}{2!} + \cdots\right)$$

$$= 1 + \frac{x}{1!} + x^2\left(\frac{1}{2!} + \frac{1}{2}\right) + x^3\left(\frac{1}{3!} + \frac{1}{1!}\frac{1/2}{1!} + \frac{1/3}{1!}\right) + \cdots$$

$$+ x^p\left(\frac{1}{p!} + \frac{1}{(p-2)!}\frac{1/2}{1!} + \cdots + \frac{1/p}{1!}\right) + \cdots.$$

The coefficient of x^p is seen to be of the form $1/p! + r/s + 1/p$, where r/s is the sum of a finite number of rational fractions that do not contain the factor p in their denominator. Hence, if $(r, s) = 1$, $p \nmid s$. The coefficient of x^p (as of all powers of x) is unity, so that $1/p! + r/s + 1/p = 1$, whence $1 - r/s = 1/p! + 1/p = (1 + (p - 1)!)/p!$ or $\alpha = (p - 1)!(s - r)/s = (1 + (p - 1)!)/p$. The right-hand term here shows that there are only two alternatives: Either $p \mid ((p - 1)! + 1)$, and then α is an integer; or else, it is a rational fraction with denominator p. However, as seen, $p \nmid s$, so that $\alpha = (p - 1)!(s - r)/s$ rules out this second alternative, and $p \mid ((p - 1)! + 1)$ as we wanted to prove. The other (trivial) implication may be proven as before.

4. LINEAR CONGRUENCES

The problem of solving single equations or systems of equations in one, respectively several unknowns, is familiar from elementary algebra. Similar problems may be asked concerning congruences. If $f(x)$ is a polynomial with integral coefficients and m is an integer, one may ask for those values of x, for which $f(x) \equiv 0 \pmod{m}$. This problem is, of course, equivalent to that of solving the Diophantine equation $f(x) = ym$ in integers x and y. The theory developed so far permits us to handle such problems, especially in case $f(x)$ is a linear polynomial.

Theorem 13.   *If* $(a, m) = 1$, *then*

$$ax \equiv b \pmod{m} \tag{1}$$

has a unique solution mod m.

PROOF. By Theorem 10, $y = a^{\phi(m)-1}$ is a solution of $ay \equiv 1$; hence, also of $aby \equiv b$. Setting $x = by$, $x = ba^{\phi(m)-1}$ satisfies (1) and the existence of a solution is proven. If x_1 and x_2 are two solutions, then $ax_1 \equiv b$, $ax_2 \equiv b \Rightarrow$ $a(x_1 - x_2) \equiv 0 \Leftrightarrow m \mid a(x_2 - x_1)$ and, using $(a, m) = 1$ and Theorem 3.7,

$m \mid x_2 - x_1 \Leftrightarrow x_1 \equiv x_2$. Hence, if x_1 and x_2 are both least positive residues mod m, $x_1 = x_2$, thus proving the uniqueness (mod m) of the solution.

Corollary 13.1. *If $(a, m) = 1$, then x is a solution of* (1) *if and only if it is of the form $x = ba^{\phi(m)-1} + km$, $k \in \mathbf{Z}$.*

PROOF. By the proof of Theorem 13 we know that $x_0 = ba^{\phi(m)-1}$ is a solution and that all other solutions of (1) differ from x_0 by an integral multiple of m. It is, therefore, sufficient to verify that for every $k \in \mathbf{Z}$, x satisfies (1):

$$ax = ba^{\phi(m)} + kma \equiv ba^{\phi(m)} \equiv b \,(\mathrm{mod}\ m)$$

by Theorem 10.

Having settled the case $(a, m) = 1$, we now consider the general case $(a, m) = d$.

Theorem 14. *If $(a, m) = d$, then* (1) *has no solution if $d \nmid b$ and has a unique solution* mod m/d *if $d \mid b$.*

PROOF. (1) is equivalent to the Diophantine equation

$$ax = b + km; \tag{2}$$

if $x = c \in \mathbf{Z}$ is a solution, then $b = ac - km$ and, by Theorem 3.1, $d \mid ac - km = b$; hence, if $d \nmid b$, no such solution can exist. If $d \mid b$, set $a = da_1$, $b = db_1$, $m = dm_1$; then $(a_1, m_1) = 1$ and after an obvious simplification (2) becomes $a_1 x = b_1 + km_1$, which is equivalent to $a_1 x \equiv b_1 \,(\mathrm{mod}\ m_1)$, $(a_1, m_1) = 1$. By Theorem 13 we know that this congruence has a unique solution modulo $m_1 = m/d$ and the proof of Theorem 14 is complete.

We observed already repeatedly that the problem of solving (1) is identical with that of solving the Diophantine equation $ax + my = b$. It is often convenient to have the results just obtained reformulated directly in terms of Diophantine equations; this, of course, involves hardly any new work, but we shall modify slightly the notation, in order to make it more symmetrical.

Theorem 15. (Bachet, ca. 1612). *Consider the Diophantine equation*

$$ax + by = c \tag{3}$$

with $(a, b) = d$. If $d \nmid c$, then (3) *has no solutions; if $d \mid c$, then* (3) *has infinitely many solutions. If x_0, y_0 is a solution of* (3), *then all other solutions are given by*

$$\begin{aligned} x &= x_0 + n(b/d) \\ y &= y_0 - n(a/d) \end{aligned} \tag{4}$$

with n running through all rational integers.

PROOF OF THEOREM 15. All statements are immediate consequences of Theorem 14, except the assertion that (4) represents all solutions of (3).

Let $a = a_1 d$, $b = b_1 d$, $c = c_1 d$; then, after cancellation of the common factor d_1, equation (3) becomes

$$a_1 x + b_1 y = c, \qquad (a_1, b_1) = 1. \tag{5}$$

All solutions x of (5) satisfy $a_1 x \equiv c_1 \pmod{b_1}$, $(a_1, b_1) = 1$. Theorem 14 guarantees that all solutions of this congruence (hence, also all solutions of (5)) are of the form $x = x_0 + n b_1$ and, by the symmetry (in x and y) of (5) it also follows that $y = y_0 + m a_1$. Substituting these in (5), $a_1 x_0 + b_1 y_0 + a_1 b_1 (m + n) = c_1$; we select now x_0 and y_0 as solutions of (5), obtaining $a_1 b_1 (m + n) = 0$, so that $m = -n$ and the proof of (4) is complete.

REMARK 3. A particular solution x_0, y_0 of (5), hence also of (3), may be found as follows: By Theorem 3 there are integers m and n such that $a_1 m + b_1 n = 1$; hence, $a_1(m c_1) + b_1(n c_1) = c_1$ and we may take $x_0 = m c_1$, $y_0 = n c_1$. A practical way to find m and n follows from the Euclidean algorithm (see Chapter 3, Problem 3).

Systems of k congruences in k unknowns, all taken to the same modulus m can be reduced to k independent congruences, involving only one unknown. Once this is done, we may use Theorem 14. It is sufficient to illustrate the situation for $k = 2$. Consider, therefore, the following system, all congruences being understood modulo m:

$$\begin{aligned} a_1 x + b_1 y &\equiv c_1, \\ a_2 x + b_2 y &\equiv c_2. \end{aligned} \tag{6}$$

Let†

$$D = \begin{vmatrix} a_1 b_1 \\ a_2 b_2 \end{vmatrix}, \quad D_1 = \begin{vmatrix} c_1 b_1 \\ c_2 b_2 \end{vmatrix}, \quad D_2 = \begin{vmatrix} a_1 c_1 \\ a_2 c_2 \end{vmatrix}.$$

Then, as in the proof of Cramer's rule, one shows that the system (6) implies

$$\begin{aligned} Dx &\equiv D_1, \\ Dy &\equiv D_2. \end{aligned} \tag{6'}$$

If $(D, m) = 1$, then Theorem 13 is applicable, (6') has solutions x_0, y_0, which are unique modulo m. By direct substitution in (6) one easily verifies (making once more use of $(D, m) = 1$) that these solutions of (6') actually

---

† For convenience we denote here these determinants, which are rational numbers, by capitals, rather than lower-case letters.

satisfy (6), so that (6) and (6′) are equivalent systems. The case $(D, m) > 1$ can be handled similarly, using Theorem 14, but we shall not pursue this matter further.

5. *THE CHINESE REMAINDER THEOREM

As we just saw, systems of linear congruences involving *several unknowns*, but all to the *same modulus*, reduce quite trivially to ordinary congruences in a single unknown. The situation is rather different, if we have to deal with a system of linear congruences in a *single unknown*, each taken to a *different modulus*. This is a famous problem; the main result, our Theorem 16, was known to Sun Tsu (see [6] and Example 1 on page 50) and, possibly even to Chinese mathematicians before the Christian era, whence the name under which it is generally known. It might be of some interest to observe that thousands of miles away from Sun Tsu, but almost exactly at the same time (ca. 100 A.D.) Nicomachus (Neo-Pythagorean born in Gerasa (Palestine)) stated and solved *exactly* the same problem of Example 1.

Theorem 16 (Chinese Remainder Theorem). *Consider the system of k linear congruences* $a_i x \equiv b_i \pmod{m_i}$, $(i = 1, 2, ..., k)$, *where* $(m_i, m_j) = 1$ *for all* $i \neq j$ *and* $(a_i, m_i) = 1$ *for* $1 \leq i \leq k$; *let* $m = m_1 m_2 \cdots m_k$.

This system has a unique solution modulo m; one solution x_0 *is given by* (7) *and all others are of the form* $x = x_0 + nm$, *where n is any rational integer.*

REMARK 4. If we try to solve the congruence $ax \equiv b \pmod{m}$, where $m = p_1^{s_1} p_2^{s_2} \cdots p_k^{s_k}$, then it follows from Corollary 7.1 that the problem is equivalent to that of solving the k congruences $ax \equiv b \pmod{m_i}$ with $m_i = p_i^{s_i}$. This shows that the problem considered by Theorem 16, as well as the condition $i \neq j \Rightarrow (m_i, m_j) = 1$ (which may seem strange, and at first sight, unduly restrictive), are actually both quite natural.

PROOF OF THEOREM 16. By $(a_i, m_i) = 1$ and Theorem 13, we know that each congruence has a solution of the form $x \equiv c_i \pmod{m_i}$. Set $t_i = m/m_i$ and let y_i be a solution of $t_i y_i \equiv 1 \pmod{m_i}$. We know, again by Theorem 13, that each of these congruences has $\pmod{m_i}$ a unique solution y_i, because also $(t_i, m_i) = 1$. Consider now

$$x_0 = y_1 t_1 c_1 + y_2 t_2 c_2 + \cdots + y_k t_k c_k. \tag{7}$$

Clearly, $t_j \equiv 0 \pmod{m_i}$ for every $i \neq j$; hence, $x_0 \equiv y_i t_i c_i \equiv c_i \pmod{m_i}$, because $y_i t_i \equiv 1 \pmod{m_i}$, and x_0 is a solution of the given system. With

x_0 also $x_0 + nm$ is a solution, because $x_0 + nm \equiv x_0 \pmod{m} \Rightarrow x_0 + nm \equiv x_0 \pmod{m_i}$ by Theorem 4(6). It only remains to verify that we obtain all solutions in this way.

Let x_1 be another solution of the system; then $x_1 - x_0 \equiv 0 \pmod{m_i}$ for every $i (1 \le i \le k)$. Hence, by Corollary 7.1, $x_1 - x_0 \equiv 0 \pmod{m}$, so that $x_1 = x_0 + nm$ and the proof is complete.

EXAMPLES

1. Find the least positive integer, which, upon division by 3 leaves a remainder of 2, upon division by 5 leaves a remainder of 3, and upon division by 7 leaves a remainder of 2 (Sun-Tsu, first century A.D.).

We have to solve the system

$$x \equiv 2 \pmod 3,$$
$$x \equiv 3 \pmod 5,$$
$$x \equiv 2 \pmod 7.$$

Following the steps of the proof of Theorem 16, set $m = 3 \cdot 5 \cdot 7 = 105$, $t_1 = 35$, $t_2 = 21$, $t_3 = 15$. Then y_1, y_2, y_3 are determined by the congruences $35y_1 \equiv 1 \pmod 3$, $21y_2 \equiv 1 \pmod 5$ and $15y_3 \equiv 1 \pmod 7$; these simplify to $2y_1 \equiv 1 \pmod 3$, $y_2 \equiv 1 \pmod 5$, and $y_3 \equiv 1 \pmod 7$, with the obvious solution $y_1 = 2$, $y_2 = 1$, $y_3 = 1$. Hence, by (7);

$$x = 2 \cdot 35 \cdot 2 + 1 \cdot 21 \cdot 3 + 1 \cdot 15 \cdot 2 = 233 \equiv 23 \pmod{105}.$$

The smallest positive solution is $x = 23$, and all solutions (not asked for by Sun-Tsu) are given by $x = 23 + 105n$.

2. Find a positive integer such that, when divided by 3, 4, 5, and 6, it should leave the remainders 2, 3, 4, and 5, respectively (Brahmegupta, 7th century A.D.).

Here the system is

$$x \equiv 2 \pmod 3,$$
$$x \equiv 3 \pmod 4,$$
$$x \equiv 4 \pmod 5,$$
$$x \equiv 5 \pmod 6.$$

Theorem 16 is not directly applicable, because the moduli† are not two by two coprime. But we may use Theorem 16 in order to solve the system formed by the first three congruences. Proceeding as in Example 1, set $m = 3 \cdot 4 \cdot 5 = 60$, $t_1 = 20$, $t_2 = 15$, $t_3 = 12$; then $20y_1 \equiv 1 \pmod 3$, $15y_2 \equiv 1 \pmod 4$,

† For the plural of modulus in the present sense, we shall use "moduli"; see footnote p. 25.

$12y_3 \equiv 1 \pmod{5}$, so that $y_1 = 2$, $y_2 = 3$, $y_3 = 3$ and

$$x_0 = 2 \cdot 20 \cdot 2 + 3 \cdot 15 \cdot 3 + 3 \cdot 12 \cdot 4 = 359 \equiv -1 \pmod{60}.$$

Hence, $x = 60n - 1$ is the general solution of the system formed by the first three congruences. Considering now also the last congruence, $x = 5$ (mod 6), we see that it is automatically satisfied by all solutions of the sub-system of the first three congruences so that $x = 60n - 1$ is the general solution of the whole system and, in particular, $x = 59$ is the smallest positive solution.

One also observes that if the last condition would have been, say, $x \equiv 2$ (mod 6) (or, generally, $x \equiv a \not\equiv 5 \pmod{6}$), then the system would have had no solution at all.

REMARK 5. Suppose that in some of the congruences $(a_i, m_i) = d_i > 1$; then (see Theorem 14) if $d_i \nmid b_i$, the i-th congruence (and, *a fortiori*, the whole system) has no solution. If $d_i \mid b_i$, then the factor d_i may be cancelled in the i-th congruence, which will become $a_i' x \equiv b_i' \pmod{m_i'}$, with $a_i' = a_i/d_i$, $m_i' = m_i/d_i$, $(a_i', m_i') = 1$ and the new system, equivalent to the original one satisfies the conditions of coprimality of the coefficients a_i' and the moduli m_i'.

We shall not discuss systematically the situations that may arise if the other coprimality conditions of Theorem 16 are violated, that is if $(m_i, m_j) = d_{ij} > 1$. The kind of difficulties that may arise were partly illustrated in the discussion of Brahmegupta's example. The interested reader is referred to LeVeque's book [3], where this problem is treated and to Dickson's History [1], Vol. 2, p. 58 where further references are given.

6. *ON PRIMITIVE ROOTS

This section has been inserted only for its intrinsic interest; its results will not be used anywhere else in this book, except in the proof of Theorem 26, which itself is not really indispensable for what follows.

Definition 11.   If $x^r \equiv c \pmod{m}$, then c is said to be an *r-th power residue* (mod *m*).

By Theorem 10, $(a, m) = 1 \Rightarrow a^{\phi(m)} \equiv 1 \pmod{m}$; hence there exists a set **K** of positive integers k such that $a^k \equiv 1 \pmod{m}$. By Remark 3.2, **K** contains a smallest positive integer h. It is easy to see that $h \mid \phi(m)$. Indeed, otherwise, $\phi(m) = hn + r$, with $1 \le r < h$. But this would imply that

$$1 \equiv a^{\phi(m)} = a^{hn+r} = a^{hn}a^r = (a^h)^n \cdot a^r \equiv 1 \cdot a^r \equiv a^r \pmod{m},$$

contrary to the definition of h as *smallest* positive exponent for which $a^h \equiv 1$ (mod m).

Definition 12. If h is the smallest positive integer such that $a^h \equiv 1$ (mod m), then a is said to *belong to the exponent h modulo m.*

REMARK 6. If $a^h \equiv 1$ (mod m), $0 < h \in \mathbf{Z}$, then $(a, m) = 1$; indeed, the congruence means that $\exists l \in \mathbf{Z} \ni a^h = 1 + lm$, or $1 = a^h - lm$ and $d = (a, m)$ divides $a^h - lm$; hence $d \mid 1 \Rightarrow d = 1$.

REMARK 7. If $a^n \equiv 1$ (mod m), then $n = kh$.

PROOF. $h \nmid n \Rightarrow n = lh + r(1 \leq r < h) \Rightarrow 1 \equiv a^n = a^{lh+r} = (a^h)^l \cdot a^r \equiv a^r$ (mod m) contrary to the definition of h.

REMARK 8. $h \leq \phi(m)$; this follows trivially (see Theorem 3.1(6)) from $h \mid \phi(m)$ already established.

Definition 13. If g belongs to the exponent $\phi(m)$ modulo m, then g is called a *primitive root* mod m.

Theorem 17. *If g is a primitive root* mod m, *then* $g, g^2, ..., g^{\phi(m)}$ *are all incongruent modulo m and form a complete set of reduced residues.*

PROOF. The number of elements in the set is exactly $\phi(m)$ (see Remark 2) and satisfies $(g^r)^{\phi(m)} = (g^{\phi(m)})^r \equiv 1$ (mod m); hence, by Remark 6, all are coprime to m; therefore, all we have to show is that they are pairwise incongruent mod m. Let us assume the contrary; that is, let $1 \leq r < s \leq \phi(m)$ and assume that $g^r \equiv g^s$ (mod m); then $g^{s-r} \equiv 1$ (mod m) with $1 \leq s - r \leq \phi(m) - 1$, contrary to the definition of g as a primitive root.

Corollary 17.1. *Necessary and sufficient condition for g to be a primitive root* mod m *are that $(g, m) = 1$ and that $g, g^2, ..., g^{\phi(m)}$ be all incongruent* mod m.

PROOF. Left to the reader.

Corollary 17.2. *If g is a primitive root* mod m, *then* $g^r \equiv 1$ (mod m) $\Rightarrow$ $\phi(m) \mid r$.

PROOF. Remark 7 with $h = \phi(m)$.

Corollary 17.3. *If g is a primitive root* mod p, *then* $g, g^2, ..., g^{p-1} \equiv 1$ (mod p) *are all incongruent* mod p *and* $g^r \equiv 1$ (mod p) $\Rightarrow (p - 1) \mid r$.

PROOF. Corollaries 17.1 and 17.2 for $m = p$.

Definition 14. If $(a, m) = 1$ and m admits the primitive root g, then the exponent k for which $a \equiv g^k$ (mod m) is called the *index of a* (mod m).

REMARK 9. The index of an integer is uniquely defined if we also require that $0 \le k < \phi(m)$. (Why?)

REMARK 10. The indices behave very much like logarithms and there exists a calculus of indices of considerable interest, but it will not be presented here; the interested reader may wish to consult [3], Chapter III, pp. 111–115.

Theorem 18. *If b belongs to the exponent $h \pmod{m}$ and $(k, h) = d$, then b^k belongs* mod m *to the exponent h/d.*

PROOF (all congruences are mod m). Let b^k belong to the exponent n; then $(b^k)^n \equiv 1$. By Remark 7,

$$h \mid kn \Rightarrow \frac{h}{d} \mid \frac{k}{d} \cdot n \Rightarrow \frac{h}{d} \mid n,$$

because $(h/d, k/d) = 1$. Conversely, $(b^k)^{h/d} = b^{kh/d} = (b^h)^{k/d} \equiv 1$; hence, still by Remark 7, $n \mid (h/d)$, so that $n = (h/d)$ (see Theorem 3.1(7)).

Corollary 18.1. *If g is a primitive root mod m, then g^k is also a primitive root, if and only if $(k, \phi(m)) = 1$.*

PROOF. Take $h = \phi(m)$ in Theorem 18.

Theorem 19. *If m has any primitive roots, then it has exactly $\phi(\phi(m))$ distinct ones.*

PROOF. Let g be a primitive root mod m. By Theorem 17, $g, g^2, ..., g^{\phi(m)}$ form a complete set of reduced residues and any primitive root has to occur among them. By Theorem 18, the exponent to which g^k belongs is $n = \phi(m)/(k, \phi(m))$. Now, g^k is a primitive root precisely when $n = \phi(m)$; for that it is necessary and sufficient to have $(k, \phi(m)) = 1$. However, the number of integers k satisfying $1 \le k \le \phi(m)$ and prime to $\phi(m)$ is, by definition, $\phi(\phi(m))$.

At this point the reader may wonder about the significance of the clause "If m has any primitive roots...." Do not all integers have *some* primitive root? The answer turns out to be NO! In fact, it is the exception rather than the rule, that an integer should have a primitive root and the following theorem holds:

Theorem 20. *An integer m has primitive roots if and only if $m = 2, 4, p^r, 2p^r(p$ an odd prime).*

We shall not prove this theorem completely but shall prove the "only if" part, and settle the cases $m = 2^c$ and $m = p$. (The proofs omitted here, i.e., the existence of primitive roots if $m = 2p^r$ and $m = p^r(r \ge 2)$ are the object of Problems 30–33 at the end of this chapter; they also may be found in [4] and [5].) In these proofs we shall have to make use of some properties of the Euler ϕ-function, which could easily be presented now; however, we shall investigate systematically the ϕ-function in Chapter 6 and prefer to simply anticipate here the needed results, which are

(A) $(m_1, m_2) = 1 \Rightarrow \phi(m_1)\phi(m_2) = \phi(m_1 m_2)$.

(B) $\phi(m) = m \prod_{p|m} (1 - \dfrac{1}{p})$.

(C)   (Corollary of B). If m is divisible by an odd prime, then $\phi(m)$ is even (in symbols: $m \neq 2^b \Rightarrow 2 \mid \phi(m)$).

(D) $\sum_{d|m} \phi(d) = m$.

Theorem 21. $(m_1,\ m_2) = 1,\ a^{h_1} \equiv 1 \,(\text{mod}\ m_1),\ a^{h_2} \equiv 1\ (\text{mod}\ m_2) \Rightarrow a^{[h_1, h_2]} \equiv 1 \,(\text{mod}\ m_1 m_2)$.

PROOF. Let $d = (h_1, h_2)$ so that $h_1 = dk_1$, $h_2 = dk_2$, $(k_1, k_2) = 1$, and set $h = [h_1,\ h_2] = h_1 h_2/d$. Then $(a^d)^{h_1/d} \equiv 1 \,(\text{mod}\ m_1)$, $(a^d)^{h_2/d} \equiv 1 \,(\text{mod}\ m_2)$; hence $a^h = (a^d)^{(h_1/d)(h_2/d)} \equiv 1^{h_2/d} \equiv 1 \,(\text{mod}\ m_1)$, and also $a^h = (a^d)^{(h_2 \cdot d)(h_1/d)} \equiv 1^{h_1/d} \equiv 1 \,(\text{mod}\ m_2)$, so that $a^h \equiv 1 \,(\text{mod}\ m_1 m_2)$, by Theorem 7.

Corollary 21.1.   *If $(m_1, m_2) = 1$ and if a belongs to $h_1 \,(\text{mod}\ m_1)$ and to $h_2 \,(\text{mod}\ m_2)$ then, setting $[h_1, h_2] = h$, $a^h \equiv 1 \,(\text{mod}\ m_1 m_2)$.*

Theorem 22.   *If b is odd and $c \geq 3$, then $b^{2^{c-2}} \equiv 1 \,(\text{mod}\ 2^c)$.*

PROOF. For $c = 3$ Theorem 22 reads $b^2 \equiv 1 \,(\text{mod}\ 8)$ which is true (observe that $1^2 \equiv 3^2 \equiv 5^2 \equiv 7^2 \equiv 1 \,(\text{mod}\ 8\ ))$. For $c > 3$ we use induction on c. If the Theorem holds for some c, then $b^{2^{c-2}} = 1 + k \cdot 2^c$ and, squaring both sides,

$$(b^{2^{c-2}})^2 = b^{2^{c-1}} = 1 + 2k \cdot 2^c + 2^{2c} \equiv 1 \,(\text{mod}\ 2^{c+1}),$$

so that Theorem 22 holds also for $c + 1$, and hence, for all $c \geq 3$.

Corollary 22.1.   *If $m = 2^c$, $c \geq 3$, then m can have no primitive roots.*

PROOF. If $(b, m) = 1$, then b is odd; also, $\phi(m) = 2^{c-1}$. Hence, $b^{(\phi(m))/2} = b^{2^{c-2}} \equiv 1 \,(\text{mod}\ m)$ by Theorem 22 and all integers b belong to exponents $\leq (\phi(m))/2 < \phi(m)$.

Theorem 23.   *If m is divisible by two distinct, odd primes, it can have no primitive root.*

PROOF. Let $m = p^s m_1$, $(p, m_1) = 1$, $m_1 \neq 2^c$. Then, if $0 < b \in \mathbf{Z}$, $(b, m) = 1$, one has $b^{\phi(p^s)} \equiv 1 \,(\text{mod}\ p^s)$, $b^{\phi(m_1)} \equiv 1 \,(\text{mod}\ m_1)$ by Theorem 10; and by

Theorem 21, $b^h \equiv 1 \pmod{m}$, where $h = [\phi(p^s), \phi(m_1)]$. By Property (C), $d = (\phi(p^s), \phi(m_1))$ is even; hence, $d \geq 2$, so that, using Property (A),

$$h = \frac{\phi(p^s)\phi(m_1)}{d} = \frac{\phi(m)}{d} \leq \frac{\phi(m)}{2}.$$

Consequently every b coprime to m belongs to an exponent $\leq (\phi(m))/2$ and m has no primitive root.

We can now settle the case $m = 2^c$ and prove the "only if" part of Theorem 20: $m = 2$ has the primitive root $g = 1$, $m = 4$ has the primitive root $g = 3$, and, on account of Corollary 22.1, $m = 2^c$ has no primitive root for $c \geq 3$. If m contains two odd primes, it can have no primitive root by Theorem 23. Consider now the case $m = 2^c p^s$. Let $c \geq 3$ and take any b such that $(b, m) = 1$. Then $b^{\phi(p^s)} \equiv 1 \pmod{p^s}$, by Theorem 10; $b^{2^{c-2}} \equiv 1 \pmod{2^c}$ by Theorem 22 and, using Theorem 21, $b^h \equiv 1 \pmod{m}$, where $h = [\phi(p^s), 2^{c-2}]$. By Property (C), $d = (\phi(p^s), 2^{c-2}) = 2d_1 \geq 2$, and, clearly, $\phi(2^c) = 2^{c-1}$; hence,

$$h = \frac{\phi(p^s) \cdot 2^{c-2}}{2d_1} = \frac{\phi(p^s) \cdot 2^{c-1}}{4d_1} = \frac{\phi(p^s)\phi(2^c)}{4d_1} = \frac{\phi(m)}{4d_1} \leq \frac{\phi(m)}{4},$$

so that $m = 2^c p^s$ can have no primitive root for $c \geq 3$. If $c = 2$, $m = 4p^s$, and, proceeding as before, for any $(b, m) = 1$, one obtains successively, that $b^2 \equiv 1 \pmod{4}$ and $b^h \equiv 1 \pmod{m}$ with $h = [\phi(p^s), 2] = \phi(p^s) = \frac{1}{2}\phi(m)$; hence, again, m can have no primitive root. As stated by Theorem 20, in all cases where the existence of a primitive root has not been ruled out, it actually exists, but we shall prove here this statement only in the special case $m = p$.

The integers $1, 2, \ldots, p - 1$ form a complete set of reduced residues mod p. Each of them belongs to some exponent $h \leq \phi(p) = p - 1$ and we know (see Remarks following Definition 11) that actually $h \mid (p - 1)$. If we select an arbitrary divisor h of $p - 1$, there might, or there might not exist positive integers $b, 1 \leq b \leq p - 1$ belonging to the exponent h. But if there exist any, then there exist exactly $\phi(h)$ of them. Indeed, if a belongs to the exponent h, then $a, a^2, \ldots, a^h \equiv 1$ are h incongruent solutions of the congruence $x^h \equiv 1 \pmod{p}$. These are actually all its solutions, because, in strong analogy with algebraic equations, the number of solutions of a congruence modulo a prime cannot exceed its degree.†

Hence, all reduced residues belonging to the exponent h are found among

---

† This fact, stated and proven as Theorem 24 could easily be established here; however, in order not to interrupt the present proof, it seems preferable to anticipate this result.

these $a^k (1 \leq k \leq h)$. As seen in the proof of Theorem 19, the power a^k
belongs to the exponent $h/(h, k)$ and this reduces to h if and only if $(h, k) = 1$;
the number of such exponents $k \leq h$ is precisely $\phi(h)$. Given an arbitrary
integer h, we shall denote by $N(h)$ the number of positive integers $b \leq p - 1$
belonging to the exponent h and we just proved that there are only two
alternatives: Either $N(h) = 0$, or else $N(h) = \phi(h)$, the last one being pos-
sible only if $h \mid (p - 1)$. Consequently, $\sum\limits_{h \mid p-1} N(h) \leq \sum\limits_{h \mid p-1} \phi(h)$. However,
each integer b belongs to some exponent $h \leq p - 1$; hence, $\sum\limits_{h \mid p-1} N(h) =$
$\sum\limits_{h \leq p-1} N(h) = p - 1$. Also, by property D, $\sum\limits_{h \mid p-1} \phi(h) = p - 1$. Putting these
results together, $p - 1 = \sum\limits_{h \mid p-1} N(h) \leq \sum\limits_{h \mid p-1} \phi(h) = p - 1$. This shows
that $\leq$ is actually an equality. However, this is not possible, unless $N(h) =$
$\phi(h)$ for every $h \mid p - 1$. In particular, for $h = p - 1$, we obtain the result
(slightly stronger than what we want to prove), that there are $N(p - 1) =$
$\phi(p - 1)$ integers $b \leq p - 1$, belonging to the exponent $p - 1 = \phi(p)$,
i.e., that are primitive roots. We have actually proven

Corollary 20.1. *Each prime p has exactly $\phi(p - 1)$ primitive roots incongruent* (mod p).

7. *CONGRUENCES OF HIGHER DEGREES

Let
$$f(x) = a_0 x^n + a_1 x^{n-1} + \cdots + a_n \tag{8}$$

be a polynomial of degree n with integer coefficients. The congruence $f(x) \equiv 0$
(mod m) is said to be of degree n, if $a_0 \not\equiv 0$ (mod m); more generally, one
has the

Definition 15. If $a_0 \equiv a_1 \equiv \cdots \equiv a_{n-j-1} \equiv 0 \,(\mathrm{mod}\, m), a_{n-j} \not\equiv 0 \,(\mathrm{mod}\, m,)$
then

$$a_0 x^n + a_1 x^{n-1} + \cdots + a_{n-j-1} x^{j+1} + a_{n-j} x^j + \cdots$$
$$+ a_{n-1} x + a_n \equiv 0 \,(\mathrm{mod}\, m)$$

is said to be a congruence of degree j.

Remark 11. If $f(x)$ is defined by (8), then it follows from Taylor's Theorem
that

$$f(x) = f(a) + (x - a)\frac{f'(x)}{1!} + \cdots + (x - a)^n \frac{f^{(n)}(a)}{n!} = f(a) + (x - a)g(x).$$

Here $g(x)$ is a polynomial with integral coefficients because $(f^{(m)}(a))/m!$ is an integer for every m (the reader is invited to give a proof of this fact); hence, if $f(a) \equiv 0 \pmod{m}$ then

$$f(x) = f(a) + (x - a)g(x) \equiv (x - a)g(x) \pmod{m}.$$

The converse, that $f(x) \equiv (x - a)g(x) \pmod{m}$ implies $f(a) \equiv 0 \pmod{m}$ is trivial. In analogy with the definition of a multiple root of an equation, Remark 11 suggests the following

Definition 16. The integer a is said to be a *k-fold solution of the congruence* $f(x) \equiv 0 \pmod{m}$, if $f(x) \equiv (x - a)^k g(x) \pmod{m}$, with k a positive integer and $g(x)$ a polynomial with integral coefficients, not all divisible by m. In particular, if $k \geq 2$, a is said to be a multiple solution.

While an algebraic equation of degree n always has exactly n complex roots (if we count properly their multiplicities), the situation is more complicated in the case of congruences mod m. We may have either no solution at all, or infinitely many, because, if x_0 is a solution, so is $x = x_0 + km$. It is, clearly, of interest to consider as distinct only solutions that are not congruent mod m. Even with this restriction, congruences may have no solution, or one single solution mod m, or a number of solutions less than the degree, or equal to it, or higher than the degree. For illustration, consider the following

EXAMPLES

$x^2 + 1 \equiv 0 \pmod{7}$ has no solution;

$x^2 - 3 \equiv 0 \pmod{6}$ has only one solution, $x \equiv 3 \pmod{6}$;

$x^2 + 1 \equiv 0 \pmod{17}$ has the two solutions $x \equiv 4$; and $x \equiv 13 \pmod{17}$;

$x^2 - 1 \equiv 0 \pmod{8}$ has four solutions (namely,

$x \equiv 1, 3, 5,$ or $7) \pmod{8}$, as already seen in the proof of Theorem 22.

As usually it is easier to bring some order into this apparent chaos, when the modulus m is a prime power p^k and we conclude this section with two theorems concerning prime and prime power moduli.

Theorem 24 (Lagrange). *If*

$$f(x) \equiv 0 \pmod{p} \qquad (9)$$

is a congruence of degree $n \geq 1$, then it has at most n solutions.

Before proving this theorem, let us make a few remarks.

REMARK 12. In general, let $f(x) \equiv x^r g(x) \pmod{p}$, with $g(0) \not\equiv 0 \pmod{p}$, $r \geq 0$; then $g(x)$ can be selected so that its degree should not exceed $p - 2$. Indeed, for integral $x \not\equiv 0 \pmod{p}$, $x^{p-1} \equiv 1$, $x^p \equiv x$, $x^{k(p-1)+s} \equiv x^s \pmod{p}$ with $0 \leq s \leq p - 2$.

REMARK 13. If all coefficients of $f(x)$ are divisible by p, then it is clear that every integer is a solution of (9). In such a case we say that $f(x)$ vanishes identically mod p.

REMARK 14. One has to be careful in the interpretation of a congruence like $f(x) \equiv g(x) \pmod{p}$, where $f(x)$ is given by (8) and $g(x) = \sum_{j=0}^{m} b_j x^{m-j}$. It may stand for the ordinary congruence $h(x) \equiv 0 \pmod{p}$, where $h(x) = f(x) - g(x)$; but usually it stands for the identical congruence, i.e., for the statement that $f(a) \equiv g(a) \pmod{p}$ holds for every integer a. By Theorem 24 that means that $a_j \equiv b_j \pmod{p}$ for $0 \leq j \leq \max(m, n)$. This is also, of course, the correct interpretation of the congruences mod m in preceding Remark 11 and Definition 16.

PROOF OF THEOREM 24. For $n = 1$, this is precisely Theorem 13 with $m = p$. For $n > 1$ we use induction on n. Assume, contrary to the assertion, that Theorem 24 holds up to a certain degree $n - 1$, but that there exists a congruence $a_0 x^n + a_1 x^{n-1} + \cdots + a_n \equiv 0 \pmod{p}$ of degree n with $n + 1$ solutions $u_1, u_2, \cdots, u_{n+1}$, all incongruent mod p. Set $g(x) = f(x) - a_0(x - u_1) \cdots (x - u_n)$. Then the degree of $g(x)$ is at most $n - 1$. If $g(x)$ vanishes identically mod p (that is, if all coefficients of $g(x)$ are divisible by p) then $f(x) \equiv a_0(x - u_1) \cdots (x - u_n) \pmod{p}$ so that

$$0 \equiv f(u_{n+1}) \equiv a_0(u_{n+1} - u_1) \cdots (u_{n+1} - u_n) \pmod{p};$$

this, however, is possible only if $a_0 \equiv 0 \pmod{p}$ (here we use the assumption $u_i \not\equiv u_j \pmod{p}$ for $i \neq j$, and Corollary 3.4.1) so that $f(x)$ vanishes identically, contrary to the assumption $n > 1$. Consequently, $g(x) \equiv 0 \pmod{p}$ is a congruence of degree n_1, with $1 \leq n_1 \leq n - 1$; hence, by the induction assumption, it can have at most $n - 1$ solutions incongruent mod p. However, $u_1, u_2, \ldots, u_n$ are clearly solutions and are also, by assumption, incongruent $\pmod{p}$; this contradiction shows that (9) could not have had $n + 1$ incongruent solutions and finishes the proof.

It is interesting to observe† that if (9) has exactly $m (\leq n)$ solutions $\pmod{p}$,

---

† This remark is of considerable importance in the study of p-adic valuations and in connection with a famous theorem known as Hensel's Lemma.

then, in general, also

$$f(x) \equiv 0 \ (\mathrm{mod}\ p^r) \tag{10}$$

has exactly m distinct solutions; this now means, of course, that (10) has m solutions incongruent mod p^r.

In order to state the result with precision, we recall the definition and an important property of the discriminant† D of the polynomial (1) with integral coefficients.

Definition 17. If $x_1, x_2, \ldots, x_n$ are the (not necessarily integral, not even necessarily real) roots of $f(x) = 0$, so that $f(x) = a_0(x - x_1)\cdots(x - x_n)$, then the product $D = a_0^{2n-2} \prod_{i<k} (x_i - x_k)^2$ is called the *discriminant of* $f(x)$; alternatively, D may be defined by

$$D = (-1)^{n(n-1)/2} a_0^{n-2} \prod_{i=1}^{n} f'(x_i),$$

where $f'(x)$ stands for the derivative of $f(x)$.

REMARK 15. The identity of the two definitions is a non-trivial theorem (see, e.g., [7], Section 28). The fact that D is an integer is not obvious from either definition, but becomes so using still another representation of D, namely,‡ $D = (-1)^{n(n-1)/2} a_0^{-1} R(f, f')$, where $R(f, f')$ stands for the resultant of $f(x)$ and $f'(x)$; this is a certain§ determinant, having as entries the (integral) coefficients of $f(x)$ and $f'(x)$ and divisible by a_0.

As an illustration, let us consider the polynomial

$$f(x) = 3(x - 1)(x + 2)(x - \tfrac{2}{3}) = 3x^3 + x^2 - 8x + 4,$$

with $n = 3$ and $f'(x) = 9x^2 + 2x - 8$. According to the first definition,

$$D = 3^4(1 + 2)^2(1 - \tfrac{2}{3})^2(-2 - \tfrac{2}{3})^2 = 3^2 \cdot 1^2 \cdot 8^2 = 576.$$

† In order to conform to a generally accepted custom, the discriminant will be denoted by a capital D, although here it is a rational integer.
‡ Observe erroneous omission of the factor $(-1)^{(n-1)/2}$ in [7].
§ In general the resultant of $f(x) = \sum_{j=0}^{m} a_j x^{n-j}$ and $g(x) = \sum_{j=0}^{n} b_j x^{m-j}$ is

$$R(f, g) = \begin{vmatrix} a_0 & a_1 & \cdots & a_n & 0 & 0 & \cdots & 0 \\ 0 & a_0 & \cdots & a_{n-1} & a_n & 0 & \cdots & 0 \\ \vdots & \vdots & & & & & & \\ 0 & 0 & \cdots & a_0 & a_1 & & \cdots & a_n \\ b_0 & b_1 & \cdots & & b_m & 0 & \cdots & 0 \\ 0 & b_0 & \cdots & & b_{m-1} & b_m & \cdots & 0 \\ \vdots & \vdots & & & & & & \\ 0 & 0 & \cdots & & b_0 & b_1 & \cdots & b_m \end{vmatrix} \begin{array}{l} \left.\rule{0pt}{22pt}\right\} m \text{ rows} \\ \left.\rule{0pt}{22pt}\right\} n \text{ rows} \end{array}$$

According to the second definition,

$$D = (-1)^{(3 \cdot 2)/2} \cdot 3^{\,3-2} f'(1) f'(-2) f'(\tfrac{2}{3}) = -3 \cdot 3 \cdot 24 \cdot (-8/3) = 576.$$

Finally,

$$R(f, f') = \begin{vmatrix} 3 & 1 & -8 & 4 & 0 \\ 0 & 3 & 1 & -8 & 4 \\ 9 & 2 & -8 & 0 & 0 \\ 0 & 9 & 2 & -8 & 0 \\ 0 & 0 & 9 & 2 & -8 \end{vmatrix}$$

$$= 3 \cdot 4 \cdot 2 \begin{vmatrix} 1 & 1 & -8 & 2 & 0 \\ 0 & 3 & 1 & -4 & 1 \\ 3 & 2 & -8 & 0 & 0 \\ 0 & 9 & 2 & -4 & 0 \\ 0 & 0 & 9 & 1 & -2 \end{vmatrix} = -3 \cdot 24^2,$$

so that $D = (-1)^{(3 \cdot 2)/2} \cdot 3^{-1} (-3 \cdot 24^2) = 576$.

Let us make still another observation: If $r \geq 2$ and $x = a$ is a solution of the congruence (10), then it is, *a fortiori*, a solution of the congruence

$$f(x) \equiv 0 \;(\mathrm{mod}\; p^{r-1}). \tag{10'}$$

The converse is not necessarily true; if $x = b$ is a solution of (10') with $0 \leq b < p^{r-1}$, it may, or may not be also a solution of (10); we may try, however, to find a solution of (10) of the form

$$a = b + k p^{r-1}, \quad 0 \leq k < p, \quad 0 \leq b < p^{r-1}. \tag{11}$$

Indeed, as observed, if a is a solution of (10), then it is also a solution of (10'); hence, so also is every b satisfying $b \equiv a \;(\mathrm{mod}\; p^{r-1})$, and, in particular, the unique $b < p^{r-1}$, congruent to $a \;(\mathrm{mod}\; p^{r-1})$. Consequently, every solution a of (10) can be written in the form (11); such a solution a of (10) is said *to correspond* to the solution b of (10'). Now the key theorem may be stated as follows.

Theorem 25. *For $r \geq 2$, to every solution $b \;(\mathrm{mod}\; p^{r-1})$ of (10') corresponds exactly one solution $(\mathrm{mod}\; p^r)$ of (10), provided that $p \nmid f'(b)$; if $p \mid f'(b)$ but $p^r \nmid f(b)$, then there are no solutions of (10) corresponding to b; finally if $p \mid f'(b)$ and $p^r \mid f(b)$, then there are exactly p solutions (distinct $\mathrm{mod}\; p^r$) of (10), corresponding to the solution b of (10').*

PROOF. By Taylor's theorem,

$$f(x) = f(c) + (f'(c)/1!)(x - c) + \cdots + (f^{(n)}(c)/n!)(x - c)^n$$

and, for integral c, as already seen, the coefficients $f^{(j)}(c)/j!$ are all integers. In particular, for $a = b + kp^{r-1}$,

$$f(b + kp^{r-1}) = f(b) + f'(b) \cdot kp^{r-1} + \sum_{j=2}^{n} \frac{f^{(j)}(b)}{j!} k^j p^{j(r-1)}.$$

If $r \geq 2$, $j \geq 2$, then $j(r-1) \geq r$, so that the last sum is divisible by p^r; hence, if $a = b + kp^{r-1}$ is a solution of (10), so that $f(a) \equiv 0 \pmod{p^r}$, we obtain $f(b) + f'(b)kp^{r-1} \equiv 0 \pmod{p^r}$. However, $p^{r-1} \mid f(b)$, because b is a solution of (10'); hence, dividing by p^{r-1}, the last congruence may be written as

$$kf'(b) \equiv -f(b)p^{1-r} \pmod{p}. \tag{12}$$

If $p \nmid f'(b)$, then it follows by Theorem 13, that the congruence (12) has a unique solution $k \pmod{p}$. If $p \mid f'(b)$, but $p \nmid f(b)p^{1-r}$, then (12) cannot be satisfied by any k, while if $p \mid f'(b)$, $p \mid f(b)p^{1-r}$ (i.e., if $p^r \mid f(b)$), then (12) is trivially satisfied for every value of $k \pmod{p}$ and the Theorem is proven.

From Theorem 25 easily follows the result we are actually aiming at, namely,

Corollary 25.1.   *If D is the discriminant of the polynomial* (1) *and if $p \nmid D$, then all congruences* (10) *have the same number $m(\leq n)$ of solutions, which is, in particular, the number of solutions of* (9).

In the proof of the Corollary we shall use the following lemmas, which are close analogues of a well-known theorem in the algebra of polynomials.

Lemma 1.   *A solution b of* (9) *is a multiple solution, if and only if $p \mid f'(b)$.*

PROOF. By Taylor's theorem,

$$f(x) = f(b) + (x - b)f'(b) + \cdots + (x - b)^n f^{(n)}(b)/n!.$$

As already observed in the proof of Theorem 25, the coefficients $f^{(k)}(b)/k!$ are integers if b is an integer; hence,

$$f(x) = f(b) + (x - b)f'(b) + (x - b)^2 g(x).$$

By assumption, $p \mid f(b)$; if $p \mid f'(b)$ also holds, then $f(x) \equiv (x - b)^2 g(x)$ $\pmod{p}$ and, in view of Definition 16, b is a multiple solution of (9). Conversely, if $x \equiv b \pmod{p}$ is a multiple solution of (9), then by Definition 16, $f(x) \equiv (x - b)^2 g_1(x) \pmod{p}$; but $p \mid f(b)$, so that, by Taylor's theorem, $f(x) \equiv (x - b)f'(b) + (x - b)^2 g(x) \pmod{p}$ also holds. Consequently, $(x - b)f'(b) \equiv (x - b)^2 (g_1(x) - g(x)) \pmod{p}$ or $f'(b) \equiv (x - b)h(x) \pmod{p}$, where $h(x) = g_1(x) - g(x)$ is a polynomial with integral coefficients (the reader should supply a justification for the cancellation of the factor $x - b$). The left-hand side being independent of x we may substitute for x on the right-hand side any integer, without changing its value (mod p); setting, in particular, $x = b$ we obtain $f'(b) \equiv 0 \pmod{p}$, and Lemma 1 is proven.

Lemma 2. *If congruence (9) has a multiple solution, then $p \mid D$.*

PROOF. If b is a multiple solution of (9), then, by Definition 16, $f(x) \equiv (x - b)^2 g(x) \pmod{p}$. By Remark 14, the coefficients $a_j (0 \le j \le n)$ of $f(x)$ are congruent mod p to the coefficients c_j of $h(x) = (x - b)^2 g(x) = \sum_{j=0}^{m} c_j x^{m-j} (m \ge n)$. Consequently, if D_h is the discriminant of $h(x)$, then $D \equiv D_h \pmod{p}$, because both discriminants are polynomials in the respective coefficients. However, $D_h = 0$, because the equation $h(x) = 0$ has the multiple root $x = b$; hence $D \equiv 0 \pmod{p}$.

PROOF OF COROLLARY 25.1. Let $b_i (i = 1, 2, ..., n)$ be one of the m solutions incongruent mod p of (9), i.e., of (10) with $r = 1$. Then $f(b_i) \equiv 0 \pmod{p}$ and, from $p \nmid D$ and Lemma 2 it follows that (9) has no multiple solutions; hence, by Lemma 1, $p \nmid f'(b_i)$. By Theorem 25 it follows that to each b_i corresponds (mod p^2) exactly one solution of (10) with $r = 2$. This proves the Corollary for $r = 2$. Let us assume then that we already know that (10′) has exactly m solutions (mod p^{r-1}), $r \ge 2$. If b_i is one of them, then $p^{r-1} \mid f(b_i)$; hence, *a fortiori*, $p \mid f(b_i)$. Consequently, using $p \nmid D$ and the two Lemmas, it follows that $p \nmid f'(b_i)$. It now follows again from Theorem 25, that to each b_i corresponds (mod p^r) exactly one solution of (10); hence, as (10′) has m solutions (mod p^{r-1}), also (10) has exactly m solutions (mod p^r) and the Corollary is proven.

Theorem 26. *Let p be a prime and n an arbitrary positive integer, and set $d = (n, p - 1)$; then*

$$(a, p) = 1 \Rightarrow x^n \equiv a \pmod{p} \text{ has} \begin{cases} d \text{ solutions mod } p \text{ if } a^{(p-1)/d} \equiv 1 \pmod{p}, \\ no \text{ solutions if } a^{(p-1)/d} \not\equiv 1 \pmod{p}. \end{cases}$$

PROOF. $a \equiv x^n \Rightarrow a^{(p-1)/d} \equiv x^{n(p-1)/d} \equiv (x^{p-1})^{n/d} \equiv 1 \pmod{p}$ by Theorem 11; hence, no solution can exist if $a^{(p-1)/d} \not\equiv 1 \pmod{p}$. On the other hand, if $a^{(p-1)/d} \equiv 1 \pmod{p}$, let g be a primitive root mod p. Then, by Theorem 17, $a \equiv g^j \pmod{p}$ for some integer j and also, any solution x of the given congruence can be written as $x = g^y$; moreover, to solutions x incongruent mod p correspond exponents y incongruent mod $p - 1$ (the reader should prove this formally). Substituting, the congruence becomes $g^{yn} \equiv a \equiv g^j \pmod{p} \Leftrightarrow ny \equiv j \pmod{p - 1}$. By Theorem 14, the last congruence has no solution, if d does not divide j, and has exactly one solution mod $(p - 1)/d$

if $d \mid j$. To decide between these two alternatives we observe that

$$(g^j)^{(p-1)/d} \equiv a^{(p-1)/d} \equiv 1 \ (\text{mod } p),$$

by assumption; hence, by Remark 7, applied to g, with $(g, p) = 1$ and $h = p - 1$, one has $p - 1 \mid (j(p - 1)/d)$, so that j/d is an integer and $d \mid j$. Consequently, $ny \equiv j \pmod{p - 1}$ has exactly one solution y_0 (mod $((p - 1)/d)$ and the d solutions $y = y_0 + k(p - 1)/d(k = 0, 1, ..., d - 1)$, incongruent mod $p - 1$. To each corresponds a solution x incongruent mod p and the Theorem is proven.

We shall not pursue further the general theory of higher congruences, but pass immediately to study in some detail a most important particular case, that of quadratic congruences. The reader interested in the general theory is advised to consult such books as the excellent *Introduction to Number Theory* by Nagell [4].

PROBLEMS

1. Prove Theorem 1 in detail.

2. Prove that Definition 5 is meaningful; that is, show that each element of the set **A** belongs to one and only one equivalence class, so that $\mathcal{R}$ induces indeed a partition of the elements of **A**.

3. (i) Consider the set whose elements are the ordered couples of integers, the second being different from zero. Two couples (a, b), (c, d) are said to be "similar" if $ad = bc$. Prove that this "similarity" is an equivalence relation.

   (ii) Define "addition" among the equivalence classes of couples by $(a, b) + (c, d) = (ad + bc, bd)$ and "multiplication" by $(a, b) \times (c, d) = (ac, bd)$. Show that

$$(a, b) + (c, d) = (e, f) \Leftrightarrow \frac{a}{b} + \frac{c}{d} = \frac{e}{f}$$

and

$$(a, b) \times (c, d) = (g, h) \Leftrightarrow \frac{a}{b} \cdot \frac{c}{d} = \frac{g}{h}.$$

Show, further, that if we establish a correspondence $(a, b) \Leftrightarrow (r/s)$, with r and s uniquely determined by $(r/s) = (a/b)$, $(r, s) = 1$, then (r/s) is independent of the couple (a, b) selected and depends only on its equivalence class. These results are expressed succinctly, by stating that the set of equivalence classes of ordered couples is *isomorphic* to the set of rational fractions in reduced form. What is the subset of equivalence classes of couples (a, b) corresponding to the rational integers? To zero? To one?

4. Prove in detail Theorem 3.

5. Prove in detail Theorem 4.

6. Write out in complete detail the proof of Theorem 5.

7. Find a complete set of residues mod 7, all of which are divisible by 10. Can you solve the same problem if 7 is replaced by 6? Why?

8. Prove Corollary 7.1.

9. Prove that for every integer n, also $n(n + 1)(2n + 1)/6$ is an integer.

10. Prove that $(a + b)^p \equiv a^p + b^p \pmod{p}$; more generally,

$$(a + b + \cdots + z)^p \equiv a^p + b^p + \cdots + z^p \pmod{p}.$$

11. Prove that if n is an integer, $3n^2 - 1$ is never the square of an integer (*Hint*: Use congruences mod 3).

12. Prove that for every odd n, $n^2 \equiv 1 \pmod{8}$.

13. Prove that for every integer n, $n^3 \equiv -1, 0,$ or $+1 \pmod{9}$.

14. Prove that the following congruences hold for every integer n:
    (a) $2^{2n} - 1 \equiv 0 \pmod{3}$;
    (b) $2^{3n} - 1 \equiv 0 \pmod{7}$; and
    (c) $2^{4n} - 1 \equiv 0 \pmod{15}$.

15. Prove that there exist infinitely many primes $p \equiv 3 \pmod{4}$.

16. Prove that if $n = 2^m + 1$ is prime, then m must be a power of 2 (n is then called a *Fermat prime*).

17. Prove that if $n = 2^m - 1$ is prime, also m is a prime (a *Mersenne prime*).

18. Prove Remark 2 in detail.

19. Find the smallest positive solution of the congruence $240^{37} \equiv x \pmod{7}$.

20. Find the greatest common divisor $(p!, (p - 1)! - 1)$, where p is a prime.

21. (Lagrange). Let p be an odd prime. Define the coefficients $a_1, a_2, \ldots, a_{p-1}$ by the identity

$$(x - 1)(x - 2) \cdots (x - p + 1) = x^{p-1} - a_1 x^{p-2} + \cdots + a_{p-1}$$

    or

$$x(x - 1) \cdots (x - p + 1) = x^p - a_1 x^{p-1} + \cdots + a_{p-1} x.$$

    Replace here x by $x - 1$, getting

$$(x - 1)(x - 2) \cdots (x - p)$$
$$= (x - p)[(x - 1)(x - 2) \cdots (x - p + 1)]$$
$$= (x - p)[x^{p-1} - a_1 x^{p-2} + \cdots + a_{p-1}]$$
$$= (x - 1)^p - a_1(x - 1)^{p-1} + \cdots + a_{p-1}(x - 1).$$

Equate coefficients of equal powers in the last two expressions, obtain equations for the $a_i(i = 1, 2, ..., p - 1)$ and infer that

$$p \mid a_i(i = 1, 2, ..., p - 2), \quad a_{p-1} \equiv -1 \pmod{p}.$$

Obtain from this a third proof of Wilson's Theorem 12. Next, observing that $x^{p-1} - a_1 x^{p-2} + \cdots + a_{p-1} \equiv x^{p-1} - 1 \pmod{p}$, find a new proof of Fermat's Theorem 11.

22. Find the general solution of the Diophantine equation $10x - 49y = 3$.

23. Find the general solution of the congruence $3^x - 2^x \equiv 5 \pmod{7}$. What can you say about the congruence $3^x - 2^x \equiv 4 \pmod{7}$?

24. Let $d = (a, b)$. Show how the Euclidean algorithm (Chapter 3, Problem 3) leads to a method of finding integers m and n such that $am + bn = d$ (*Hint*: Observe that $d = r_{m-1} = r_{m-3} - r_{m-2}q_{m-1}$, and that one may continue to replace r_k by $r_{k-2} - r_{k-1}q_k$ all the way back to a and b.) *Application*: $a = 12, b = 22$.

25. Solve the system of simultaneous congruences:

$$3x + 7y - 10 \equiv 0 \pmod{14},$$

$$11x - 8y + 8 \equiv 0 \pmod{14}.$$

26. Let g be a primitive root mod p. Then $p - g$ is also a primitive root mod p if $p \equiv 1 \pmod{4}$, and belongs to the exponent $((p - 1)/2)$ if $p \equiv 3 \pmod{4}$.

27. Justify the last example on top of p. 44: $\phi(p^r) = p^r - p^{r-1}$.

28. Prove Corollary 17.1.

29. Prove that if $m = p^r$, then g is a primitive root if and only if $g, g^2, ..., g^{\phi(m)}$ are all incongruent mod m (*Hint*: Use Problem 27.)

30. Prove that for every prime p, there exists a primitive root g, such that $g^{p-1} \not\equiv 1 \pmod{p^2}$.
    (*Hint*: With g, also $g_1 = g + p$ is a primitive root mod p and if $g^{p-1} \equiv 1 \pmod{p^2}$, then $g_1^{p-1} \not\equiv 1 \pmod{p^2}$.)

31. Let g be a primitive root mod p, with $g^{p-1} \not\equiv 1 \pmod{p^2}$; then $g^{(p-1)p^{m-2}} \not\equiv 1 \pmod{p^m}$ for every integer $m \geq 2$).

(*Hint*: By Problem 30, the statement is true for $m = 2$ and some g; now use induction, by assuming the statement true with $m - 1$ instead of m. By Theorem 10, $g^{\phi(p^{m-2})} = g^{p^{m-3}(p-1)} \equiv 1 \pmod{p^{m-2}}$, so that by the induction hypothesis, $g^{p^{m-3}(p-1)} = 1 + qp^{m-2}, p \nmid q$. The proof by induction may be concluded, by elevating both sides to the power p.)

32. If g is a primitive root mod p and $g^{p-1} \not\equiv 1 \pmod{p^2}$, then g is a primitive root mod p^m.

(*Hint*: From $(g, p^m) = 1$ it follows (see Definition 12 and the remarks preceding it) that there exists a positive integer v to which g belongs mod p^m, so that $g^v = 1 \pmod{p^m}$ and $v \mid p^{m-1}(p - 1)(= \phi(p^m))$. But also $g^v \equiv 1 \pmod{p}$ holds; hence, $p - 1 \mid v$, so that $v = (p - 1)p^a$, with $0 \leq a \leq m - 1$ and $g^{(p-1)p^a} \equiv 1 \pmod{p^m}$. Assuming $a < m - 1$, one gets a contradiction with Problem 31; hence, $v = \phi(p^m)$.)

33. If $n = 2p^m$, then n has a primitive root.

(*Hint*: If g is an odd primitive root mod p^m, then it is also a primitive root mod $2p^m$; if g is an even primitive root mod p^m, then $g + p^m$ is an odd primitive root mod p^m, hence also mod $2p^m$.)

34. Prove that $x^p - x \equiv 0 \pmod{p}$ has all rational integers as solutions.

35. Justify Remark 9.

36. Let $f(x) \equiv 0 \pmod{p}$ be a congruence of degree n. Prove that it has exactly n solutions mod p if and only if $f(x)$ is a factor of $x^p - x \pmod{p}$, that is, if $x^p - x + pg(x) = f(x)h(x)$ for some polynomials $g(x)$, $h(x)$ with integral coefficients.

37. Let $F(x)$ be a polynomial with integral coefficients and let a and n be integers, $n \geq 0$; prove that $F^{(n)}(a)/n!$ is an integer.

38. Show that if $(x - b)h(x) \equiv 0 \pmod{p}$ holds identically, then one may cancel the factor $x - b$. (This fact has been used in the proof of Lemma 1, pp. 61–62.)

BIBLIOGRAPHY

1. L. E. Dickson, *History of the Theory of Numbers*. New York: Chelsea, 1952.
2. C. F. Gauss, "Disquisitiones Arith.," *Art.*, **24**, p. 77.
3. W. J. LeVeque, *Topics in Number Theory*, Vol. 1. Reading, Mass.: Addison Wesley Publishing Co., 1956.
4. N. H. McCoy, *The Theory of Numbers*. New York: The Macmillan Co., 1965.

5. T. Nagell, *Introduction to Number Theory*. New York: John Wiley & Sons, 1951.

6. M. A. Stern, *Lehrbuch der Algebraischen Analysis*. Leipzig: Winter'sche Verlagsbuchhandlung (1860).

7. Sun Tsu, "Suan-ching" (arithmetic), edited by Y. Mikaini, *Abhandlungen-Geschichte der Mathematischen Wissenschaften*; **30**, 1912, p. 32.

8. B. L. Van der Waerden, *Modern Algebra*, Vol. 1. New York: Frederick Ungar Publishing Co., 1953.

CHAPTER **5**

Quadratic Residues

1. INTRODUCTION

Consider the general congruence of second degree modulo† an odd prime p:

$$ax^2 + bx + c \equiv 0, \quad p \nmid a.$$

On account of $p \nmid a$, (1) is equivalent to

$$4a(ax^2 + bx + c) = (2ax + b)^2 - (b^2 - 4ac) \equiv 0.$$

$p \nmid a$ also implies (Theorem 4.13) that $2ax + b \equiv x_1$ has a unique solution mod p; hence, setting $2ax + b \equiv x_1$ and $b^2 - 4ac \equiv a_1$,

(1) is seen to be equivalent to the system

$$x_1^2 \equiv a_1, \tag{2}$$

$$2ax \equiv x_1 - b. \tag{2'}$$

(2′) is a linear congruence and can be handled according to Section 4.4 (see in particular Theorem 4.13); hence, the general problem of quadratic congruences reduces to that of solving (2). Concerning (2), the following fundamental theorem holds:

---

† In this section all congruences without indication of a modulus are understood to be mod p, with p an *odd* prime.

Theorem 1.   (Legendre).

(1) $p \nmid a \Rightarrow x^2 \equiv a$ has $\begin{cases} 2 \text{ solutions if } a^{(p-1)/2} \equiv 1, \\ 0 \text{ solutions otherwise.} \end{cases}$

(2) $a^{(p-1)/2} \not\equiv 1 \Rightarrow a^{(p-1)/2} \equiv -1$.

FIRST PROOF. The first assertion follows by taking $n = 2$ in Theorem 4.25. For the second observe that, by Theorem 4.11, one has for every $a \not\equiv 0$ that $0 \equiv a^{p-1} - 1 = (a^{(p-1)/2} - 1)(a^{(p-1)/2} + 1)$; hence, $a^{(p-1)/2} \not\equiv 1 \Rightarrow a^{(p-1)/2} \equiv -1$ and also the last assertion now follows from Theorem 4.25.

We present also a second proof of Theorem 1, independent of Theorem 4.25 and of the concept of primitive roots.

SECOND PROOF. Assertions (2) follows as before from the remark $a \not\equiv 0 \Rightarrow$ either $a^{(p-1)/2} \equiv -1$, or $a^{(p-1)/2} \equiv 1$. It only remains to prove (1). If $a^{(p-1)/2} \equiv -1$, then $x^2 \equiv a$ can have no solution. Indeed if $x \equiv c$ were a solution, then

$$a^{(p-1)/2} \equiv (c^2)^{(p-1)/2} \equiv c^{p-1} \equiv 1$$

(by Theorem 4.11), contrary to the assumption $a^{(p-1)/2} \equiv -1$. This proves the last assertion of (1). Next, if $a^{(p-1)/2} \equiv 1$, then by Theorem 4.24, a is one of the at most $(p-1)/2$ solutions (incongruent mod p) of $x^{(p-1)/2} \equiv 1$. A set of $(p-1)/2$ solutions, incongruent mod p, is furnished by $1^2, 2^2, ...,$ $(p-1)/2)^2$. These are indeed solutions, because, for $1 \leq n \leq (p-1)/2$, $(n^2)^{(p-1)/2} = n^{p-1} \equiv 1$ by Theorem 4.11; and they are incongruent because if $1 \leq n < m \leq (p-1)/2$, then $0 < m - n < m + n \leq p - 1 < p$, so that $m^2 - n^2 = (m-n)(m+n) \not\equiv 0$. Consequently, a is necessarily of the form $a = n^2(1 \leq n \leq (p-1)/2$.

Now, let $a \equiv n^2$ be any of these $(p-1)/2$ residues; then $x^2 \equiv a$ has the two incongruent solutions $x \equiv n$ and $x \equiv p - n(n \equiv p - n \Rightarrow p \mid n$, impossible for $1 < n < (p-1)/2)$, and this finishes also the proof of the first assertion of (1).

2. THE LEGENDRE SYMBOL AND THE LAW OF QUADRATIC RECIPROCITY

In view of Theorem 1, it seems appropriate to introduce

Definition 1.   Let $(r, m) = 1$; then r is said to be a *quadratic residue modulo m*, if there exists some integer x, such that $x^2 \equiv r \pmod{m}$. We call n a *quadratic non-residue modulo m*, if the congruence $x^2 \equiv n \pmod{m}$ has no solutions.

Corollary 1.1. *There exist exactly $(p-1)/2$ quadratic residues and $(p-1)/2$ quadratic non-residues modulo p.*

PROOF. Left to the reader.

Definition 2. For $p \nmid a$ we define the *Legendre Symbol* $\left(\dfrac{a}{p}\right)$ of quadratic residuacy as follows:

$\left(\dfrac{a}{p}\right) = +1$ if a is a quadratic residue and $\left(\dfrac{a}{p}\right) = -1$ if a is a quadratic non-residue modulo p.

EXAMPLE

Modulo 7 one has $1^2 \equiv 6^2 \equiv 1$; $2^2 \equiv 5^2 \equiv 4$; $3^2 \equiv 4^2 \equiv 2$; hence, 1, 2, and 4 are quadratic residues and 3, 5, 6 are quadratic non-residues mod 7.

Using Legendre's symbol, $\left(\dfrac{1}{7}\right) = \left(\dfrac{2}{7}\right) = \left(\dfrac{4}{7}\right) = 1$ and $\left(\dfrac{3}{7}\right) = \left(\dfrac{4}{7}\right) = \left(\dfrac{6}{7}\right) = -1$.

Theorem 2. *Let p be an odd prime, $p \nmid a \cdot b$; then*

(1) $\quad a \equiv b \pmod{p} \Rightarrow \left(\dfrac{a}{p}\right) = \left(\dfrac{b}{p}\right)$;

(2) $\quad \left(\dfrac{a^2}{p}\right) = 1$;

(3) $\quad \left(\dfrac{1}{p}\right) = 1$;

(4) $\quad \left(\dfrac{a}{p}\right)\left(\dfrac{b}{p}\right) = \left(\dfrac{ab}{p}\right)$;

(5) $\quad \left(\dfrac{a}{p}\right) \equiv a^{(p-1)/2} \pmod{p}$;

(6) $\quad \left(\dfrac{-1}{p}\right) = (-1)^{(p-1)/2} = \begin{cases} 1 \text{ if } p \equiv 1 \pmod 4, \\ -1 \text{ if } p \equiv 3 \pmod 4. \end{cases}$

PROOFS. Assertions (1) and (2) should be evident; (3) is the particular case $a = 1$ of (2); (5) is a rephrasing of Theorem 1 and (6) is the particular case $a = -1$ of (5). Proof of (4):

$$\left(\dfrac{a}{p}\right)\left(\dfrac{b}{p}\right) \equiv a^{(p-1)/2}b^{(p-1)/2} = (ab)^{(p-1)/2} \equiv \left(\dfrac{ab}{p}\right) \pmod{p} \text{ (we used (5) twice).}$$

However $\left(\dfrac{a}{p}\right)\left(\dfrac{b}{p}\right) = \pm 1$, $\left(\dfrac{ab}{p}\right) = \pm 1$; hence, $\left(\dfrac{a}{p}\right)\left(\dfrac{b}{p}\right) \equiv \left(\dfrac{ab}{p}\right) \pmod{p} \Rightarrow$
$\left(\dfrac{a}{p}\right)\left(\dfrac{b}{p}\right) = \left(\dfrac{ab}{p}\right)$ because $p > 2$.

The Theory of quadratic residues is dominated by the famous Law of Quadratic Reciprocity of Gauss and our next aim is its proof.

Theorem 3 (Quadratic Reciprocity Law of Legendre-Gauss). *If p and q are distinct odd primes, then*

$$\left(\frac{p}{q}\right)\left(\frac{q}{p}\right) = (-1)^{[(p-1)/2][(q-1)/2]}$$

REMARK 1. Theorem 3 may be rephrased as follows: The symbols $\left(\dfrac{p}{q}\right)$ and $\left(\dfrac{q}{p}\right)$ are equal, except when p and q are both congruent to 3 (mod 4), in which case $\left(\dfrac{p}{q}\right) = -\left(\dfrac{q}{p}\right)$.

Theorem 3 had already been stated by Euler and an incomplete proof of it was given by Legendre. Gauss gave eight proofs of it. Many other mathematicians have given proofs (Bachmann counts 45, Gerstenhaber claims that there are 152, the last one his own). The shortest proof known today is probably due to Frobenius (See [1]; for recent versions of it, see [2], pp. 69–71 and [3].) We shall present a version of one of Gauss' own proofs, due essentially to his student Eisenstein. The reader may be interested to know that in Gauss' opinion the three greatest mathematicians were Archimedes, Newton, and Eisenstein. Most people today would replace Eisenstein's name by that of Gauss himself, but, nevertheless, Eisenstein's contribution to mathematics is highly impressive, in particular, if one keeps in mind that he died in 1852 at the age of only 29, and who knows whether we would not have agreed with Gauss' opinion, if Eisenstein would have lived as long as Gauss himself! As most other proofs (including Frobenius'), ours will make essential use of *Gauss' Lemma*, which we state as

Theorem 4 (Gauss' Lemma). *Let p be an odd prime, $p \nmid a$. Let $S = \{r\}$ consist of the least positive residues of the set $\{ma\}$, $m = 1, 2, \ldots$, $(p - 1)/2$. Denote by n the number of integers $r \in S$, $r > p/2$; then $\left(\dfrac{a}{p}\right) = (-1)^n$.*

PROOF. We make two observations: First, all elements of S are incongruent (mod p) (indeed, if $m_1 \neq m_2$, then $m_1 a \equiv m_2 a \Rightarrow p \mid (m_1 - m_2)a \Rightarrow p \mid m_1 - m_2$, which is impossible, because $0 < m_1$, $m_2 \leq (p - 1)/2$; next, denoting by $s_1, s_2, \ldots, s_n$ the values of $r > p/2$ and by $t_1, t_2, \ldots, t_k$ the values of $r < p/2$, also $p - s_i \not\equiv t_j$ (indeed $p - s_i \equiv t_j \Rightarrow s_i + t_j \equiv 0 \Rightarrow p \mid m_i a + m_j a \Leftrightarrow p \mid m_i + m_j$, impossible, because $2 \leq m_i + m_j \leq p - 1$). Consequently, $p - s_1, p - s_2, \ldots, p - s_n; t_1, \ldots, t_k$ are a set of $n + k = (p - 1)/2$ integers, all belonging to the interval 1 to $(p - 1)/2$ and incongruent to each other mod p; hence, they are precisely the integers $1, 2, \ldots, (p - 1)/2$ in some order and their product $(p - s_1)(p - s_2) \cdots (p - s_n)t_1 t_2 \cdots t_k$ equals $((p - 1)/2)!$ However, the product, multiplied out, equals $(-1)^n s_1 s_2 \cdots s_n t_1 \cdots t_k$ plus a multiple of p, or, taking congruences mod p and replacing s_i and t_j by their values $m_i a$ and $m_j a$, $(-1)^n a^{(p-1)/2}((p - 1)/2)! \equiv ((p - 1)/2)!$ From, $(p, ((p - 1)/2)!) = 1$, follows, by Corollary 4.6.1, that $a^{(p-1)/2} \equiv (-1)^n$, and further, by Theorem 2(5), that $(-1)^n \equiv \left(\dfrac{a}{p}\right)$, whence, using $p > 2$, that $\left(\dfrac{a}{p}\right) = (-1)^n$, as in the proof of Theorem 2(4).

In the proof of Theorem 3, and often afterwards, we shall use

Definition 3. The *greatest integer function*, in symbols $y = [x]$, is defined as the largest rational integer not in excess of x.

EXAMPLES

$[3] = 3$, $[-1] = -1$; in general, for every integer n, $[n] = n$; $[5/2] = 2$, $[e] = 2$, $[\pi] = 3$, $[-\pi] = -4$; in general, for non-integral $x > 0$, $[-x] = -[x] - 1$.

Lemma 1 (Eisenstein). *Let m, n be odd, coprime integers, $m \neq 1$, $n \neq 1$. Set $m' = \frac{1}{2}(m - 1)$, $n' = \frac{1}{2}(n - 1)$; then*

$$\sum_{r=1}^{m'} \left[\frac{nr}{m}\right] + \sum_{r=1}^{n'} \left[\frac{mr}{n}\right] = m'n'.$$

PROOF. The result is geometrically evident, if we observe that the sum on the left counts the points with integral coordinates (so-called *lattice points*) *inside* the rectangle of sides $m/2$ and $n/2$; indeed, there are no lattice points on the diagonal. (The coordinates (s, t) of a point of the diagonal satisfy $(s/t) = (m/n)$ with $s < m$, $t < n$, and m/n is in reduced form, because $(m, n) = 1$; hence, s and t cannot both be integers.) In the lower triangle, the vertical of abscissa r, meets the diagonal at the ordinate rm/n; hence, there are exactly $[rm/n]$ points with integral ordinates on it and if we let $r = 1, 2, ..., m'$, $m' = (m - 1)/2$, we obtain all together $\sum_{r=1}^{m'} [rm/n]$ lattice points inside the lower triangle. Similarly, there are $\sum_{r=1}^{n'} [rn/m]$ lattice points in the upper triangle, while the total number of lattice points inside the rectangle is clearly $m' \cdot n'$ and the Lemma is proven.

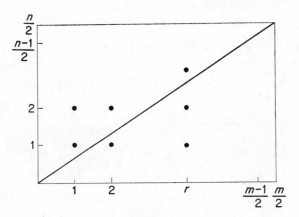

Figure 1

Lemma 2. *If $p \nmid a$, $p' = (p - 1)/2$ and n is defined as in Theorem* 4, *then*

$$\sum_{m=1}^{p'} \left[\frac{ma}{p} \right] + \frac{1}{8}(a - 1)(p^2 - 1) \equiv n (\text{mod } 2).$$

PROOF. As in Gauss' Lemma (Theorem 4), consider the set $\mathbf{S} = \{r\}$ of least positive residues $ma \equiv r \pmod{p}$, where $m = 1, 2, ..., p', p' = (p - 1)/2$. Given m, the corresponding r is the difference $ma - p[ma/p]$. Summing over all m, $a\sum_{m=1}^{p'} m - p\sum_{m=1}^{p'} [ma/p] = \sum r$, or

$$a \sum_{m=1}^{p'} m = p \sum_{m=1}^{p'} \left[\frac{ma}{p} \right] + \sum r. \tag{3}$$

Again, as in Gauss' Lemma, we distinguish between the r's less than $p/2$, and denote them by $t_1, ..., t_k$; and those larger than $p/2$ denoted by $s_1, s_2, ..., s_n$. Then $\sum r = \sum_{j=1}^{n} s_j + \sum_{j=1}^{k} t_j$. We also recall that the set $\{p - s_j, t_j\}$ is precisely the set of all integers from 1 to p' in some order; hence,

$$\sum_{j=1}^{n} (p - s_j) + \sum_{j=1}^{k} t_k = np - \sum_{j=1}^{n} s_j + \sum_{j=1}^{k} t_k$$

$$= \sum_{m=1}^{p'} m = \frac{[(p - 1)/2][(p + 1)/2]}{2} = \frac{p^2 - 1}{8}. \tag{4}$$

(3) and (4) may be rewritten as

$$a \frac{p^2 - 1}{8} = p \sum_{m=1}^{p'} \left[\frac{ma}{p} \right] + \sum_{j=1}^{m} s_j + \sum_{j=1}^{k} t_j,$$

and

$$-\frac{p^2 - 1}{8} = -np + \sum_{j=1}^{n} s_j - \sum_{j=1}^{k} t_j,$$

respectively. Adding, we obtain

$$(a - 1) \frac{p^2 - 1}{8} = p \left\{ \sum_{m=1}^{p'} \left[\frac{ma}{p} \right] - n \right\} + 2 \sum_{j=1}^{n} s_j.$$

Modulo 2, the right-hand side is congruent to

$$p \left\{ \sum_{m=1}^{p'} \left[\frac{ma}{p} \right] - n \right\} \equiv \sum_{m=1}^{p'} \left[\frac{ma}{p} \right] - n \equiv n - \sum_{m=1}^{p'} \left[\frac{ma}{p} \right],$$

because $p \equiv 1 \pmod 2$ and $2u \equiv 0 \pmod 2 \Leftrightarrow u \equiv -u \pmod 2$, and the Lemma is proven.

PROOF OF THEOREM 3. By Gauss' Lemma, we know how to define integers n and m, so that $\left(\frac{q}{p} \right) = (-1)^n$, $\left(\frac{p}{q} \right) = (-1)^m$; whence $\left(\frac{p}{q} \right)\left(\frac{q}{p} \right) = (-1)^{n+m}$. By Lemma 2,

$$n \equiv \sum_{r=1}^{p'} \left[\frac{rq}{p} \right] + \frac{(q-1)(p^2-1)}{8} \equiv \sum_{r=1}^{p'} \left[\frac{rq}{p} \right] \bmod 2,$$

because p and q are odd, so that

$$(q - 1)(p^2 - 1) = (q - 1)(p + 1)(p - 1) \equiv 0 \pmod{16}.$$

In the same way $m \equiv \sum_{r=1}^{q'}[rp/q] \pmod 2$, where $q' = (q - 1)/2$. Hence, $m + n \equiv \sum_{r=1}^{p'}[rq/p] + \sum_{r=1}^{q'}[rp/q] \pmod 2$. By Lemma 1, the second member equals $p'q'$, so that $\left(\frac{p}{q} \right)\left(\frac{q}{p} \right) = (-1)^{m+n} = (-1)^{p' \cdot q'}$ and the Theorem is proven.

Theorem 3 is valid only when the "numerator" and "denominator" in Legendre's symbol are both odd primes. One complements it by indicating the corresponding results for $\left(\frac{-1}{p} \right)$ and $\left(\frac{2}{p} \right)$. These are often called the "complementary laws."

Theorem 5   (Complementary Laws of Quadratic Reciprocity). *If p is an odd prime, then* $\left(\dfrac{-1}{p}\right) = (-1)^{(p-1)/2}$ *and* $\left(\dfrac{2}{p}\right) = (-1)^{(p^2-1)/8}$.

PROOF. The first result is a restatement of Theorem 2(6). To prove the second, set $a = 2$ in Lemma 2:

$$\sum_{m=1}^{p'} \left[\frac{2m}{p}\right] + \frac{2-1}{8}(p^2-1) \equiv n \ (\text{mod } 2).$$

In the first member, $2m/p \leq 2p'/p = (p-1)/p < 1$; hence $[2m/p] = 0$ and $n \equiv (p^2-1)/8 \ (\text{mod } 2)$. The result now follows from Theorem 4.

Corollary 5.1. -1 *is a quadratic residue of the primes* $p \equiv 1 \ (\text{mod } 4)$ *and a quadratic non-residue of the primes* $p \equiv 3 \ (\text{mod } 4)$.

Corollary 5.2. 2 *is quadratic residue of the primes* $p \equiv \pm 1 \ (\text{mod } 8)$, *and a quadratic non-residue of the primes* $p \equiv \pm 3 \ (\text{mod } 8)$.

PROOF. Left to the reader.

So far, the Legendre Symbol $\left(\dfrac{a}{p}\right)$ has been defined only for $p \nmid a$. It often is convenient to have a meaning attached to $\left(\dfrac{a}{p}\right)$ for all a. Therefore, Definition 2 is complemented by

Definition 2'.   If $p \mid a$, then $\left(\dfrac{a}{p}\right) = 0$.

To illustrate the advantages of Definition 2', we observe, for instance, how simply one can now state, in full generality and without any need for case distinctions that the number of solutions of the congruence $x^2 \equiv a$ (mod p) is $1 + \left(\dfrac{a}{p}\right)$. The cases $\left(\dfrac{a}{p}\right) = \pm 1$ are settled by Theorem 1, while for $p \mid a$ there is only one solution, namely, $x \equiv 0 \ (\text{mod } p)$. To illustrate the usefulness of the Reciprocity Law let us compute the following Legendre Symbol.

$\left(\dfrac{213}{499}\right) = \left(\dfrac{3}{499}\right)\left(\dfrac{71}{499}\right)$ by Theorem 2(4); $\left(\dfrac{3}{499}\right) = -\left(\dfrac{499}{3}\right)$ by the Recipro-

city Law, because $499 \equiv 3 \ (\text{mod } 4)$; $-\left(\dfrac{499}{3}\right) \equiv -\left(\dfrac{1}{3}\right) \equiv -1$ by Theorem

2(1) and 2(3). Similarly, $\left(\dfrac{71}{499}\right) = -\left(\dfrac{499}{71}\right) = -\left(\dfrac{2}{71}\right) = -(-1)^{(71^2-1)/8} \equiv$

-1 by Theorems 3, 2(1), and 5, respectively; consequently, $\left(\dfrac{213}{499}\right) = +1$.

3. *THE JACOBI AND KRONECKER SYMBOLS

Definition 4. Let a, b be odd, $(a, b) = 1$, $b = p_1 p_2 \cdots p_r$ (the prime factors need not be distinct); then the Jacobi Symbol $\left(\dfrac{a}{b}\right)$ is defined by $\left(\dfrac{a}{b}\right) = \prod_{i=1}^{r} \left(\dfrac{a}{p_i}\right)$, where $\left(\dfrac{a}{p_i}\right)$ are Legendre Symbols.

Paralleling Definition 2′ we might also add

Definition 4′. If $(a, b) > 1$ then the Jacobi Symbol $\left(\dfrac{a}{b}\right)$ is defined and $\left(\dfrac{a}{b}\right) = 0$.

REMARK 2. The Legendre symbol $\left(\dfrac{a}{p_i}\right)$ occurs in the product as often as the highest power of p_i that divides b.

REMARK 3. If a is a quadratic residue mod b, then the congruence $x^2 \equiv a$ (mod b) has solutions, $b \mid c^2 - a$ for appropriate c and, *a fortiori*, $p_i \mid c^2 - a$; consequently, $x^2 \equiv a$ (mod p_i) has solutions for $p_i \mid b$, $\left(\dfrac{a}{p_i}\right) = 1$ and, hence, $\left(\dfrac{a}{b}\right) = 1$. Therefore, if a is a quadratic residue mod b, then $\left(\dfrac{a}{b}\right) = 1$, as in the case of the Legendre symbol. But the converse is not true any more; it is possible to have $\left(\dfrac{a}{p_i}\right) = -1$ for an even number (say, $2h$) of prime factors p_i, so that $x^2 \equiv a$ (mod p_i) has no solutions; hence, *a fortiori*, $x^2 \equiv a$ (mod b) has none, while $\left(\dfrac{a}{b}\right) = \prod_i \left(\dfrac{a}{p_i}\right) = (-1)^{2h} = +1$.

From the definition of Legendre and Jacobi symbols immediately follows:

Theorem 6. *Let* a, a_i, b, b_i *be odd with* $(a, b) = (a_i, b) = (a, b_i) = 1$; *then*

(1) $a_1 \equiv a_2 \pmod{b} \Rightarrow \left(\dfrac{a_1}{b}\right) = \left(\dfrac{a_2}{b}\right);$

(2) $\left(\dfrac{a^2}{b}\right) = +1;$

(3) $\left(\dfrac{a}{b^2}\right) = +1;$

(4) $\quad a = a_1 m^2, \; b = b_1 n^2 \Rightarrow \left(\dfrac{a}{b}\right) = \left(\dfrac{a_1}{b_1}\right);$

(5) $\quad \left(\dfrac{a}{b_1}\right)\left(\dfrac{a}{b_2}\right) = \left(\dfrac{a}{b_1 b_2}\right);$

(6) $\quad \left(\dfrac{a_1}{b}\right)\left(\dfrac{a_2}{b}\right) = \left(\dfrac{a_1 a_2}{b}\right).$

PROOF. The proofs are left to the reader.

Also the Law of Reciprocity and the Complementary Laws generalize immediately to Jacobi symbols, as follows:

Theorem 7. *If a, b are odd, $(a, b) = 1$, then*

(1) $\quad \left(\dfrac{a}{b}\right)\left(\dfrac{b}{a}\right) = (-1)^{a' \cdot b'}$ *with* $a' = \tfrac{1}{2}(a - 1)$, $b' = \tfrac{1}{2}(b - 1)$;

(2) $\quad \left(\dfrac{-1}{b}\right) = (-1)^{(b-1)/2};$

(3) $\quad \left(\dfrac{2}{b}\right) = (-1)^{(b^2 - 1)/8}.$

PROOFS. Let a_1 and a_2 be odd integers. Then one checks easily the congruences $(a_1 - 1)(a_2 - 1) \equiv 0 \pmod 4 \Rightarrow a_1 a_2 - a_1 - a_2 + 1 \equiv 0 \pmod 4 \Rightarrow a_1 a_2 - 1 \equiv (a_1 - 1) + (a_2 - 1) \pmod 4 \Rightarrow (a_1 a_2 - 1)/2 \equiv (a_1 - 1)/2 + (a_2 - 1)/2 \pmod 2$, and, by induction on the number r of factors,

$$\frac{a_1 a_2 \cdots a_r - 1}{2} \equiv \sum_{j=1}^{r} \frac{a_j - 1}{2} \pmod 2. \tag{5}$$

To prove Theorem 7(1), let $a = p_1 p_2 \cdots p_r$, $b = p_1' \cdots p_s'$. By Definition 4, $\left(\dfrac{a}{b}\right) = \displaystyle\prod_{1 \le j \le s} \left(\dfrac{a}{p_j'}\right)$ so that, using also Theorem 2(4)

$$\left(\frac{a}{b}\right) = \prod_{1 \le j \le s} \left(\frac{a}{p_j'}\right) = \prod_{1 \le j \le s} \prod_{1 \le i \le r} \left(\frac{p_i}{p_j'}\right).$$

By Theorem 3,

$$\left(\frac{p_i}{p_j'}\right) = \left(\frac{p_j'}{p_i}\right)(-1)^{[(p_i - 1)/2][(p_j' - 1)/2]},$$

so that

$$\prod_{1 \le i \le r} \left(\frac{p_i}{p_j'}\right) = (-1)^{[(p_j' - 1)/2]\sum_{i=1}^{r} (p_i - 1)/2} \prod_{1 \le i \le r} \left(\frac{p_j'}{p_i}\right)$$

and

$$\left(\frac{a}{b}\right) = (-1)^{\Sigma^s_{j=1}\,(p_j'-1)/2\,\Sigma^r_{i=1}\,(p_i-1)/2} \prod_{i\le j\le s} \prod_{i\le i\le r} \left(\frac{p_j'}{p_i}\right)$$

Having a finite number of factors, we may rearrange the last product and obtain

$$\prod_{1\le i\le r} \prod_{1\le j\le s} \left(\frac{p_j'}{p_i}\right) = \prod_{1\le i\le r} \left(\frac{b}{p_i}\right) = \left(\frac{b}{a}\right),$$

by Theorem 2(4) and Definition 4, respectively. Also, by (5),

$$\sum_{j=1}^{s} \frac{p_j' - 1}{2} \equiv \frac{p_1' \cdots p_s' - 1}{2} \equiv \frac{b' - 1}{2} = b' \;(\text{mod } 2);$$

similarly, $\sum_{i=1}^{r}(p_i - 1)/2 \equiv a'$ (mod 2), so that $\left(\frac{a}{b}\right) = (-1)^{a'\cdot b'}\left(\frac{a}{b}\right)$, as claimed. Similarly,

$$\left(\frac{-1}{b}\right) = \prod_{1\le j\le s} \left(\frac{-1}{p_j'}\right) = \prod_{1\le j\le s} (-1)^{(p_j'-1)/2} = (-1)^{\Sigma^r_{j=1}\,(p_j'-1)/2} = (-1)^{b'}$$

(use being made, successively, of Definition 4, Theorem 5 and the congruence (5)), which proves Theorem 7(2).

Theorem 7(3) is similarly proven, using instead of (5) the congruence

$$\frac{(a_1 a_2 \cdots a_r)^2 - 1}{8} \equiv \sum_{i=1}^{r} \frac{a_i^2 - 1}{8} \;(\text{mod } 2), \qquad (6)$$

obtained as follows: $a_1 \equiv a_2 \equiv 1$ (mod 2)

$$\Rightarrow (a_1^2 - 1)(a_2^2 - 1) \equiv 0\,(\text{mod } 16) \Rightarrow a_1^2 a_2^2 - 1$$

$$\equiv (a_1^2 - 1) + (a_2^2 - 1)\,(\text{mod } 16)$$

$$\Rightarrow \frac{a_1^2 a_2^2 - 1}{8} \equiv \frac{a_1^2 - 1}{8} + \frac{a_2^2 - 1}{8}\,(\text{mod } 2) \Rightarrow (6) \text{ by induction on } r.$$

Using (6),

$$\left(\frac{2}{b}\right) = \prod_{1\le j\le s} \left(\frac{2}{p_j'}\right) = \prod_{1\le j\le s} (-1)^{(p_j'^2-1)/8} = (-1)^{\Sigma^s_{j=1}\,(p_j'^2-1)/8}$$

$$= (-1)^{((p_1' \cdots p_s')^2 - 1)/8} = (-1)^{(b^2-1)/8},$$

and Theorem 7(3) is proven.

While the definition of the Jacobi symbol is more general than that of Legendre's symbol, it is still restricted by the conditions that a and b be odd and coprime. We already dispensed with the last restriction, simply by the stipulation that $(a, b) > 1 \Rightarrow \left(\dfrac{a}{b}\right) = \left(\dfrac{b}{a}\right) = 0$. It is somewhat less trivial to discard the restriction that a and b have to be odd. This is partially done by

Definition 5. The *Kronecker symbol* $\left(\dfrac{a}{b}\right)$ is defined as follows:

(i) $\left(\dfrac{a}{b}\right) = 0$ if $(a, b) > 1$;

(ii) $\left(\dfrac{a}{b}\right)$ is identical with the Jacobi symbol if

$$a \equiv b \equiv 1 \;(\text{mod } 2) \quad \text{and} \quad (a, b) = 1;$$

(iii) *If $a \equiv 0$ or $1 \;(\text{mod } 4)$ and $b = 2^c b_1$, $b_1 \equiv 1 \;(\text{mod } 2)$,*

then $\left(\dfrac{a}{b}\right) = \left(\dfrac{a}{2}\right)^c \left(\dfrac{a}{b_1}\right)$; here $\left(\dfrac{a}{b_1}\right)$ is a Jacobi symbol

and $\qquad \left(\dfrac{a}{2}\right) = \left(\dfrac{a}{-2}\right) = \begin{cases} 0 & \text{if } a \text{ is even,} \\ +1 & \text{if } a \equiv 1 \;(\text{mod } 8), \\ -1 & \text{if } a \equiv 5 \;(\text{mod } 8). \end{cases}$

REMARK 4. By Theorem 7(3),

$$\left(\frac{2}{a}\right) = (-1)^{(a^2-1)/8} = \begin{cases} 1 & \text{if} \quad a \equiv 1 \;(\text{mod } 8), \\ -1 & \text{if} \quad a \equiv 5 \;(\text{mod } 8); \end{cases}$$

hence, for $a \equiv 1 \;(\text{mod } 4)$, one has $\left(\dfrac{a}{2}\right) = \left(\dfrac{2}{a}\right)$; this also holds for $a \equiv 0$ (mod 4), if we use Definition 4′.

We finish this chapter by listing some properties of the Kronecker symbol, not covered by those of the Jacobi symbol.

Theorem 8. *Let m, n, a, a_1, a_2, k be positive integers; then*

(1) $a_1 \equiv a_2 \;(\text{mod } 8) \Rightarrow \left(\dfrac{a_1}{2}\right) = \left(\dfrac{a_2}{2}\right)$;

(2) $\left(\dfrac{a_1}{2}\right)\left(\dfrac{a_2}{2}\right) = \left(\dfrac{a_1 a_2}{2}\right)$;

(3) $\left(\dfrac{a}{2}\right) = \left(\dfrac{2}{a}\right)$;

(4) $\left(\dfrac{a}{2}\right)^k = \left(\dfrac{a}{2^k}\right)$;

(5) $a \equiv 0 \text{ or } 1 \;(\text{mod } 4) \Rightarrow \left(\dfrac{a}{m}\right)\left(\dfrac{a}{n}\right) = \left(\dfrac{a}{mn}\right)$;

(6) $m \equiv n \,(\text{mod } a) \Rightarrow \left(\dfrac{a}{m}\right) = \left(\dfrac{a}{n}\right).$

All proofs, except that of (6), are very simple; they are left as an exercise for the reader.

One of the important advantages of the Jacobi and Kronecker symbols is that they permit a rapid calculation of Legendre symbols. The computation of $\left(\dfrac{213}{499}\right)$, performed already using exclusively the Theory of the Legendre symbol, can now proceed as follows:

$$\left(\frac{213}{499}\right) = \left(\frac{499}{213}\right) = \left(\frac{73}{213}\right) = \left(\frac{213}{73}\right) = \left(\frac{67}{73}\right) = \left(\frac{73}{67}\right) = \left(\frac{6}{67}\right) = \left(\frac{2}{67}\right)\left(\frac{3}{67}\right)$$

$$= -\left(\frac{3}{67}\right) = \left(\frac{67}{3}\right) = \left(\frac{1}{3}\right) = +1;$$

there are more steps than in the previous method, but each step can be performed mentally with ease. In practice, of course, one would combine both methods so as to obtain the greatest simplification of the numerical work.

PROBLEMS

1. Prove in detail the equivalence of the congruence (1) with the system (2), (2′) of Section 1.

2. Prove Corollary 1.1.

3. Find a complete set of quadratic residues and of quadratic non-residues modulo 11 and modulo 13.

4. Find $\left(\frac{3}{5}\right)$ and $\left(\frac{5}{11}\right)$ by Gauss' Lemma, that is, by determining in each case the integer n, for which $\left(\dfrac{a}{p}\right) = (-1)^n$.

5. Prove Corollaries 5.1 and 5.2.

6. Compute $\left(\dfrac{101}{131}\right) \cdot \left(\dfrac{100}{131}\right),\ \left(\dfrac{99}{131}\right)$ using only the theory of the Legendre symbol. Compute the same symbols, considered as Jacobi symbols.

7. Prove that the product of two quadratic residues or two quadratic non-residues (mod p) is a quadratic residue, while the product of a quadratic residue and of a quadratic non-residue is a quadratic non-residue mod p.

8. Prove Theorem 6.

9. Prove Theorem 8 in detail; special care is needed for (6). (*Hint:* Use the reciprocity formula to replace $\left(\dfrac{a}{m}\right)$ and $\left(\dfrac{a}{n}\right)$ by $\left(\dfrac{m}{a}\right)$ and $\left(\dfrac{n}{a}\right)$, respectively; then use Theorem 6(1) and Theorem 8(1).)

10. Find all primes for which 3 is a quadratic residue and all primes for which 3 is a quadratic non-residue. Solve the same problem for -5.

11. Prove that for every $p > 3$, the sum of the quadratic residues is divisible by p.

12. Show that $p \nmid a \Rightarrow \sum_{m=0}^{p-1} \left(\dfrac{am + b}{p}\right) = 0$

   (*Hint:* Show first that $\sum_{m=0}^{p-1} \left(\dfrac{m}{p}\right) = 0.$

13. Let $S(a) = \sum_{m=1}^{p-1} \left(\dfrac{m^2 + a}{p}\right)$. Show that $S(a)$ depends only on $\left(\dfrac{a}{p}\right)$, in particular show that $p \mid a \Rightarrow S(a) = p - 1$.

   (*Hint:* Show that for every $k \not\equiv 0 \pmod{p}$, $S(a) = \left(\dfrac{k^2}{p}\right) S(a) = S(ak^2)$

   and use Problem 7).

14. Prove that $\sum_{m=0}^{p-1} S(a) = 0$.
   (*Hint:* invert the order of summations and use Problem 11).

15. Prove

   (i) $\left(\dfrac{a}{p}\right) = -1 \Rightarrow S(a) = 0,$

   (ii) $\left(\dfrac{a}{p}\right) = +1 \Rightarrow S(a) = -2,$

   (iii) $p \nmid a \Rightarrow S(a) + \left(\dfrac{a}{p}\right) = -1.$

   (*Hints:* For (i) observe that by Problem 13,

   $$S(a) = S(an^2) = \sum_{m=0}^{p-1} \left(\frac{m^2 + an^2}{p}\right)$$

   for every $n \not\equiv 0 \pmod{p}$; hence,

   $$\left(\frac{a}{p}\right) = -1 \Rightarrow S(a) = \left(\frac{a}{p}\right) \sum_{m=1}^{p-1} \left(\frac{m^2 a + a^2 n^2}{p}\right).$$

Sum over $n(1 \leq n \leq p - 1)$ and conclude that $S(a) = -S(a)$. For (ii) split the sum in Problem 14 into 3 parts according to the values of $\left(\dfrac{a}{p}\right)$, use Problem 13 and Part (i); (iii) follows immediately from (i) and (ii).)

16. Let $f(x) = ax^2 + bx + c$, set $d = b^2 - 4ac$ and

$$T(f) = \sum_{m=0}^{p-1} \left(\frac{f(m)}{p}\right).$$

Prove the following:

(i)   if $p \nmid ad$ then $T(f) = -\left(\dfrac{a}{p}\right)$;

(ii)   if $p \mid a$ but $p \nmid d$ or $p \nmid a$ but $p \mid d$, then

$$T(f) = (p - 1)\left(\frac{a}{p}\right);$$

(iii)   if $p \mid a$ and $p \mid d$ then $T(f) = (p - 1)\left(\dfrac{c}{p}\right)$.

(*Hints*:   The case $p \mid a$, $p \nmid d$ of Part (ii) follows from Problem 12. If $p \nmid a$ then

$$\left(\frac{a}{p}\right)T(f) = \left(\frac{4a}{p}\right)T(f) = \sum_{m=0}^{p-1} \left(\frac{(2am + b)^2 - d}{p}\right)$$

$$= \sum_{m=0}^{p-1}\left(\frac{k^2 - d}{p}\right) \text{ or } T(f) = \left(\frac{a}{p}\right)\sum_{m=0}^{p-1}\left(\frac{m^2 - d}{p}\right);$$

if $p \mid d$, the result of (ii) follows immediately; if $p \nmid d$, use Problem 15 (iii) to obtain (i); case (iii) is trivial.)

17. Prove: (i) if b is kept fixed, the Jacobi symbol $\left(\dfrac{a}{b}\right)$ is a periodic function of a; find its least period.

(ii)   If a is kept fixed, the Jacobi symbol $\left(\dfrac{a}{b}\right)$ is a periodic function of b; find its least period.

18. (i)   Let $a \equiv 1 \pmod 4$ and $b = 2^k b_1$, $2 \nmid b_1$. Using the definition of the Jacobi symbol $\left(\dfrac{a}{b_1}\right)$ and of the Kronecker symbols $\left(\dfrac{a}{2}\right)$ and $\left(\dfrac{a}{b}\right) = \left(\dfrac{a}{2}\right)^k \left(\dfrac{a}{b_1}\right)$, find the relation between $\left(\dfrac{a}{b}\right)$ and $\left(\dfrac{b}{a}\right)$.

(ii)   Same question in case $a \equiv 0 \pmod 4$ (*Caution:*   If $a = a_1 \cdot 2^k$, $k > 0$ and $b \equiv 3 \pmod 4$, then $\left(\dfrac{a}{b}\right)$ is defined, but $\left(\dfrac{b}{a}\right)$ is not.)

19. Determine the number of solutions of the following two congruences:

(a) $x^2 \equiv 231 \pmod{997}$,

(b) $x^2 \equiv 997 \pmod{231}$. (*Hint:*   997 is a prime.)

BIBLIOGRAPHY

1.   G. Frobenius, "Ueber das quadratische Reziprozitätsgesetz," *Sitzungsber. der königl. Preuss. Akad. der Wiss.* Berlin: 1914, pp. 335–349 and 484–488.

2.   W. J. LeVeque, *Topics in Number Theory*, Vol. 1. Reading, Mass.: Addison-Wesley Publishing Co., 1956.

3.   D. Shanks, *Solved and Unsolved Problems in Number Theory*. Washington, D.C.: Spartan Books, 1962.

CHAPTER 6

Arithmetical Functions

1. INTRODUCTION

Let us denote by Z^+ the set of natural integers; clearly $Z^+ \subset Z$. Functions whose domain is Z or Z^+ are usually called arithmetical functions (sometimes also number theoretic functions), regardless of their range. It is, of course, easy to fabricate such functions out of any functions defined over Q, R, or C, simply by considering their restrictions to Z or Z^+. But this rarely leads to interesting results. So, for instance, if we restrict the function $y = x^2$ to $x \in Z$, we obtain simply the sequence of squares; if we restrict $y = \sin \pi x$ to $x \in Z$, we obtain $y = 0$ for all $x \in Z$, and so on. It is much more interesting to consider functions that have Z or Z^+ as their *natural domain*, which means that we cannot give them a simple, sensible interpretation, unless the independent variable is an integer. So, for instance it makes sense to speak about the number of divisors of an integer m, but no simple meaning can be attached to the number of divisors of π, or of e, or of i. We already met with some arithmetical functions. One of them, the Legendre-Jacobi-Kronecker symbol has been discussed in Chapter 5; another one is the number of divisors of an integer; still another one is Euler's ϕ-function. In the present chapter we shall study these and also a few other arithmetical functions. Besides, we shall discuss also two functions, that are not, properly speaking, arithmetic functions, being defined over the reals; but their connection with arithmetical functions is so close, that this seems the logical place to study them. One, the function $y = [x]$ which we already met, has **Z**, at least, as its range; the other, $y = x - [x] - \frac{1}{2}$, not even that.

2. THE FUNCTION [x]

The function $[x]$ has already been defined verbally (see Definition 5.3); it stands for the greatest integer not in excess of the real number x. If we think of the integers as being represented by equidistant dots on the real line, then, if x is one of the dots, $[x] = x$; otherwise, $[x]$ stands for the dot next to the left of x. For convenience we define once more the function $y = [x]$.

Definition 1.

$[x] = n \ni x - 1 < n \leq x, n \in \mathbf{Z}.$

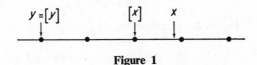

Figure 1

The reader is invited to convince himself that Definition 5.3 and the present one are equivalent. From the definition follow almost immediately the statements of the following theorem.

Theorem 1.   *Let n be an integer and x be a real number; then*

(1) $[x + n] = [x] + n;$

(2) $\left[\dfrac{[x]}{n}\right] = \left[\dfrac{x}{n}\right];$

(3) $\displaystyle\sum_{1 \leq n \leq x} 1 = [x];$

(4) $0 \leq x - [x] < 1;$

(5) $|x - [x] - \frac{1}{2}| \leq \frac{1}{2};$

(6) $[x] + [y] \leq [x + y] \leq [x] + [y] + 1;$

(7) $x \notin \mathbf{Z}^+ \Rightarrow [-x] = -[x] - 1;$

(8) $[2x] - 2[x] = \begin{cases} 1 & \text{if } [2x] \text{ is odd,} \\ 0 & \text{if } [2x] \text{ is even.} \end{cases}$

PROOF. To prove the last assertion, let $x = n + \alpha, 0 \leq \alpha < 1$; then $[x] = n.$

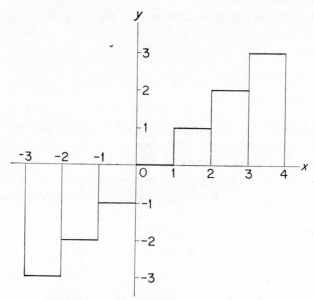

Figure 2.   Graph of the function $y = [x]$

If $0 \le \alpha < \frac{1}{2}$, then $[2x] = [2n + 2\alpha] = 2n$ is even and $[2x] - 2[x] = 2n - 2n = 0$; if $\frac{1}{2} \le \alpha < 1$, then $[2x] = [2n + 2\alpha] = 2n + 1$ is odd and $[2x] - 2[x] = 2n + 1 - 2n = 1$. The proof of the other statements is left to the reader.

Theorem 2. $n! = \prod_{p \le n} p^{e_p}$, *where* $e_p = \sum_{m \ge 1} [n/p^m]$.

REMARK 1. If $p^m > n$ (i.e., for $m > \log n/\log p$), then $[n/p^m] = 0$; therefore, the sum in e_p contains exactly $[\log n/\log p]$ nonvanishing terms.

PROOF OF THEOREM 2. Consider all integers $m \le n$, written in natural order. Every p-th integer is divisible by p; if we divide p out of them, we obtain the factor p exactly $[n/p]$ times. At the same time, integers that contained p precisely to the first power, are no more divisible by p, while those that contained p to the k-th power $(k > 1)$, now contain it only to the $(k - 1)$st power. In particular, every p^2-th integer had been divisible by p^2 and is now divisible by p (at least!). We factor out p from each of these integers, obtaining another $[n/p^2]$ times the factor p; all integers $m \le n$ that had contained p to the first, or second power, do not contain the factor p any more, while every p^3-th integer, which originally were divisible by p^3, now are still divisible at least by the first power of p. In general, let k_a be the exact power of p that divides a given integer a and set $v_a = \max(0, k_a - m)$; then, after m operations of the kind described, the factor p has been obtained $[n/p] + [n/p^2] \cdots + [n/p^m]$ times and $n! = p^{\{[n/p] + \cdots + [n/p^m]\}} \cdot c$, where $c = b_1 \cdot b_2 \cdots b_n$, and the power of p that divides b_a is v_a. In particular, if $m = [\log n/\log p]$, then $v_a = 0$ for all b_a; hence $p \nmid c$ and $e_p = \sum_{m \geq 1} [n/p^m]$, as asserted.

3. THE FUNCTION $y = ((x))$

Definition 2. $((x)) = x - [x] - \frac{1}{2}$ if $x \notin \mathbf{Z}$, $((n)) = 0$ *for* $n \in \mathbf{Z}$.

From Theorem 1 we know that $|((x))| \leq \frac{1}{2}$. Actually, $-\frac{1}{2} < ((x)) < \frac{1}{2}$, because $((x)) = 0$ for integral x. We observe that $((x))$ is a periodic function, of period one, which, for $0 < x < 1$ reduces to the straight-line segment $((x)) = x - \frac{1}{2}$. This function is sometimes called the " sawtooth function."

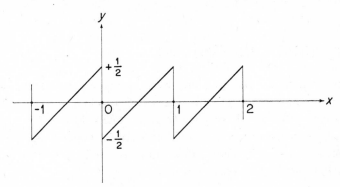

Figure 3.   Graph of the function $y = ((x))$

Consider the first degree polynomial $B_1(x) = x - \frac{1}{2}$. Then $((x)) = B_1(x - [x])$. The following theorem is an immediate consequence of preceding remarks.

Theorem 3.

(1)   *The function* $y = ((x))$ *is periodic, of period one and piecewise linear.*

(2)   *Let* $B_1(x) = x - \frac{1}{2}$; *then* $((x)) = B_1(x - [x])$;

(3) $-\frac{1}{2} < ((x)) < \frac{1}{2}$;

(4) $((-x)) = -((x))$;

(5) $\displaystyle\int_0^1 ((x))\, dx = 0$;

(6) $\left| \displaystyle\int_\alpha^\beta ((x))\, dx \right| \leq /18$ for all real α, β;

(7) $y(x) = \displaystyle\int_1^x ((x))\, dx$ satisfies $|y(x)| \leq 1/8$;

(8) $h, k \in \mathbf{Z}^+ \Rightarrow \displaystyle\sum_{m=1}^{k-1} \left(\left(\frac{mh}{k}\right)\right) = 0$.

PROOF. The proofs for statements (1) to (7) are very easy and are left to the reader. For statement (8), observe that setting $m = k - n$, one has

$$\sum_{m=1}^{k-1} \left(\left(\frac{mh}{k} \right) \right) = \sum_{n=1}^{k-1} \left(\left(\frac{(k-n)h}{k} \right) \right) = \sum_{m=1}^{k-1} \left(\left(\frac{(k-m)h}{k} \right) \right) = \sum_{m=1}^{k-1} \left(\left(\frac{-mh}{k} \right) \right)$$

$$= \sum_{m=1}^{k-1} \left\{ - \left(\left(\frac{mh}{k} \right) \right) \right\} = - \sum_{m=1}^{k-1} \left(\left(\frac{mh}{k} \right) \right)$$

so that $2 \sum_{m=1}^{k-1} ((mh/k)) = 0$ and the statement is proven. The first, second, and last equality are trivially justified, the third holds by Theorem 3(1) and the fourth by Theorem 3(4).

4. THE EULER FUNCTION $\phi(n)$

The Euler function $\phi(n)$ has already been defined (see Definition 4.10) as the number of integers not exceeding $n(\in \mathbf{Z}^+)$ and coprime to n. Some of its important properties have already been stated. Most of them follow quite easily from the property denoted by (A) in Chapter 4, Section 6, and which $\phi(n)$ shares with many other arithmetic functions; this property, called *multiplicativity*, is described as follows.

Definition 3.   A function $f(n)$, defined on $\mathbf{Z}^+$ is said to be *multiplicative*, if $(m, n) = 1 \Rightarrow f(m)f(n) = f(mn)$; $f(n)$ is said to be *totally multiplicative*, if $f(m)f(n) = f(mn)$ for all $m, n \in \mathbf{Z}^+$ (without the restriction $(m, n) = 1$).

Theorem 4. $\phi(n)$ *is multiplicative.*

This statement is precisely Property (A), anticipated in Chapter 4. In the proof we shall use two lemmas.

Lemma 1.   *Let* $(m_1, m_2) = 1$; *let* h_1 *run through a complete set of residues* mod m_1 *and let* h_2 *run through a complete set of residues* mod m_2. *Then* $h = h_2 m_1 + h_1 m_2$ *runs through a complete set of residues* $m_1 m_2$.

PROOF. h_1 takes m_1 values, h_2 takes m_2 values, all integral; the set $\mathbf{H} = \{h\}$ consists, therefore, of $m_1 m_2$ integers. Hence, we shall have proven Lemma 1, if we show that these $m_1 m_2$ integers are all incongruent mod $m_1 m_2$. To do this, assume that $h = h_2 m_1 + h_1 m_2$ and $h' = h_2' m_1 + h_1' m_2$ are two integers of $\mathbf{H}$, congruent mod $m_1 m_2$ and that h_1, h_2 are not both the same as h_1', h_2'. Then $(h_2 - h_2')m_1 + (h_1 - h_1')m_2 \equiv 0 \pmod{m_1 m_2} \Rightarrow (h_2 - h_2')m_1 + (h_1 - h_1')m \equiv 0 \pmod{m_1} \Rightarrow (h_1 - h_1')m_2 \equiv 0 \pmod{m_1} \Rightarrow h_1 - h_1' \equiv 0 \pmod{m_1}$, because $(m_1, m_2) = 1$. However, h_1 and h_1' belong to the same complete set of residues mod m_1; hence, they can be congruent (mod m_1) only if they are identical, and $h_1 = h'_1$. In the same way we obtain also $h_2 = h'_2$, contrary to our assumption that $(h_1, h_2) \neq (h'_2, h'_2)$ and the Lemma is proven.

Lemma 2. *Let $(m_1, m_2) = 1$, let h_1 run through a complete set of reduced residues mod m_1 and h_2 through a complete set of reduced residues mod m_2; then $h = m_1 h_2 + m_2 h_1$ runs through a complete set of reduced residues mod $m_1 m_2$.*

PROOF. Consider the set $\mathbf{H} = \{h\}$ discussed in Lemma 1. We already know that all its elements are incongruent mod $m_1 m_2$. We now have to show that $(h, m_1 m_2) = 1$ if and only if $(h_1, m_1) = 1$ *and* $(h_2, m_2) = 1$. On account of $(m_1, m_2) = 1$ the condition $(m_1 h_2 + m_2 h_1, m_1 m_2) = 1$ is equivalent to the two simultaneous conditions $(m_1 h_2 + m_2 h_1, m_1) = 1$ and $(m_1 h_2 + m_2 h_1, m_2) = 1$, which simplify to $(m_2 h_1, m_1) = 1$ and $(m_1 h_2, m_2) = 1$. Using once more $(m_1, m_2) = 1$, these conditions reduce to $(h_2, m_2) = 1$ and $(h_1, m_1) = 1$; hence,

$$(h, m_1 m_2) = 1 \Leftrightarrow \begin{cases} (h_1, m_1) = 1 \\ (h_2, m_2) = 1 \end{cases}$$

and Lemma 2 is proven.

PROOF OF THEOREM 4. By the definition of Euler's ϕ-function, there are $\phi(m_1)$ distinct values of h_1 with $1 \leq h_1 \leq m$, $(h_1, m_1) = 1$; $\phi(m_2)$ distinct values of h_2 with $1 \leq h_2 \leq m_2$, $(h_2, m_2) = 1$; and $\phi(m_1 m_2)$ distinct values of h with $1 \leq h \leq m_1 m_2$, $(h, m_1 m_2) = 1$. By Lemma 2, each of these $\phi(m_1 m_2)$ values of h is obtained exactly once, by setting $h = m_1 h_1 + m_2 h_2$, with h_1 running through a complete set of reduced residues modulo m_1 and h_2 through a complete set of reduced residues modulo m_2. Consequently, there are $\phi(m_1)\phi(m_2)$ distinct values of h, $\phi(m_1 m_2) = \phi(m_1)\phi(m_2)$ and the Theorem is proven.

Theorem 5. $\phi(p^r) = p^r - p^{r-1}$.

PROOF. If $n \leq p^r$, then $(n, p^r) = 1$, except for $n = kp$, where k may take the values $1, 2, ..., p^{r-1}$ (see Chapter 4, Problem 21).

Theorem 6. $\phi(m) = m \prod_{p \mid m} \left(1 - \dfrac{1}{p}\right)$.

This is Property (B) anticipated in Chapter 4.

PROOF. Let $m = p_1^{s_1} p_2^{s_2} \cdots p_s^{s_r}$; then, by Theorem 4, $\phi(m) = \prod_{p_i \mid m} \phi(p_i^{s_i})$; by Theorem 5, $\phi(p_i^{s_i}) = p_i^{s_i} - p_i^{s_i - 1}$, so that $\phi(m) = \prod_{p_i \mid m} p_i^{s_i}(1 - (1/p_i)) = m \prod_{p \mid m} (1 - (1/p))$.

Corollary 6.1. *If $m \neq 1, 2$ then $2 \mid \phi(m)$.*

This implies, of course, Property (C) of Chapter 4.

PROOF. By Theorem 6,

$m = p_1^{s_1} p_2^{s_2} \cdots p_r^{s_r} \Rightarrow \phi(m) = p_1^{s_1-1} p_2^{s_2-1} \cdots p_r^{s_r-1}(p_1 - 1)(p_2 - 1) \cdots (p_r - 1)$
and, by assumption, either some odd $p_j \mid m$ so that $2 \mid (p_j - 1) \Rightarrow 2 \mid \phi(m)$;
or $m = 2^s$, $s \geq 2$, so that $\phi(m) = 2^{s-1}$ and again $2 \mid \phi(m)$.

Theorem 7. $\displaystyle\sum_{d \mid m} \phi(d) = m$.

This is Property (D) anticipated in Chapter 4.

PROOF. Let $m = p_1^{s_1} p_2^{s_2} \cdots p_r^{s_r}$ and consider the product $P = \displaystyle\prod_{p_i \mid m} (1 + \phi(p_i) +$
$\cdots + \phi(p_i^{s_i}))$. Multiplying it out and observing that $(p_i^t, p_j^s) = 1$ if
$p_i \neq p_j$, we obtain, by Theorem 4, that P consists of a sum of terms of
the form

$$\phi(p_1^{t_1})\phi(p_2^{t_2}) \cdots \phi(p_r^{t_r}) = \phi(d),$$

where $d = p_1^{t_1} p_2^{t_2} \cdots p_r^{t_r}(0 \leq t_i \leq s_i)$ runs precisely through all the divisors
of m; furthermore, Theorem 3.3 guarantees that each divisor is obtained
exactly once. Hence, $P = \displaystyle\sum_{d \mid m} \phi(d)$. However, by Theorem 5,

$1 + \phi(p) + \cdots + \phi(p^s) = 1 + (p - 1) + (p^2 - p) + \cdots$
$$+ (p^{s-1} - p^{s-2}) + (p^s - p^{s-1}) = p^s;$$

hence, $P = \displaystyle\prod_{p_i \mid m} p_i^{s_i} = m$. Writing that the two expressions of P are equal
we obtain the Theorem. A different, neater proof of Theorem 7 will be given
in Section 5.

One should observe that the proof of the equality $P = \displaystyle\sum_{d \mid m} \phi(d)$ uses only
the fact that $\phi(n)$ is multiplicative; hence, we have proven incidentally the
following corollary.

Corollary 7.1. *Let $f(n)$ be multiplicative and let $n = p_1^{s_1} p_2^{s_2} \cdots p_r^{s_r}$ be
the canonical factorization of $n > 1$; then $\displaystyle\sum_{d \mid n} f(n) = \prod_{p \mid n}(1 + f(p) + \cdots + f(p^s))$.
If $n = 1$, then $\displaystyle\sum_{d \mid n} f(n) = 1$.*

The last statement follows from the fact that $f(1) = 1$, because $f(n)$ is
multiplicative.

5. THE MÖBIUS FUNCTION $\mu(n)$

The Möbius Function $\mu(n)$ is defined on the set $\mathbf{Z}^+$ of natural integers
$n = p_1^{s_1} p_2^{s_2} \cdots p_r^{s_r} (s_j \geq 1)$ as follows.

Definition 4.

$$\mu(n) = \begin{cases} 0 & \text{if } \sum_{i=1}^{r} s_i > r \text{ (i.e., if } \exists\, j,\, 1 \le j \le r \ni p_j^2 \mid n), \\[2mm] (-1)^r & \text{if } \sum_{i=1}^{r} s_i = r \text{ (i.e., if } s_1 = s_2 = \cdots = s_r = 1). \end{cases}$$

$M(x) = \sum_{n \le x} \mu(n)$ is called *the sum function of $\mu(n)$*.

In particular, for $r = 0$, we obtain $\mu(1) = 1$; for $r = 1$, $\mu(p) = -1$ for every prime p; also

$$\mu(p_1 p_2) = 1, \qquad \mu(p^2) = \mu(p^3) = \cdots = 0.$$

REMARK 2. $M(x)$ is defined over $\mathbf{R}$, not only over $\mathbf{Z}^+$; by the general convention on empty sums, $M(x) = 0$ if $x < 1$.

Definition 5. An integer not divisible by the square of any integer $n \ne 1$ is called *squarefree*.

Theorem 8. $\mu(n)$ *is multiplicative.*

PROOF. Let $(m, n) = 1$; hence, $p^2 \mid mn$ only if either $p^2 \mid m$, or $p^2 \mid n$, and in either case $\mu(m)\mu(n) = \mu(mn) = 0$. If m and n are both squarefree, then $m = p_1 p_2 \cdots p_r$, $n = q_1 q_2 \cdots q_s$, $mn = p_1 p_2 \cdots p_r q_1 q_2 \cdots q_s$, the primes p_i and q_j being all distinct. Then $\mu(m) = (-1)^r$, $\mu(n) = (-1)^s$ and $\mu(mn) = (-1)^{r+s}$, so that the Theorem holds.

Theorem 9.

$$\sum_{d \mid n} \mu(d) = \begin{cases} 1 & \text{if } n = 1; \\ 0 & \text{otherwise.} \end{cases}$$

FIRST PROOF. By Theorem 8, $\mu(n)$ is multiplicative; hence, remembering that for any p, $1 + \mu(p) + \mu(p^2) + \cdots = 1 + \mu(p) = 0$, the result follows from Corollary 7.1.

SECOND PROOF. Let $n = p_1^{s_1} \cdots p_r^{s_r}$, $n_1 = p_1 p_2 \cdots p_r$. Then $\mu(d) = 0$, unless $d \mid n_1$. Hence, $\sum_{d \mid n} \mu(d) = \sum_{d \mid n_1} \mu(d)$. The divisors of n_1 are 1; $p_1, p_2, \ldots, p_r$; $p_1 p_2, \ldots, p_{r-1} p_r$; $\cdots$; $p_1 p_2 \cdots p_r = n$. In general there are $\binom{r}{k} = \dfrac{r!}{k!(r-k)!}$ distinct divisors $d_s^{(k)}\left(s = 1, 2, \ldots, \binom{r}{k}\right)$ of n_1, containing exactly $k(\le r)$ prime factors; the corresponding $\mu(d_s^{(k)})$ equals $(-1)^k$ and $\sum_{s=1}^{\binom{r}{k}} \mu(d_s^{(k)}) = (-1)^k \binom{r}{k}$. Hence, $\sum_{d \mid n} \mu(d) = \sum_{k=0}^{r} (-1)^k \binom{r}{k} = (1-1)^r = 0$, provided that $r > 0$. In case $r = 0$, $n = 1$, and $\sum_{d \mid 1} \mu(d) = \mu(d) = 1$. If in this proof we replace everywhere $\mu(d)$ by $|\mu(d)|$, we obtain

*Corollary 9.1.   *Let r be the number of distinct primes that divide n; then*
$\sum_{d|n} |\mu(d)| = 2^r.$

Still another proof of Theorem 9 may be based on the function $\zeta(s) = \sum_{n=1}^{\infty} n^{-s}$.

Let $s > 1$; then one observes (for a proof see Chapter 7) that the series which defines $\zeta(s)$ converges and equals $\prod_p (1 - p^{-s})^{-1}$, the product being taken over all primes. Hence, $\zeta(s)^{-1} = \prod_p (1 - p^{-s}) = \sum_{n=1}^{\infty} a_n n^{-s}$. It may easily be checked that only squarefree numbers actually occur in the last sum; hence, $a_n = 0$ if $p^2 \mid n$; also, $a_n = +1$, or -1, depending on whether n is a product of an even, or an odd number of primes. This identifies a_n as the Möbius function $\mu(n)$ and $\zeta(s)^{-1} = \sum_{n=1}^{\infty} \mu(n)n^{-s}$. But $\zeta(s) \cdot \zeta(s)^{-1} = 1$, so that $\sum_{k=1}^{\infty} k^{-s} \sum_{m=1}^{\infty} \mu(m)m^{-s} = 1$. The double sum may be written as $\sum_{k=1}^{\infty} \sum_{m=1}^{\infty} (km)^{-s} \mu(m)$, or, setting $km = n$, as $\sum_{n=1}^{\infty} n^{-s} \sum_{m|n} \mu(m)$, so that

$$\sum_{n=1}^{\infty} n^{-s} \sum_{m|n} \mu(m) = 1. \tag{1}$$

Both sides in equation (1) are *Dirichlet series*, that is, series of the form $\sum_{n=1}^{\infty} a_n n^{-s}$ and (1) may be written as $\sum_{n=1}^{\infty} a_n n^{-s} = \sum_{n=1}^{\infty} b_n n^{-s}$, with $a_n = \sum_{m|n} \mu(m)$; $b_1 = 1$, $b_n = 0 \ (n > 1)$. It is clear that if a Dirichlet series converges for $s = s_0 (\in \mathbf{R})$, then it converges also for $s \geq s_0$.

The following uniqueness theorem holds for Dirichlet series. Assuming it for a moment the proof of Theorem 9 reduces to the remarks that $a_1 = \sum_{m|1} \mu(m) = b_1 = 1$ and $a_n = \sum_{m|n} \mu(m) = b_n = 0$ for $n > 1$.

Theorem 10.   *If the Dirichlet series $\sum_{n=1}^{\infty} a_n n^{-s}$ and $\sum_{n=1}^{\infty} b_n n^{-s}$ converge both for $s \geq s_0$, then they are equal for all $s \geq s_0$ if and only if $a_n = b_n$ for all n.*

PROOF.   The "if" part is trivial. To prove the "only if" part, assume the equality of the two series and let $s \to +\infty$; then all terms with $n > 1$ tend to zero in both series. One easily shows (by first proving, then using the uniformity of the convergence) that $\lim_{s \to \infty} \sum_{n=2}^{\infty} a_n n^{-s} = \lim_{s \to \infty} \sum_{n=2}^{\infty} b_n n^{-s} = 0$ so that $a_1 = b_1$ and the statement is proven for $n = 1$. Having established that $a_n = b_n$ for $n = 1, 2, ..., k - 1$ it remains to show that also $a_k = b_k$ and the proof by induction of the Theorem will be complete. From $a_n = b_n \ (n = 1, 2, ..., k - 1)$ and $\sum_{n=1}^{\infty} a_n n^{-s} = \sum_{n=1}^{\infty} b_n n^{-s}$ it follows that $\sum_{n=k}^{\infty} a_n n^{-s} = \sum_{n=k}^{\infty} b_n n^{-s}$, or, multiplying by k^s, that $a_k + \sum_{n=k+1}^{\infty} a_n (k/n)^s = b_k + \sum_{n=k+1}^{\infty} b_n (k/n)^s$.

Observing that for $n \geq k + 1$, $k/n < 1$, it follows as before, that both infinite sums approach zero when $s \to \infty$; consequently, $a_k = b_k$ and Theorem 10 is proven.

While Theorem 9 may strike the reader as comparatively trivial (and he may well wonder why one should prove it in three different ways), it actually is a very powerful tool. As an illustration we shall use it to prove a corollary, which, to the best of my knowledge, is due to I. M. Vinogradov (see [11]) and is surprisingly general and versatile.

Corollary 9.2. (Vinogradov). *Consider an arbitrary set of n couples $\{(\alpha_j, d_j)\}$, $1 \le j \le n$, where the α_j may be arbitrary real, or even complex numbers and the d_j are positive integers. For any integer m set*

$$S_m = \sum_{d_j \equiv 0 (\text{mod } m)} \alpha_j$$

and let $S' = \sum_{d_j = 1} \alpha_j$; then

$$S' = \sum_{m=1}^{\infty} \mu(m) S_m .$$

COMMENTS. S_m is the sum of those α_j, whose companions d_j are multiples of the integer m; clearly, $S_m = 0$, unless $m \mid d_j$ for at least some $j (1 \le j \le n)$. S' is the sum of those α_j, whose companions satisfy $d_j = 1$.

PROOF. By the definition of S_d, $\sum_{m=1}^{\infty} \mu(m) S_m = \sum_{m=1}^{\infty} \mu(m) \sum_{d_j \equiv 0(m)} \alpha_j$; rearranging the terms we obtain $\sum_{j=1}^{n} \alpha_j \sum_{m \mid d_j} \mu(m) = \sum_{d_j = 1} \alpha_j = S'$, because, if $d_j \ne 1$, the inner sum vanishes on account of Theorem 9. The Corollary is proven.

To illustrate the power of Corollary 9.2, let us prove

Corollary 9.3. *For every real $x \ge 1$, $\sum_{m=1}^{x} \mu(m) [x/m] = 1$.*

PROOF. In Corollary 9.2 with $n = [x]$, let $d_j = j$, $\alpha_j = 1(1 \le j \le x)$; then $S' = 1$, $S_m = \sum_{j \le x, j \equiv 0(m)} 1 = [x/m]$ and, by Corollary 9.2, $1 = S' = \sum_{m=1}^{\infty} \mu(m) S_m = \sum_{m=1}^{\infty} \mu(m)[x/m] = \sum_{m=1}^{x} \mu(m)[x/m]$ as claimed.

Theorem 11. (Möbius' inversion formula). *If $f(n)$ is a function defined on $\mathbf{Z}^+$ and $F(n)$ is defined by $F(n) = \sum_{d \mid n} f(d)$, then $f(n) = \sum_{d \mid n} \mu(d) F(n/d)$. Conversely, if $F(n)$ is a function on $\mathbf{Z}^+$ and $f(n)$ is defined by $f(n) = \sum_{d \mid n} \mu(d) F(n/d)$, then $F(n) = \sum_{d \mid n} f(d)$.*

PROOF. $\sum_{d \mid n} \mu(d) F(n/d)$

$$= \sum_{d \mid n} \mu(d) \sum_{d_1 \mid (n/d)} f(d_1) = \sum_{d_1 \mid n} f(d_1) \sum_{d_1 d \mid n} \mu(d)$$

$$= \sum_{d_1 \mid n} f(d_1) \sum_{d \mid (n/d_1)} \mu(d).$$

The last sum vanishes, by Theorem 5, unless $n/d_1 = 1$, that is, unless $n = d_1$, when it reduces to one and $\sum_{d|n} \mu(d)F(n/d) = \sum_{d_1=n} f(d_1) \cdot 1 = f(n)$. For the converse, one has, successively, $\sum_{d|n} f(d) = \sum_{d|n} \sum_{d_1|d} \mu(d_1)F(d/d_1) = \sum_{d|n} \sum_{d_1|d} F(d_1)\mu(d/d_1)$; inverting the order of summation, this equals $\sum_{d_1|n} F(d_1) \sum_{d_1|d|n} \mu(d/d_1)$. Setting $k = d/d_1$, the inner sum equals $\sum_{k|(n/d_1)} \mu(k)$ and is zero, except for $d_1 = n$, when $\sum_{k|1} \mu(k) = 1$; $d_1 = n$ also implies $F(d_1) = F(n)$ and that finishes the proof of the statement.

Theorem 11 makes no assumption concerning the multiplicative character of the functions involved. However, we have

Theorem 12.   (i)   *If $f(n)$ is multiplicative, and $F(n) = \sum_{d|n} f(d)$, then also $F(n)$ is multiplicative; and conversely,*

(ii)   *if $F(n)$ is multiplicative, then, so is $f(n)$.*

PROOF. (i)   If $(m, n) = 1$, then it is clear that we obtain each divisor r of mn exactly once, if we set $r = dd_1$ and let d and d_1 run independently through the divisors of m and of n, respectively. Hence, $F(mn) = \sum_{r|mn} f(r) = \sum_{dd_1|mn} f(dd_1)$ $= \sum_{d|m} \sum_{d_1|n} f(d)f(d_1)$, by the multiplicativity of $f(n)$. The double sum, however, equals $\sum_{d|m} f(d) \sum_{d_1|n} f(d_1) = F(m)F(n)$. The proof of (ii) is similar and is left as an exercise for the reader.

SECOND PROOF OF THEOREM 7. In Theorem 11 take $F(n) = n$. Then $f(n) = \sum_{d|n} \mu(n/d)d$ and $F(n) = n = \sum_{d|n} f(d)$. But $f(n) = \sum_{d|n} \mu(d)(n/d) = n\sum_{d|n} \frac{\mu(d)}{d} = n\prod_{p|n} (1 - (1/p)) = \phi(n)$; hence, $F(n) = n = \sum_{d|n} f(d)$ becomes $n = \sum_{d|n} \phi(d)$.

The "sum function" of the Möbius function $\mu(n)$ has been defined by $M(x) = \sum_{n \leq x} \mu(n)$. It is completely trivial to observe that for $x \geq 2$, $|M(x)| \leq \sum_{n \leq x} |\mu(x)| < \sum_{n \leq x} 1 = x$. It seems, however, reasonable to assume that there are roughly speaking, about as many squarefree integers with an even, as with an odd number of distinct primes; therefore, it would seem plausible that many cancellations occur in the sum $\sum_{n \leq x} \mu(n)$ and one would expect $M(x)$ to increase less fast than x. If this guess is correct, then the ratio $M(x)/x$ should decrease to zero, as x increases indefinitely. This is in fact so, but the proof is far from simple. The ease with which we just proved

Thereom 13. $|M(x)| < x,$

should be contrasted with the long and difficult considerations needed for the apparently simple improvement of Theorem 13 to

Theorem 13'. *If* $\varepsilon > 0$, *but arbitrarily small, then, for all sufficiently large* x, $|M(x)| < \varepsilon x$.

A proof of Theorem 13' will be given at the end of this chapter, under anticipation of two results to be proven only later.

6. *LIOUVILLE'S FUNCTION

As an example of a totally multiplicative function, that behaves in many ways like Möbius' μ-function, one may mention Liouville's function $\lambda(n)$.

Definition 6. Let $n = p_1^{s_1} p_2^{s_2} \cdots p_r^{s_r}$; then $\lambda(n) = (-1)^s$, where $s = \sum_{i=1}^{r} s_i$.

The multiplicativity follows directly from the definition.

7. THE FUNCTION $\sigma_k(n)$

Definition 7. The sum of the k-th powers of the divisors of the integer n is denoted by $\sigma_k(n)$. In particular, $\sigma_0(n)$ is the number of divisors of n (sometimes, although not in this book, $\sigma_0(n)$ is denoted by $\tau(n)$); $\sigma_1(n)$ (usually denoted simply by $\sigma(n)$) is the sum of the divisors of n. In symbols, $\sigma_k(n) = \sum_{d|n} d^k$.

Theorem 14. $\sigma_k(n)$ *is multiplicative.*

PROOF. The function $f(n) = n^k$ is trivially (even totally) multiplicative; if we use it in Theorem 12, the result follows from the definition $\sigma_k(n) = \sum_{d|n} d^k$.

Theorem 15.

$$\sigma_k(n) = \prod_{p|n} \frac{p^{(s_p+1)k} - 1}{p^k - 1},$$

where s_p *stands for the highest power of* p *that divides* n.

PROOF. By the multiplicative property,

$$\sigma_k(n) = \prod_{p|n} \sigma_k(p^{s_p}) = \prod_{p|n} (1 + p^k + p^{2k} + \cdots + p^{s_p k})$$

$$= \prod_{p|n} (p^{(s_p+1)k} - 1)/(p^k - 1).$$

Corollary 15.1.

$$\sigma(n) = \prod_{p|n} \frac{p^{s_p+1} - 1}{p - 1}.$$

Corollary 15.2.

$$\sigma_0(n) = \prod_{p|n} (s_p + 1).$$

PROOFS. For Corollary 15.1, set $k = 1$ in Theorem 15; for Corollary 15.2, set $k = 0$ in the proof of the Theorem.

8. *PERFECT NUMBERS

Definition 8. *A number n is called* perfect, *if the sum of all its proper divisors (i.e., of divisors $d \neq n$) adds up to n, that is, if $\sigma(n) = 2n$.*

Examples of even perfect numbers are $6(= 1 + 2 + 3)$, $28(= 1 + 2 + 4 + 7 + 14)$ and not many are known.

No odd perfect numbers are known and their existence is highly unlikely, but has never been disproven. It has been shown, however (see [1], [3] p. 21–22, [4], [5]) that if any odd perfect numbers exist at all, they must be very large ($> 10^{20}$) and must contain very many distinct primes. Except for finding more, and more stringent necessary conditions for the existence of odd perfect numbers (and thus making their existence so much more unlikely), almost all our present knowledge about perfect numbers goes back to Euclid, who already knew the following

Theorem 16. *If $2^{n+1} - 1 = p$ is a prime, then $m = \frac{1}{2}p(p + 1)$ is a perfect number; and if m is an even perfect number, then $m = 2^n(2^{n+1} - 1)$, with $2^{n+1} - 1 = p$, a prime.*

PROOF. Let $2^{n+1} - 1 = p$ be a prime. Then, $(p + 1)/2 = 2^n$, $m = 2^n p$, and, by Corollary 15.1, $\sigma(m) = \sigma(2^n p) = ((2^{n+1} - 1)/(2 - 1))((p^2 - 1)/(p - 1)) = (2^{n+1} - 1)(p + 1) = p(p + 1) = 2m$ and m is perfect.

Conversely, if m is even and perfect, $m = 2^n m_1, n > 0, m_1$ odd. By Corollary 15.1

$$\sigma(m) = \sigma(2^n)\sigma(m_1) = (2^{n+1} - 1)\sigma(m_1)$$

and, if m is perfect, $\sigma(m) = 2m = 2^{n+1}m_1$. Hence,

$$2^{n+1}m_1 = (2^{n+1} - 1)\sigma(m_1).$$

Let $d = (m_1, \sigma(m_1))$; then, observing that $(2^{n+1} - 1, 2^{n+1}) = 1$, it follows that $m_1 = d(2^{n+1} - 1)$ and $\sigma(m_1) = 2^{n+1}d$. We assert that $d = 1$; indeed, if $d \neq 1$, then m_1 would have at least the distinct divisors $m_1, d, (2^{n+1} - 1)$, 1, so that

$$\sigma(m_1) \geq m_1 + d + 2^{n+1} - 1 + 1 = d(2^{n+1} - 1) + d + 2^{n+1}$$
$$= 2^{n+1}(d + 1) > 2^{n+1}d = \sigma(m_1),$$

which is a contradiction. Hence, $d = 1$, $m_1 = 2^{n+1} - 1$ and $m = 2^n m_1 = 2^n \cdot (2^{n+1} - 1)$. Now, $\sigma(m)$ becomes

$$\sigma(m) = \sigma(2^n)\sigma(m_1) = (2^{n+1} - 1)(m_1 + 1 + \sum_{\substack{1 < c < m_1 \\ c \mid m_1}} c)$$

$$\geq (2^{n+1} - 1)(2^{n+1} - 1 + 1) = 2m,$$

with equality possible only if the sum over the divisors c of m_1, $1 < c < m_1$ vanishes; but that means precisely, that $m_1 = 2^{n+1} - 1$ has to be a prime, and the proof is complete.

Prime numbers of the form $p = 2^{n+1} - 1$ are called *Mersenne primes* and $n + 1 = q$ must itself be a prime; otherwise, if $q = m \cdot k, m > 1, k > 1$, $2^{m \cdot k} - 1 = (2^m)^k - 1$ is divisible at least by $1, 2^m - 1$, and $2^q - 1$, all distinct because $q = mk > m > 1$. It is known that $2^q - 1$ is prime for $q = 2, 3, 5, 7, 13, 17, 19, 31, 67, 127, 257$, and composite for all other primes less than 257. Hence, the condition that $n + 1$ be a prime, is a necessary but *not a sufficient* condition for the primality of $2^q - 1$. In some cases it is known that $2^q - 1$ is composite, without knowing any factor of it, on the basis of different tests of primality, some of which were devised specially for Mersenne numbers. The oldest seems to be Euler's (in 1736, see [2]); the most useful is, presumably, due to Lucas (see [7] p. 310; also [3] pp. 80–81; 223, and 231), who published his paper in volume 1 of the newly launched American Journal of Mathematics, (1878)).

9. *RAMANUJAN SUMS

These sums, important especially in the theory of representation of integers as sums of squares, occur since shortly after 1900, in the work of many mathematicians (for instance, Jensen, Landau, etc.). However, in view of Ramanujan's contribution to their study (in 1918; see [8], pp. 179–199) Hardy's choice of calling them " Ramanujan's Sums " seems well justified.

We shall list some of their principal properties and give sketches for the proofs. For more details, one may consult [3] and [8]. Concerning notations, there is no universal agreement; here we shall again follow Hardy and denote Ramanujan's sums by $c_n(m)$. Before we define them formally, we recall that a complex number $a + ib$ may be represented by a point in the plane, of coordinates $x = a$ and $y = b$; its distance from the origin, $(a^2 + b^2)^{1/2}$ is called the absolute value of the complex number, is usually denoted by $|a + ib|$, and the angle θ formed by the ray from the origin to $a + ib$ with the x-axis is called the argument; clearly $\theta = arctg\ (b/a)$. The series expansion of the exponential function of real argument, $e^x = \sum_{n=0}^{\infty} (x^n/n!)$ is taken as the definition of the exponential function in case of complex argument. In particular, if θ is real, $e^{i\theta} = \sum_{n=0}^{\infty} (i\theta)^n/n!$ and separating the real from the purely imaginary part,

$$e^{i\theta} = \sum_{n=0}^{\infty} (-1)^n \frac{\theta^{2n}}{(2n)!} + i \sum_{n=0}^{\infty} (-1)^n \frac{\theta^{2n+1}}{(2n+1)!} ;$$

or, identifying these well-known series, $e^{i\theta} = \cos \theta + i \sin \theta$. It is easy to show (use the addition formulas for sine and cosine) that with this definition the usual formal rules of computation with exponentials continue to hold, in particular, $e^{a+ib} = e^a(\cos b + i \sin b)$, and $e^{ix} \cdot e^{iy} = e^{i(x+y)}$. Also $|e^{i\theta}| = (\cos^2 \theta + \sin^2 \theta)^{1/2} = 1$, for real θ. Clearly, $e^{2\pi i k} = \cos (2\pi k) + i \sin (2\pi k) = 1$ for every integer k.

Definition 9. The sums $c_n(m) = \sum_h e^{2\pi ihm/n}$, where h runs through a complete set of reduced residues modulo n, depend on the two parameters n (the index) and m (the argument) and are called *Ramanujan's sums*.

REMARK 3. Each summand $s = e^{2\pi ihm/n}$ entering the Ramanujan sums satisfies $s^n = e^{2\pi imh} = 1$; hence, such summands are called *n-th roots of unity*; taking, as one always may, the fraction m/n in reduced form, it is clear that $s^k \neq 1$ for $0 < k < n$. Such n-th roots of unity, that are not roots of unity of any lower order, are called *primitive n-th roots of unity*.

Theorem 17. *Ramanujan's sums are multiplicative functions of their indices; that is, if $(m, n) = 1$, then $c_m(k)c_n(k) = c_{mn}(k)$ for all integers k.*

PROOF.

$$c_m(k)c_n(k) = \sum_{\substack{h_1 \bmod m \\ (h_1,m)=1}} e^{2\pi ih_1k/m} \sum_{\substack{h_2 \bmod n \\ (h_2,n)=1}} e^{2\pi ih_2k/n} = \sum_{h_1} \sum_{h_2} e^{2\pi ik(h_1n + h_2m)/mn}$$

the summation being over h_1 and h_2 with the same conditions. By Lemma 2 we know that for $(m, n) = 1$, if h_1 runs through a complete reduced set of residues modulo m, and h_2 runs independently through a complete set of reduced residues modulo n, then $h = h_1n + h_2m$ runs through a complete set of reduced residues modulo mn; hence, the last sum can be written as $\sum_{\substack{h \bmod mn \\ (h,mn)=1}} e^{2\pi ikh/mn}$ and equals, by definition, $c_{mn}(k)$.

Theorem 18. $c_p(m) = -1$ *for every prime p and every integer $m \not\equiv 0$* (mod p).

PROOF. If h runs through a complete set of reduced residues mod p, so does mh, because $(m, p) = 1$. Hence,

$$c_p(m) = \sum_{h=1}^{p-1} e^{2\pi i h m/p} = \sum_{\substack{h' \bmod p \\ (h',p)=1}} e^{2\pi i h'/p} = \sum_{h''=1}^{p-1} e^{2\pi i h''/p} = \sum_{h=1}^{p} e^{2\pi i h/p} - 1.$$

The proof is completed by verifying that the finite sum vanishes. To do that, set $x = e^{2\pi i/p}$; then $\sum_{h=1}^{p} e^{2\pi i h/p} = \sum_{h=1}^{p} x^h = (x^{p+1} - x)/(x - 1) = x(x^p - 1)/(x - 1) = 0$, because, as already observed, $x^p = e^{2\pi i} = \cos 2\pi + i \sin 2\pi = 1$. More generally, we have

Theorem 19. *Let* $(m, n) = d$; *then* $c_n(m) = \sum_{k|d} k\mu(n/k)$.

REMARK 4. If $n = p$, $(m, p) = 1$, then Theorem 19 yields $c_p(m) = \sum_{k|1} k\mu(p/k)$ $= \mu(p) = -1$, so that Theorem 18 is actually a Corollary of Theorem 19.

PROOF. From Theorem 9 we know that $\sum_{k|u} \mu(k) = 1$, or 0, depending on whether $u = 1$, or $u \neq 1$. This permits us to simplify the summation conditions in the definition of Ramanujan's sums. Instead of letting h range only over a complete set of *reduced* residues mod n, we let h range over *all* residues (thus ignoring the annoying side condition $(h, n) = 1$), but introduce the extra factor $\sum_{d|(h,n)} \mu(d)$, which vanishes when $(h, n) \neq 1$ and reduces conveniently to unity, precisely when h is prime to n. Hence,

$$c_n(m) = \sum_{h \bmod n} e^{2\pi i h m/n} \sum_{c|(h,n)} \mu(c) = \sum_{c|n} \mu(c) \sum_{\substack{h \equiv 0 (\bmod c) \\ 1 \leq h \leq n}} e^{2\pi i h m/n}.$$

Setting $h = rc$, $r = 1, 2, \ldots, n/c$, $c_n(m) = \sum_{c|n} \mu(c) \sum_{r=1}^{n/c} e^{2\pi i r c m/n} = \sum_{c|n} \mu(c) \sum_{r=1}^{n/c} e^{2\pi i r m/(n/c)}$. If $(n/c) \mid m$, $e^{2\pi i r m/(n/c)} = 1$, $\sum_{r=1}^{n/c} e^{2\pi i r m/(n/c)} = n/c$; otherwise, as seen in the proof of Theorem 18, the sum vanishes. Hence,

$$c_n(m) = \sum_{c|n,(n/c)|m} \mu(c)n/c, \quad \text{or with } k = n/c, c = n/k,$$

$c_n(m) = \sum_{k|n,k|m} k\mu(n/k)$. However, $k \mid n$, $k \mid m$, if and only if $k \mid d = (m, n)$ and Theorem 19 is proven.

10. FUNCTIONS RELATED TO PRIME NUMBERS

In the theory of primes, there are several functions that play an important role. Some of these are defined by the following formulas:

Definition 10.

(1) $\pi(x) = \sum\limits_{p \le x} 1$, the number of primes not exceeding the real number x;

(2) $\theta(x) = \sum\limits_{p \le x} \log p$;

(3) $\psi(x) = \sum\limits_{p^m \le x} \log p = \sum\limits_{p \le x} \left[\dfrac{\log x}{\log p}\right] \log p = \sum\limits_{n \le x} \Lambda(n)$, with

(4) $\Lambda(n) = \begin{cases} \log p & \text{if } n = p^m, \\ 0 & \text{if } n \ne p^m. \end{cases}$

$\psi(x)$ may be interpreted as the logarithm of the least common multiple of all integers n up to x (including x, if x is an integer).

REMARK 5. The smallest prime is $p = 2$; hence $\pi(x) = \theta(x) = \psi(x) = 0$, for $x < 2$.

REMARK 6. The functions $\pi(x)$, $\theta(x)$, $\psi(x)$ are defined for all real x; the function $\Lambda(n)$ is defined only for integral n. While the function $\pi(x)$ is a very "natural" one, it is not immediately apparent, why $\theta(x)$ and $\psi(x)$ had to be introduced (by Tchebycheff, see [6] and [10]). In fact, it turns out that $\theta(x)$ and $\psi(x)$ are easier to handle than $\pi(x)$. Indeed, for large x, $\theta(x)$ and $\psi(x)$ behave practically like x itself; in fact, they are *asymptotically equal to x*, which means that $\lim\limits_{x \to \infty} \{\theta(x)/x\} = \lim\limits_{x \to \infty} \{\psi(x)/x\} = 1$. Actually, it is possible to prove the Prime Number Theorem (denoted from here on by PNT) directly in the form $\lim\limits_{x \to \infty} \dfrac{\pi(x) \cdot \log x}{x} = 1$, and this is precisely what we are going to do. However, in the classical approach it turned out that a direct proof of the PNT was more difficult than the proof of $\lim\limits_{x \to \infty} (\theta(x)/x) = 1$, or of $\lim\limits_{x \to \infty} (\psi(x)/x) = 1$; and it is very easy to show, that either of these equalities is equivalent to the PNT. Indeed, we have

Theorem 20. *If one of the three functions $\theta(x)/x$, $\psi(x)/x$, $(\pi(x) \log x)/x$ approaches a limit when $x \to \infty$, then all three do, and the three limits are equal.*

Nothing of the material presented from here on to the end of the chapter will be used anywhere else in the book except the O and o notations explained in the next paragraph. However, the material is not only of great historic importance, but also intrinsically very beautiful and most likely to remain useful in the future. Indeed, the modern elementary proofs of the PNT make use of $\theta(x)$ or $\psi(x)$. Also, the deeper theory of the distribution of primes is inextricably connected with that of the Möbius sum function $M(x)$. For these reasons the author feels compelled to make this material available to his readers.

Before we prove Theorem 20, it is convenient to introduce some very useful notations, due to E. Landau, and which have received widespread acceptance. Let $f(x)$ and $g(x)$ be any two functions; then, if there exist positive constants C and ε such that $|f(x)| < C|g(x)|$ holds for all x satisfying $|x - x_0| < \varepsilon$, we write $f(x) = O(g(x))(x \to x_0)$. If $|f(x)| < C|g(x)|$ holds for all sufficiently large x, we write $f(x) = O(g(x))(x \to \infty)$. Usually, it is unnecessary to mention x_0, which is understood from the context and then the last bracket is omitted. This notation is particularly useful, if $g(x)$ is a much simpler function than $f(x)$. If, for instance, we want to state that $f(x)$ stays bounded, $|f(x)| < C$, we take $g(x) = 1$ and write $f(x) = O(1)$. The following are a few further examples of the use of the O-notation: When $x \to +\infty$, then $\sin x = O(1)$; $e^{-x} = O(x^{-n})$ for every n; $[x] = O(x)$; $x/[x] = O(1)$.

If an inequality $|f(x)| < \varepsilon|g(x)|$ $(x \to x_0)$ holds for every $\varepsilon > 0$, provided only that $|x - x_0|$ is small enough (or, provided that x is sufficiently large, if $x_0 = \infty$), then we write $f(x) = o(g(x))$. In previous examples, for instance, when $x \to \infty$, $\sin x = o(x^{1/2})$, $e^{-x} = o(x^{-n})$, for every n; also, $x = o(x^2)$, $x^{1/2} = o(x)$, and so on. If $f(x) \to 0$, we may express this by writing $f(x) = o(1)$.

Theorem 20 will follow easily from a few preliminary theorems.

Theorem 21. $\psi(x) = \theta(x) + \theta(x^{1/2}) + \theta(x^{1/3}) + \theta(x^{1/4}) + \cdots$.

REMARK 7. The sum breaks off after k terms, if k is the first integer such that $x^{1/(k+1)} < 2$ (see Remark 1).

PROOF. $\psi(x) = \sum\limits_{p^m \le x} \log p = \sum\limits_{m \ge 1} \sum\limits_{p \le x^{1/m}} \log p = \sum\limits_{m \ge 1} \theta(x^{1/m})$.

Theorem 22.   For $x > 1$, $\theta(x) < x \log x$.

PROOF.

$$\theta(x) = \sum_{p \le x} \log p \le \sum_{p \le x} \log x = \log x \sum_{p \le x} 1 < \log x \sum_{n \le x} 1 = x \log x.$$

Theorem 23.   For $x > 1$, $\theta(x) \le \psi(x) < \theta(x) + x^{1/2} \log^2 x$, or, *less precisely*, $\psi(x) - \theta(x) = O(x^{1/2} \log^2 x)$.

PROOF. The first inequality follows from Theorem 21; for the second, let $k = [\log x/\log 2]$ and observe that

$$\psi(x) - \theta(x) = \sum_{m=2}^{k} \theta(x^{1/m}) \le \sum_{m=2}^{k} x^{1/m} \log x^{1/m} = \sum_{m=2}^{k} \frac{1}{m} \log x \cdot x^{1/m}$$

by Theorem 22. Hence, *a fortiori*,

$$\psi(x) - \theta(x) \leq \sum_{m=2}^{k} \tfrac{1}{2}x^{1/m} \log x = \tfrac{1}{2} \log x \sum_{m=2}^{k} x^{1/m} \leq \tfrac{1}{2} \log x \sum_{m=2}^{k} x^{1/2}$$

$$= \tfrac{1}{2}(k-1)x^{1/2} \log x < \frac{k}{2} x^{1/2} \log x \leq \frac{1}{2 \log 2} x^{1/2} \log^2 x < x^{1/2} \log^2 x,$$

which proves the theorem.

Theorem 24 (Tchebycheff). *There exist positive constants* A, A'; B, B', *such that, for* $x > 2$, $Ax < \theta(x) < A'x$, $Bx < \psi(x) < B'x$.

Proof. On account of Theorem 23, it is sufficient to prove $\theta(x) < A'x$ and $\psi(x) > Bx$, because then

$$\psi(x) < \theta(x) + O(x^{1/2} \log^2 x) < A'x + O(x^{1/2} \log^2 x)$$
$$= x(A' + O(x^{-1/2} \log^2 x)) < (A' + 1)x$$

and

$$\theta(x) > \psi(x) - O(x^{1/2} \log^2 x) > Bx(1 - O(x^{-1/2} \log^2 x)) > \tfrac{1}{2}Bx$$

follow immediately for sufficiently large x. We shall actually prove rather more, namely, that $\theta(x) < (2 \log 2)x$ and $\psi(x) > ((\log 8)/10)x$.

For $n = 1$ and $n = 2$, $\theta(n) < (2 \log 2)n$ holds trivially. In order to complete the induction on n, we observe that in the expansion of $(1 + 1)^{2m+1}$, the binomial coefficient† $M = (2m + 1)!/m!(m + 1)! = N/D$ occurs twice, so that $M < 2^{2m}$. All primes p satisfying $m + 1 < p \leq 2m + 1$ divide N, but not D; hence, $\left(\prod_{p>m+1}^{2m+1} p \right) \mid M$ and, in particular, $\left(\prod_{p>m+1}^{2m+1} p \right) \leq M$. On taking logarithms, $\theta(2m + 1) - \theta(m + 1) = \sum_{p>m+1}^{2m+1} \log p \leq \log M < 2m \log 2$. The proof that $\theta(k) < (2 \log 2)k$ can now be completed by induction on k. Let us assume that the inequality, already checked for $k = 1$ and $k = 2$, holds up to $k = n - 1$. We show that it then also holds for $k = n$. If n is even this is trivial, because n (being divisible by 2) cannot be a prime; hence,

$$\theta(n) = \theta(n - 1) < (2 \log 2)(n - 1) < (2 \log 2)n.$$

If n is odd, it is of the form $n = 2m + 1$, and we just proved that $\theta(n) = \theta(2m + 1) < \theta(m + 1) + (2 \log 2)m$; by the induction hypothesis, this is $< (2 \log 2)(m + 1) + (2 \log 2)m = (2 \log 2)(2m + 1) = (2 \log 2)n$ and this finishes the proof of the statement. Indeed, having proven the inequality for integers, it holds for all real numbers, because, if $n < x < n + 1$ then

$$\theta(x) = \theta(n) < (2 \log 2)n < (2 \log 2)x.$$

---

† The binomial coefficient, its numerator and its denominator are denoted here, for convenience by capitals, although they are rational integers.

In order to prove $\psi(x) > \dfrac{\log 8}{10} x$, we proceed in a similar way. One easily checks that

$$\psi(1) = 0,$$
$$\psi(2) = \log 2 > 2(\cdot 346),$$
$$\psi(3) = \log 2 + \log 3 = \log 6 > 3(\cdot 597),$$
$$\psi(4) = 2 \log 2 + \log 3 > 4(\cdot 621),$$
$$\psi(5) = \psi(4) + \log 5 > 5(\cdot 818),$$

so that, for $x \le 5$, $\psi(x) > \left(\dfrac{\log 8}{10}\right) x \cong (\cdot 2079)x$ is amply satisfied and from here on we may assume that $x > 5$. Now

$$2^n < \frac{2n}{n} \cdot \frac{2n-1}{n-1} \cdot \dots \cdot \frac{n+1}{1} = \frac{(2n)!}{n!\,n!}.$$

By Theorem 2,

$$\frac{(2n)!}{n!\,n!} = \prod_{p \le 2n} p^{k_p}, \quad \text{with} \quad k_p = \sum_{1 \le m \le m_1} \left(\left[\frac{2n}{p^m}\right] - 2\left[\frac{n}{p^m}\right]\right),$$

where $m_1 = [\log 2n/\log p]$ (clearly, all terms are zero for $m > (\log 2n/\log p)$). By Theorem 1(8) the bracket is either 0, or 1; hence, $k_p \le \sum\limits_{1 \le m \le m_1} 1 = [\log 2n/\log p]$. Consequently,

$$n \log 2 = \log 2^n \le \log \prod_{p \le 2n} p^{k_p} = \sum_{p \le 2n} k_p \log p \le \sum_{p \le 2n} \left[\frac{\log 2n}{\log p}\right] \log p = \psi(2n).$$

For given x, set $n = [\tfrac{1}{2}x]$; then

$$\psi(x) \ge \psi(2n) \ge n \log 2 > (\tfrac{1}{2}x - 1) \log 2 = \frac{\log 2}{2} x \left(1 - \frac{2}{x}\right)$$

$$> \left(1 - \frac{2}{5}\right) \frac{\log 2}{2} x = \frac{3 \log 2}{10} x \quad \text{for } x > 5.$$

This finishes the proof of Theorem 24.

PROOF OF THEOREM 20. First, by Theorem 23,

$$\frac{\theta(x)}{x} \le \frac{\psi(x)}{x} \le \frac{\theta(x)}{x} + 0(x^{-1/2} \log^2 x),$$

so that

$$\lim_{x \to \infty} \frac{\theta(x)}{x} = \lim_{x \to \infty} \frac{\psi(x)}{x},$$

if either limit exists. Next,

$$\theta(x) = \sum_{p \le x} \log p < \sum_{p \le x} \log x = \log x \sum_{p \le x} 1 = \pi(x) \log x,$$

so that $\theta(x)/x \le (\pi(x) \log x)/x$. Finally, for any $\varepsilon > 0$, but arbitrarily small,

$$\theta(x) \ge \sum_{x^{1-\varepsilon} < p \le x} \log p \ge \sum_{x^{1-\varepsilon} < p \le x} \log x^{1-\varepsilon} = (1 - \varepsilon) \log x \sum_{x^{1-\varepsilon} < p \le x} 1$$

$$= (1 - \varepsilon)(\log x)(\pi(x) - \pi(x^{1-\varepsilon})) > (1 - \varepsilon)(\log x)(\pi(x) - x^{1-\varepsilon}).$$

Consequently,

$$\frac{\theta(x)}{x} > (1 - \varepsilon)\frac{\pi(x) \log x}{x}\left(1 - \frac{x^{1-\varepsilon}}{\pi(x)}\right);$$

but we just proved that $\theta(x) < \pi(x) \log x$, so that $\pi(x) > \theta(x)/(\log x)$ and $x^{1-\varepsilon}/\pi(x) < (x^{1-\varepsilon}/\theta(x)) \log x$. By Theorem 24, this is less than $(x^{1-\varepsilon}/ax)\log x = (\log x)/ax^{\varepsilon}$ with $a > 0, \varepsilon > 0$; hence, the fraction becomes arbitrarily small, say $< \varepsilon$, as $x \to \infty$ and

$$\frac{\theta(x)}{x} > (1 - \varepsilon)\frac{\pi(x) \log x}{x}\left(1 - \frac{x^{1-\varepsilon}}{\pi(x)}\right) > (1 - 2\varepsilon)\frac{\pi(x) \log x}{x}.$$

Combining the results it follows that the inequalities,

$$\frac{\theta(x)}{x} \le \frac{\pi(x) \log x}{x} < \frac{1}{1 - 2\varepsilon} \cdot \frac{\theta(x)}{x}$$

hold for arbitrarily small $\varepsilon > 0$. It follows that if $\lim_{x \to \infty} \theta(x)/x$ exists, so does $\lim_{x \to \infty} (\pi(x) \log x)/x$ and conversely, and that, if these limits exist, then they are equal. This finishes the proof of Theorem 20.

11. **ON THE SUM FUNCTION $M(x)$

At the end of Section 5 occurs Theorem 13′, which can be restated now in the following neater form.

Theorem 13′.   *If $x \to \infty$, then $M(x) = \sum_{n \le x} \mu(n) = o(x)$.*

We made the remark that, while $M(x) = O(x)$ is trivial, the apparently modest sharpening represented by Theorem 13′ is far from trivial. In the remaining part of this chapter, we shall prove Theorem 13′, by anticipating two results that will be proven only later.

1. The PNT holds, that is,

$$\pi(x) = \frac{x}{\log x} + o\left(\frac{x}{\log x}\right);$$

we know from Theorem 20 that this statement is equivalent to $\psi(x) = x + o(x)$.

2. If σ is the real part of $s = \sigma + it$, then for $\sigma > 1$, $\zeta(s) = \sum_{n=1}^{\infty} n^{-s} = \prod_p (1 - p^{-s})^{-1}$ converges; the convergence is uniform for $\sigma \geq 1 + \varepsilon$ and every $\varepsilon > 0$. The reader may convince himself that these results will be proven without the use of anything developed in the present section, so that no circularity vitiates the reasoning.

Let $H(x) = \sum_{n=1}^{x} \mu(n) \log n$; then $\mu(n) = (H(n) - H(n-1))/(\log n)$, so that $M(x) = 1 + \sum_{n=2}^{x} (H(n) - H(n-1))/(\log n)$. We may regroup the terms, by combining those with the same $H(n)$ in consecutive summands and, observing also that $H(1) = 0$, we obtain

$$M(x) = 1 + \sum_{n=2}^{x} H(n)\left(\frac{1}{\log n} - \frac{1}{\log(n+1)}\right) + \frac{H(x)}{\log([x]+1)}.$$

We shall presently show that, as $x \to \infty$, $H(x) = o(x \log x)$. Assuming this result for a moment, and observing that

$$\frac{1}{\log n} - \frac{1}{\log(n+1)} = \frac{\log(n+1) - \log n}{\log n \cdot \log(n+1)} < 2\frac{\log(1 + 1/n)}{\log^2 n} < \frac{2}{n \log^2 n},$$

it follows that

$$M(x) = o\left(\sum_{n=2}^{x} n \log n \cdot \frac{1}{n \log^2 n}\right) + o(x) = o\left(\sum_{n=2}^{x} \frac{1}{\log n} + x\right) = o(x),$$

and this is the statement we wanted to prove. Hence, in order to finish the proof of Theorem 13' it only remains to show (besides the two anticipated results) that $H(x) = o(x \log x)$, which means that $\lim_{x \to \infty} H(x)/(x \log x) = 0$.

In the proof, we shall need the

Lemma 3.
$$\left|\sum_{n=1}^{n_0} \frac{\mu(n)}{n}\right| \leq 1.$$

We use the result of Corollary 9.3, stating that, for every x, $\sum_{n=1}^{x} \mu(n)[x/n] = 1$. We take for x the integer n_0 and denote the fractional part $(n_0/n) - [n_0/n]$

by α_n; clearly, $\alpha_1 = 0$, and $0 \leq \alpha_n < 1$ for $2 \leq n \leq n_0$. Hence,

$$1 = \sum_{n=1}^{n_0} \mu(n) \left[\frac{n_0}{n} \right] = \sum_{n=1}^{n_0} \mu(n) \frac{n_0}{n} - \sum_{n=2}^{n_0} \alpha_n \mu(n).$$

The last sum is less, in absolute value, than $\sum_{n=2}^{n_0} 1 = n_0 - 1$; hence,

$$\left| \sum_{n=1}^{n_0} \mu(n) \frac{n_0}{n} \right| = n_0 \cdot \left| \sum_{n=1}^{n_0} \frac{\mu(n)}{n} \right| \leq 1 + (n_0 - 1) = n_0$$

and the Lemma is proven.

In order to show that $H(x) = o(x \log x)$, we first find a different expression for $H(x)$. As already seen in the second proof of Theorem 9, $\zeta(s)^{-1} = \sum_{n=1}^{\infty} \mu(n) n^{-s}$, so that

$$\frac{d}{ds} \frac{1}{\zeta(s)} = -\frac{\zeta'(s)}{\zeta^2(s)} = -\sum_{n=1}^{\infty} \mu(n) (\log n) n^{-s}.$$

Also,

$$\log \zeta(s) = -\sum_{p} \log(1 - p^{-s}) = \sum_{p} \sum_{m} \frac{p^{-ms}}{m},$$

by the expansion of the logarithm. Differentiating,

$$\zeta'(s)/\zeta(s) = -\sum_{p} \sum_{m} (\log p)/p^{ms},$$

or, using Definition 10(4) of $\Lambda(n)$, $\zeta'(s)/\zeta(s) = -\sum_{n=1}^{\infty} \Lambda(n)/n^s$. The validity of these formal operations can easily be proven, on account of the uniform convergence (for $\sigma \geq 1 + \varepsilon, \varepsilon > 0$) of all series involved.

We observe that $-\zeta'(s)/\zeta^2(s) = 1/\zeta(s) \, (-\zeta'(s)/\zeta(s))$; hence,

$$-\sum_{n=1}^{\infty} \frac{\mu(n) \log n}{n^s} = \sum_{k=1}^{\infty} \frac{\mu(k)}{k^s} \sum_{m=1}^{\infty} \frac{\Lambda(m)}{m^s}.$$

Setting $km = n$ in the second member, this can be written as

$$\sum_{n=1}^{\infty} \frac{1}{n^s} \sum_{k|n} \mu(k) \Lambda(n/k) = \sum_{n=1}^{\infty} \frac{a_n}{n^s},$$

so that

$$-\sum_{n=1}^{\infty} \frac{\mu(n) \log n}{n^s} = \sum_{n=1}^{\infty} \frac{a_n}{n^s}, \qquad \text{with} \quad a_n = \sum_{k|n} \mu(k) \Lambda(n/k).$$

By Theorem 10, two such Dirichlet series can coincide for all values of s with $\sigma \geq 1 + \varepsilon$, only if they are equal termwise; that is, if they have the same coefficients. Hence, $a_n = \sum_{k|n} \mu(k) \Lambda(n/k) = -\mu(n) \log n$, and $H(x)$

becomes

$$H(x) = \sum_{n=1}^{x} \mu(n) \log n = - \sum_{n=1}^{x} \sum_{k|n} \mu(k)\Lambda(n/k)$$

$$= - \sum_{k=1}^{x} \mu(k) \sum_{\substack{n=mk \\ 1 \le m \le x/k}} \Lambda(n/k) = - \sum_{k=1}^{x} \mu(k) \sum_{m=1}^{[x/k]} \Lambda(m)$$

$$= - \sum_{k=1}^{x} \mu(k)\psi(x/k)$$

by the definition of $\psi(x)$. Until now we have made no use of the PNT. Now we shall use it, by observing that, according to it, the following is true: Given $\varepsilon > 0$, but arbitrarily small, we can find a constant y (depending only on ε, but not on x) such that, for $x \ge y$, $|\psi(x) - x| < \varepsilon x$. If we set $n_0 = [x/y]$, then

$$- H(x) = \sum_{n=1}^{x} \mu(n)\psi(x/n) = \sum_{n=1}^{n_0} \mu(n)\psi(x/n) + \sum_{n=n_0+1}^{x} \mu(n)\psi(x/n).$$

In the first sum, $x/n \ge x/n_0 \ge y$; hence,

$$\left| \sum_{n=1}^{n_0} \mu(n)\psi\left(\frac{x}{n}\right) \right| = \left| \sum_{n=1}^{n_0} \mu(n) \left(\frac{x}{n} + \left(\psi\left(\frac{x}{n}\right) - \left(\frac{x}{n}\right) \right) \right) \right|$$

$$\le \left| \sum_{n=1}^{n_0} \mu(n)\frac{x}{n} \right| + \varepsilon \cdot \sum_{n=1}^{n_0} \left| \frac{\mu(n)x}{n} \right|$$

$$\le x \sum_{n=1}^{n_0} \frac{\mu(n)}{n} + \varepsilon \cdot x \cdot \sum_{n=1}^{n_0} \frac{1}{n}.$$

Using Lemma 3 and the fact that $\sum_{n=1}^{N}(1/n) < \log N + 1$, it follows that the last sums add up to less than $x + \varepsilon x(\log n_0 + 1) < x + \varepsilon x \log x$ (for $y > e$; the other alternative is trivial). In the second sum occurring in $- H(x)$, $\psi(x/n) \le \psi(x/(n_0 + 1)) < \psi(y)$, a constant, independent of x. Hence, the second sum is less in absolute value than $\sum_{n=n_0}^{x} |\mu(n)\psi(y)| < \psi(y) \sum_{n=n_0}^{x} 1 < x\psi(y)$, so that, finally,

$$|H(x)| < x + \varepsilon x \log x + x\psi(y).$$

Consequently, $|H(x)| < x(1 + \psi(y)) + \varepsilon x \log x$, and $|H(x)|/(x \log x) < \varepsilon + (1 + \psi(y))/(\log x) < 2\varepsilon$ if x is sufficiently large. Hence, $H(x) = o(x \log x)$, as asserted, and (except for the two anticipated results) our proofs are complete.

PROBLEMS

1. Prove Theorem 1 in detail.

2. Let k_p be the highest power of the prime p that divides $(2n)!/(n!)^2$. Show that

$$k_p = \sum_{m \geq 1} \left(\left[\frac{2n}{p^m} \right] - 2 \left[\frac{n}{p^m} \right] \right).$$

3. Find the highest power of 5 that divides 3000!

4. Find $\sigma_0(24)$, $\sigma_1(24)$, $\sigma_2(24)$ (a) directly; and (b) using Theorem 15.

5. Find $\sigma(1728)$.

6. Prove: $\sum_{d|n} \lambda(d) = \begin{cases} 1 & \text{if } n = m^2 \text{ for some integer } m, \\ 0 & \text{otherwise.} \end{cases}$

7. Prove the second part of Theorem 12: If $F(n) = \sum_{d|n} f(d)$ and $F(n)$ is multiplicative, then so is $f(n)$.

8. Let $\phi(n)$ be the Euler function. Prove: $\phi(n) = \sum_{dc=n} d\mu(c)$. (*Hint:* $n = \sum_{d|n} \phi(d)$; use the Möbius inversion formula or Corollary 9.2.)

9. Compute $\sum_{d|6000} \phi(d)$.

10. Let $F(x) = \sum_{n \leq x} \phi(n)$. Prove that $F(x) = (3/\pi^2)x^2(1 + o(1))$. (*Hint:* Use Problem 8, change order of summation; use Corollary 9.2 and approximate $[x/d]^2$ by $((x/d) - \alpha)^2$; finally, remember that $\zeta(2) = \sum_{n=1}^{\infty} n^{-2} = \pi^2/6$ (see 7.3.31).

11. (Landau). Compute $(\phi(5186), \phi(5187), \phi(5188))$, and $[\phi(5186), \phi(5187), \phi(5188)]$.

12. Show that n cannot be a perfect number, if it is a prime, or the product of two odd primes; also, find all exceptions to the statement that n cannot be a perfect number, if it is the product of two primes.

13. Prove in detail the equalities occurring in the definition of $\psi(x)$.

14. Prove Theorem 3 in detail.

15. Define the Dedekind sum (see [9], where the notation is slightly different) $s(h, k) = \sum_{m \bmod k} ((m/k))((mh/k))$. Prove:
  (a) $h_1 \equiv h_2 \pmod{k} \Rightarrow s(h_1, k) = s(h_2, k)$,
  (b) $h\bar{h} \equiv 1 \pmod{k} \Rightarrow s(h, k) = s(\bar{h}, k)$,
  (c) $s(-h, k) = -s(h, k)$,
  (d) $hh^* \equiv -1 \pmod{k} \Rightarrow s(h^*, k) = -s(h, k)$,
  (e) $h^2 \equiv -1 \pmod{k} \Rightarrow s(h, k) = 0$.

16. Find the perfect numbers corresponding to the Mersenne primes $2^q - 1$, for $q = 5$ and $q = 7$; check the result.

17. Compute the Ramanujan sums $c_3(5)$ and $c_6(10)$ directly and by Theorems 18 and 19.

18. Prove: $c_n(1) = \mu(n)$.

19. Prove: $\sum_{d|n} \mu(d)\sigma_0(n/d) = 1$.

20. Prove: $\sum_{n \leq x} \psi(n)/n = (6/\pi^2)x + O(\log x)$.

    (*Hint:* Use Problem 8.)

BIBLIOGRAPHY

1. L. E. Dickson, *History of the Theory of Numbers*, Vol. 1. Washington, D.C.: Carnegie Inst. of Washington, 1919–1923.

2. L. Euler, *Comm. Acad. Petrop.* **6** (1732–3), pp. 103–107; *Opera Omnia* (1) **2**, pp. 1–5.

3. G. H. Hardy, and E. M. Wright, *An Introduction to the Theory of Numbers*, 3rd ed. Oxford: The Clarendon Press, 1954.

4. H. J. Kanold, *Journal für die reine und angewandte Mathem.* **186**, 1944, pp. 25–29; **197**, 1957, pp. 82–96.

5. U. Kühnel, *Mathem. Zeitschrift*, **52**, 1949, pp. 202–211.

6. E. Landau, *Handbuch der Lehre von der Verteilung der Primzahlen*, 2nd ed. New York: Chelsea Publishing Co., 1953.

7. E. A. Lucas, *Amer. Journal of Mathem.* **1**, 1878, pp. 185–240 and pp. 289–321.

8. S. Ramanujan, *Collected Papers*, edited by G. H. Hardy, P. V. Sashu Aiyar, and B. M. Wilson. Cambridge University Press, Cambridge: 1927.

9. B. Riemann–R. Dedekind, "Erläuterung zu den Fragmenten XXVIII," *Collected Works of B. Riemann*, edited by H. Weber, 2nd ed. (1892–1902). New York: Dover Publications, Inc., 1953.

10. P. Tchebycheff, Several memoirs, see in partic. *Journal des Math. pures et appliquées* (1) **17**, 1852, pp. 366–390.

11. I. M. Vinogradov, *Elements of Number Theory*. New York: Dover Publishing, Inc., 1954.

PART THREE

Topics from Analytic and Algebraic Number Theory

CHAPTER 7

The Distribution of Primes and the Riemann Zeta Function

1. THE DISTRIBUTION OF PRIMES AND THE SIEVE METHOD

We recall that the problem of the distribution of primes had been raised at least as far back as the Greek antiquity. The proof given in these notes, that there are infinitely many primes, appears in Euclid (book 9, Section 20); and Eratosthenes† devised a systematic method for obtaining all primes up to any given number x. This is called the *sieve method* and is easily described. First, it is clear that if n is not a prime, then there exists a prime $p \leq \sqrt{n}$ that divides n. Indeed, n not being a prime, it can be factored, $n = a \cdot b$; if $a > \sqrt{n}$ and $b > \sqrt{n}$, then $n = a \cdot b > (\sqrt{n})^2 = n$, a contradiction. Hence, if $a \leq b$, then $a \leq \sqrt{n}$ and every prime $p \mid a$ satisfies $p \leq a \leq \sqrt{n}$. This remark suggests the following procedure for the construction of a list of primes. Consider all integers from 2 up to x listed in their natural order; let us keep 2, but cancel (by a slash /) all its multiples, starting with 2^2, i.e., $2 \cdot 2, 3 \cdot 2, 4 \cdot 2. \cdots, n \cdot 2, \cdots$ for all $n \leq \frac{1}{2}x$. Next, we keep the first number after 2, that has not yet been canceled, that is, 3 but cancel (by an inverted slash \) all multiples of 3, starting with 3^2, i.e., $3 \cdot 3, 4 \cdot 3, 5 \cdot 3,$

† School of Alexandria, born 276 B.C., died apparently of voluntary starvation, at 80 years of age, ca. 196 B.C.

$\cdots, n \cdot 3, \cdots$ up to $n \le x/3$. The next integer remaining in our list, after 3 is 5; we keep it, but cancel (by a double slash \\) all its multiples, starting with 5^2, i.e., $5 \cdot 5$, $6 \cdot 5$, $\cdots$, and so on. From the previous remark, we know that any integer remaining in our set must be either a prime, or else larger than $5^2 = 25$. In general, having removed the multiples of some prime p_r, the first remaining integer after p_r is also a prime, say p_{r+1}; otherwise it would have to be divisible by some prime less than itself (actually, less than its square root) and would have been removed. We also do not have to look at integers less than p_{r+1}^2, because we observed that the composite ones among them had been removed already, all having a prime factor less than p_{r+1}; hence, it is sufficient to start removing the multiples of p_{r+1}, starting with p_{r+1}^2. An example of the way in which we proceed follows:

2, 3, 4̸, 5, 6̸, 7, 8̸, 9̸, 1̸0̸, 11, 1̸2̸, 13, 1̸4̸, 1̸5̸, 1̸6̸, 17, 1̸8̸, 19, 2̸0̸, 2̸1̸, 2̸2̸, 23, 2̸4̸, 2̸5̸, 2̸6̸, 2̸7̸, 2̸8̸, 29, 3̸0̸, 31, ...

We realize, of course, that some of the integers had been crossed out more than once; for instance, 12 had to be canceled both as a multiple of 2 and of 3; 30, as a multiple of 2, of 3, and of 5, and so on. The sieve method is quite effective for obtaining a list of primes up to a reasonably small limit; but if we try to keep track of the number of integers canceled, in order to find a formula for the (exact, or approximate) number of primes $p \le x$, we run into a serious difficulty: The number of integers canceled is expressed by square brackets; for instance, when we cancel the multiples of 2 up to x, we cancel $[\frac{1}{2}x] - 1$ integers. When we now try to replace $[\frac{1}{2}x]$ by $\frac{1}{2}x$ (or, more generally, $[x/n]$ by x/n), we introduce an error, which may be as big as unity. It soon appears that these errors accumulate so fast, that they swamp completely the principal term that we try to compute.

The simple approach of Eratosthenes has been much improved by Viggo Brun (see [4]) and later by H. Rademacher [13] and especially A. Selberg [17].

Some old problems can now be solved with the help of these improved "sieve methods"; for instance, one can show that the sum $\sum(1/p)$ extended over all twin primes converges (see [5]), or that every even number is the sum of two odd numbers, each containing only a small number of primes (see [3], [14], and [23]). But the sieve method has some natural limitations that seem by now fairly well established (see Selberg, [18], last paragraph). In particular, there seems to be no way to use it for a counting of the primes, sufficiently accurate to yield the PNT (prime number theorem).

2. FROM TCHEBYCHEFF TO LANDAU

Around the middle of the 19th century, Tchebycheff approached the problem differently. As already seen, he introduced the functions† $\theta(x) = \sum_{p \le x} \log p$ and $\psi(x) = \sum_{p^m \le x} \log p$ and proved that the PNT is equivalent to either of the relations $\lim_{x \to \infty} \theta(x)/x = 1$, $\lim_{x \to \infty} \psi(x)/x = 1$; furthermore, he also showed that there exist numerical constants A and A', with $\log (2^{1/2}\, 3^{1/3}\, 5^{1/5}/30^{1/30})\, (\approx 0{\cdot}921) \le A$, $1 \le A' \le 6A/5\, (\approx 1{\cdot}105)$ and such that, for sufficiently large x, all three ratios, $\theta(x)/x$, $\psi(x)/x$, and $(\pi(x) \log x)/x$ stay between A and A'. Tchebycheff's method can be refined to give values of A and A' still closer to unity; but no direct way seems to lead to the conclusion (needed for the PNT) that, for increasing x, a sequence of couples (A_n, A_n') can be found, such that, for $x > n$, $A_n x < \theta(x) < A_n' x$, with $\lim_{n \to \infty} A_n = \lim_{n \to \infty} A_n' = 1$. A few years after Tchebycheff's work, Riemann published his famous memoir "Ueber die Anzahl der Primzahlen unter einer gegebenen Grösse" (see [15], pp. 145–155), in which he approaches the problem from a completely different angle. He considers the function $\zeta(x) = \sum_{n=1}^{\infty} n^{-s}$, whose connection with the theory of primes had been recognized already by Euler. Riemann does not restrict himself, as Euler did, only to real values of s, but studies the behavior of $\zeta(s)$ in the whole plane of the complex variable $s = \sigma + it$. Riemann's paper is relatively short (less than 10 pages) and is beautifully written. Still, we are not going to follow it here. Indeed, as it stands, it is incomplete. While, at first reading, it might strike us as quite clear and convincing, some reflection reveals several gaps. These could not be filled until some 37 years later (and more than 30 years after Riemann's early death in 1866), through the work of Hadamard on the theory of entire functions and that of Hadamard and de la Vallée-Poussin on the zeta function. At present, it is possible to give a completely satisfactory proof along the lines of Riemann's approach. However, this requires several rather deep theorems of analysis and we prefer instead to present here one along somewhat different lines. At this point, we shall have to start using some analysis and, for ease of reference, we shall list in the next section some results needed in what follows. Sketches of proofs for some of them may be found in Appendix A and complete proofs are available in standard textbooks; at least one pertinent reference will be given for each theorem quoted.

† In order to avoid breaking with an old tradition, variable quantities will be denoted by lower case latin letters taken from the end of the alphabet, such as x, y, z and t (in addition to σ). Up to this point, lower-case latin letters have represented rational integers only, but the context should make any confusion or misinterpretation highly unlikely.

3. SOME RESULTS OF ANALYSIS

In this section we shall make no distinction between theorems, corollaries, remarks, and even definitions, but number them consecutively. Also, occasionally, lower-case latin letters do not stand for rational integers.

A. ADVANCED CALCULUS

1. Termwise integration of a uniformly convergent series over a finite interval is legitimate. This means the following. If (i) $\sum_{n=1}^{\infty} c_n(x)$ is uniformly convergent and (ii) $\int_a^b c_n(x)dx$ exists for each n, then $\int_a^b (\sum_{n=1}^{\infty} c_n(x))\, dx = \sum_{n=1}^{\infty} \int_a^b c_n(x)\, dx$.

If in addition this equality holds for each (arbitrarily large) b, and $c_n(x) \geq 0$ for $x \geq a$ then also $\int_a^{\infty} (\sum_{n=1}^{\infty} c_n(x))\, dx = \sum_{n=1}^{\infty} \int_a^{\infty} c_n(x)\, dx$. For proof of a more general statement see, for instance [1], p. 451. Termwise differentiation of a convergent series is legitimate, if the differentiated series converges uniformly (see [24], p. 305).

2. The infinite product $\prod_{n=1}^{\infty} (1 - a_n)$ is said to converge, if $a_n \neq 1$ at least for $n \geq n_0$ and if $\lim_{k \to \infty} \prod_{n=n_0}^{k} (1 - a_n)$ exists and is different from zero. If $a_n > 0$, then the infinite product converges if and only if, $\sum_{n=1}^{\infty} a_n$ converges. If $a_n \neq 1$ for all n and the product converges, then its value is not zero. For proof see, for instance, [1], p. 382.

3. If $f(x) = \int_a^b g(x, t)\, dt$ exists for each x of some interval, then $f'(x) = \int_a^b (\partial g(x, t)/\partial x)\, dt$ provided that $\partial g(x, t)/\partial x$ is continuous in x and t; (see [1], p. 219, [20], p. 59, or [24], p. 352). The conclusion remains valid if $\partial g/\partial x$ has a countable set of discontinues in t, at which $\partial g/\partial x$ stays uniformly bounded.

4. Let $z = x + iy$ be a complex number; if $x > 0$, then the improper integral $\int_0^{\infty} t^{z-1}e^{-t}\, dt$ converges and defines a function of z denoted by $\Gamma(z)$ (see [1], p. 436; also Section 8 of Appendix A).

5. The Γ-function satisfies the functional equation $z\Gamma(z) = \Gamma(z + 1)$ and $n \in \mathbf{Z} \Rightarrow \Gamma(n) = (n - 1)!$ (see [24], p. 368; also Appendix A.8).

6. $\int_0^{\infty} (\sin x/x)\, dx = \pi/2$ (see [22], pp. 150–151, or [19], pp. 275–277; also Section 7 of Appendix A).

7. If $z = x + iy$ and $0 < x < 1$, then $\int_0^{\infty} y^{z-1} \sin y\, dy = \Gamma(z) \sin \pi z/2$ (see [20], p. 107 and p. 162; also Appendix A, Section 9).

B. COMPLEX VARIABLES

8. An open, connected point set of the plane is called a *domain*. If every closed curve $\mathscr{C}$ of a domain $\mathscr{D}$ can be deformed continuously into a point, without ever going outside $\mathscr{D}$, then $\mathscr{D}$ is said to be *simply connected* ($\mathscr{D}$ has no "holes").

9. A single valued function $f(z)$, of a complex variable $z = x + iy$, defined on a domain $\mathscr{D}$, is said to be *regular analytic*, or simply, *analytic* at a point $z_0 \in \mathscr{D}$, provided that $\lim_{z \to z_0} (f(z) - f(z_0))/(z - z_0)$ exists, is finite, and is independent of the direction along which $z \to z_0$, that is, independent of $\arg(z - z_0)$; this limit is called the *derivative* of $f(z)$ at $z = z_0$, is denoted by $f'(z_0)$ and may be obtained formally by the ordinary rules of differentiation (of functions of a real variable) (see [22], p. 321).

10. If we split $f(x + iy)$ into its real and purely imaginary parts, $f(x + iy) = u(x, y) + iv(x, y)$ and $f(z)$ is analytic at $z = z_0 = x_0 + iy_0$, then the equations $\partial u/\partial x = \partial v/\partial y$, $\partial u/\partial y = -\partial v/\partial x$ hold at $z = x_0 + iy_0$. These equations are called the *Riemann-Cauchy equations*. Conversely, if the partial derivatives of u and v exist and satisfy the Riemann-Cauchy equations in some $\mathscr{D}$, $z_0 \in \mathscr{D}$, and if u and v satisfy some mild additional condition (e.g., if u and v have all second derivatives at z_0) then $f(z)$ is analytic at z_0 (see [1], p. 125 and 509, [20], pp. 65–69; also Appendix A, Section 2).

11. If $f(z)$ is analytic at all points of a domain $\mathscr{D}$, it is said to be *analytic in $\mathscr{D}$*.

12. If $f(z)$ is defined and single valued in $\mathscr{D}$, denote by $\mathscr{R}g\{f\}$ the *range* of $f(z)$, that is, the set $\{f(z) \mid z \in \mathscr{D}\}$. Then, if $g(w)$ is defined and single valued for $w \in \mathscr{R}g\{f\}$ the *composition* function $h(z) = g\{f(z)\}$ is defined and single valued for $z \in \mathscr{D}$ (see [1], p. 30).

13. The set of functions analytic in $\mathscr{D}$ is closed under addition, subtraction, multiplication and division (except at zeros of the denominator) and the composition of single valued analytic functions is single valued and analytic (see [22], pp. 321–322).

14. A uniformly convergent sequence of continuous (or of analytic) functions has as limit a continuous (or analytic, respectively) function (see [1], p. 394, or [20], p. 95).

15. Let $f(z) = f(x + iy) = u(x, y) + iv(x, y)$ be a complex valued (not necessarily analytic) function of a complex variable $z = x + iy$; let $u(x, y)$, $v(x, y)$ be real and let $\mathscr{C}$ be a curve in the plane of the complex variable $z = x + iy$ defined by the equations $x = g(t)$, $y = h(t)$, the functions $g(t)$ and $h(t)$ being defined and differentiable for $0 \leq t \leq 1$. By an integral

$\int_{\mathscr{C}} f(z)\,dz$ of $f(z)$ along $\mathscr{C}$ we understand, by definition, the line integral

$$\int_{\mathscr{C}} (u + iv)(dx + idy) = \int_{\mathscr{C}} (u(x, y)\,dx - v(x, y)\,dy)$$

$$+ i \int_{\mathscr{C}} (u(x, y)\,dy + v(x, y)\,dx), \qquad \text{with } x = g(t),\ y = h(t)$$

and where we replace dx and dy by $g'(t)\,dt$ and $h'(t)\,dt$, respectively. In case each parallel to the y-axis meets $\mathscr{C}$ in a single point, $\mathscr{C}$ may be represented by an equation of the form $y = \phi(x)$, and then $\int_{\mathscr{C}} f(z)\,dz = \int_{x_1}^{x_2} \{u(x, \phi(x)) - v(x, \phi(x))\phi'(x)\}\,dx + i \int_{x_1}^{x_2} \{u(x, \phi(x))\phi'(x) + v(x, \phi(x))\}\,dx$, where x_1 and x_2 are the abscissae of the end points of $\mathscr{C}$ (see [24], pp. 217–219, or [1], pp. 275–277).

16. If $\max_{z \in \mathscr{C}} |f(z)| = M$ and the length of $\mathscr{C}$ is L, then $|\int_{\mathscr{C}} f(z)\,dz| \le ML$ (see [1], p. 278).

17. (Cauchy's Theorem). If $f(z)$ is analytic in a simply connected domain $\mathscr{D}$ and $\mathscr{C}$ is a closed curve in $\mathscr{D}$, then $\int_{\mathscr{C}} f(z)\,dz = 0$ (see [1], p. 510; also Appendix A, Section 3).

18. If $f(z)$ is analytic in a simply connected domain $\mathscr{D}$, containing an interval of the real axis, and if $f(z)$ is real on that interval, then $f(\bar{z}) = \overline{f(z)}$ whenever z or $\bar{z}$ belong to $\mathscr{D}$ (see [20], p. 155).

19. Let $\mathscr{D}$ be simply connected, $z_0 \in \mathscr{D}$, $f(z)$ analytic in $\mathscr{D}$, except, possibly, at z_0; then z_0 is called an *isolated singularity* of $f(z)$.

(a) If $\lim_{z \to z_0} (z - z_0)f(z) = 0$, then also $\lim_{z \to z_0} f(z)$ exists and is finite and we may define $f(z_0) = \lim_{z \to z_0} f(z)$. If $f(z)$ is *continued into* z_0 by this definition of $f(z_0)$, then $f(z)$ is analytic in all of $\mathscr{D}$, and z_0 is called a *removable singularity*; z_0 is an ordinary point of $f(z)$ (see [21]).

(b) If condition (a) does not hold, but if there exists an integer $k > 0$, such that $\lim_{z \to z_0} (z - z_0)^k f(z) = g(z)$ is analytic at z_0, then z_0 is a *pole* of $f(z)$; the smallest such integer k is called the *order* of the pole.

(c) If neither (a) nor (b) hold, then z_0 is said to be an *essential isolated singularity* of $f(z)$ (see [1], p. 522, or [20], pp. 91–92).

20. If $f(z)$ is single valued and analytic in $\mathscr{D}$, $z_0 \in \mathscr{D}$ and $f(z_0) = 0$, then there exists a positive integer k such that $f(z) = (z - z_0)^k g(z)$ with $g(z)$ analytic in $\mathscr{D}$ and $g(z_0) \neq 0$; z_0 is called a *zero of order k* of $f(z)$ (see [1], p. 518, or [20] pp. 87–88).

21. Let $f(z)$ be single valued in $\mathscr{D}$ and also analytic, except, possibly, at

a finite number of points, $z_1, z_2, \ldots, z_m$; then, if $z_0 \in \mathscr{D}$, $f(z)$ can be represented by a series $\sum_{n=-\infty}^{\infty} a_n(z - z_0)^n$, convergent at least in some "punctured disk" $0 < |z - z_0| < r_0$ around z_0, for some $r_0 > 0$. If $z_0 \neq z_i (1 \leq i \leq m)$, then $a_n = 0$ for $n < 0$, the series is the ordinary Taylor series of $f(z)$ and converges (trivially) also at $z = z_0$ (namely to a_0) and z_0 is said to be an ordinary point of $f(z)$. If $z_0 = z_i (1 \leq i \leq m)$, finitely, or infinitely many coefficients $a_n(n < 0)$ may be different from zero and the series is called a *Laurent series*; if in the Laurent series $a_n = 0$ for $n < -k$, $a_{-k} \neq 0$, then z_0 is a pole of order k. If $a_n \neq 0$ for infinitely many negative values of n, then z_0 is an essential singularity (see [1], pp. 519–523 or [20], pp. 89–94; see also Appendix A, Section 6).

22. If z_0 is an ordinary point of the analytic function $f(z)$, then $\lim_{z \to z_0} f(z) = f(z_0)$ and is finite; if z_0 is a pole then $|f(z)| \to \infty$ as $z \to z_0$; if z_0 is an essential singularity $\lim_{z \to z_0} f(z)$ does not exist and $|f(z)|$ does not stay bounded in any neighborhood of z_0. (All statements follow almost trivially from 19 and 21.)

23. If $f(z)$ and $g(z)$ are analytic in $\mathscr{D}$ and $f(z) = g(z)$ at an infinite sequence of points $\{z_n\}$ with a limit point $z_0 \in \mathscr{D}$, then $f(z) = g(z)$ for all $z \in \mathscr{D}$. If $f(z)$ is defined and analytic in $\mathscr{D}_1 \supset \mathscr{D}$ and $g(z)$ is defined and analytic in $\mathscr{D}_2 \supset \mathscr{D}$, with $\mathscr{D} = \mathscr{D}_1 \cap \mathscr{D}_2$, then $g(z)$ is said to *continue $f(z)$ analytically* into $\mathscr{D}_2$ and $f(z)$ is said to *continue $g(z)$ analytically* into $\mathscr{D}_1$ (see [1], p. 519, or [20], p. 89).

24. If z_0 is a pole or essential singularity of $f(z)$, then the coefficient $a_{-1} = a_{-1}(z_0)$ of the Laurent expansion at $z = z_0$ is called the *residue* of $f(z)$ at z_0.

25. (Cauchy's Theorem on Residues). Let $\mathscr{C}$ be a simple closed curve in the z plane, let $f(z)$ be analytic inside $\mathscr{C}$, except, possibly, for a finite number of isolated singularities $z_1, z_2, \ldots, z_m$, and let $f(z)$ be continuous on $\mathscr{C}$; then $\int_{\mathscr{C}} f(z)\,dz = 2\pi i \sum_{i=1}^{m} a_{-1}(z_i)$ (see [1], pp. 524–525, or [20], p. 102; also Appendix A, Section 6).

26. Let $z = x + iy$ have modulus $r = |z| = \sqrt{x^2 + y^2}$ and argument $\theta = \arctan(y/x)$; then $\log z = \log r + i\theta$. Here θ is defined by x and y only up to integral multiples of 2π; hence, $\log z$ is *not* single valued in the whole plane. However, we can select a single valued "branch" in any bounded, simply connected domain $\mathscr{D}$, which does not contain the origin (see [1], p. 17; also Appendix A, Section 1).

27. A single valued branch of $g(z) = \log f(z)$ can be defined in any simply connected domain $\mathscr{D}$, where $f(z)$ is analytic and $f(z) \neq 0$. (Proof follows from (26) by setting $Z = f(z)$ and using 13.)

C. HARMONIC ANALYSIS

28. Let $f(t)$ be periodic and piecewise smooth, that is, $\exists\, T \ni n \in \mathbf{Z} \Rightarrow f(t) = f(t + nT)$ and $f'(t)$ exists and is continuous, except, possibly, for a finite set of points on each interval T, where $f(t)$, or $f'(t)$, or both, may have finite discontinuities. To each such $f(t)$ corresponds a *Fourier series*

$$S(t) = \frac{\alpha_0}{2} + \sum_{n=1}^{\infty} \left\{ \alpha_n \cos \frac{2\pi nt}{T} + \beta_n \sin \frac{2\pi nt}{T} \right\},$$

where

$$\alpha_n = \frac{2}{T} \int_{\gamma}^{\gamma+T} f(t) \cos \frac{2\pi nt}{T}\, dt \quad \text{and} \quad \beta_n = \frac{2}{T} \int_{\delta}^{\delta+T} f(t) \sin \frac{2\pi nt}{T}\, dt$$

(γ, δ arbitrary real numbers). Furthermore, if we let $\varepsilon \to 0$ either only through positive values, or only through negative values and denote the corresponding (possibly different) limits of $f(t + \varepsilon)$ by $f(t + 0)$ and $f(t - 0)$, respectively, then $S(t) = \frac{1}{2}\{f(t + 0) + f(t - 0)\}$ (see [9], p. 24, or [1], Chapter 15; also Appendix A, Section 10).

29. The function $y = ((t))$ is piecewise smooth, has the period $T = 1$ and the Fourier series $y = -(1/\pi) \sum_{n=1}^{\infty} (\sin 2\pi nt)/n$. (This is an immediate consequence of 28; see also [9], p. 209, or Appendix A, Section 11(a)).

30. Whenever the improper integral $\int_0^{\infty} f(x)x^{-s}\, dx$ converges, it defines a function $F(s)$, called the *Mellin transform of $f(x)$*. In particular, if $f(x) = O(x^{\alpha-1})$ for $x \to \infty$, then $\lim_{X \to \infty} \int_0^X f(x)x^{-s}\, dx$ exists, provided that $\sigma = \operatorname{Re} s > \alpha$; similarly, if $f(x) = O(x^{\beta-1})$ for $x \to 0$, $\lim_{\eta \to 0} \int_{\eta}^{x_0} f(x)x^{-s}\, dx$ exists for $\sigma < \beta$. Should $\alpha < \beta$ hold, then $\lim_{\eta \to 0} \lim_{X \to \infty} \int_{\eta}^X f(x)x^{-s}\, dx = \int_0^{\infty} f(x)x^{-s}\, dx = F(s)$ exists for $\alpha < \sigma < \beta$, and the convergence is uniform in every interior strip $\alpha + \varepsilon \leq \sigma \leq \beta - \varepsilon (\varepsilon > 0)$. In this case, $F(s)$ is a function analytic in the strip $\alpha < \sigma < \beta$ and the *inversion formula*

$$f(x) = \frac{1}{2\pi i} \lim_{T \to \infty} \int_{\gamma-iT}^{\gamma+iT} F(s)x^{s-1}\, ds$$

holds, the integral being taken along a parallel to the imaginary axis, of abscissa γ with $\alpha < \gamma < \beta$, otherwise arbitrary; the improper integral then converges and its value is independent of γ. (With different variables ($t = \log x$, $z = s - 1$), the proof is in [1], p. 498; see also Appendix A, Section 12).

31. $\sum_{n=1}^{\infty} 1/n^2 = \pi^2/6$ (see Appendix A, Section 11(b)).

4. THE ZETA FUNCTION OF RIEMANN

Theorem 1. *Let $s = \sigma + it$ be a complex variable. Then, for $\sigma > 1$, the series $\sum_{n=1}^{\infty} n^{-s}$ converges. The convergence is uniform for $\sigma \geq 1 + \varepsilon$, and any $\varepsilon > 0$, arbitrarily small. Hence, in the half plane $\sigma > 1$, $\sum_{n=1}^{\infty} n^{-s}$ represents an analytic function of s (see 3.14).*

PROOF. For any two positive integers $m < k$ one has

$$\left| \sum_{n=m+1}^{k} n^{-s} \right| \leq \sum_{n=m+1}^{k} |n^{-s}| = \sum_{n=m+1}^{k} n^{-\sigma} \leq \int_{m}^{k} x^{-\sigma}\, dx =$$

$$x^{1-\sigma}/(1-\sigma)|_{m}^{k} \leq m^{1-\sigma}/(\sigma - 1) < m^{-\varepsilon}/\varepsilon$$

because $\sigma \geq 1 + \varepsilon$. For fixed $\varepsilon > 0$, $m^{-\varepsilon}/\varepsilon$ can be made arbitrarily small, by taking m sufficiently large and this proves the uniform convergence of the series. Differentiating termwise we observe that the differentiated series, $-\sum_{n=2}^{\infty} n^{-s} \log n$ also converges for $\sigma > 1$, and uniformly so for $\sigma \geq 1 + \varepsilon$ ($\varepsilon > 0$), the proof being essentially the same as for $\sum_{n=1}^{\infty} n^{-s}$; hence, by 3.1, for $\sigma > 1$, $-\sum_{n=2}^{\infty} n^{-s} \log n$ is the derivative of the function $\sum_{n=1}^{\infty} n^{-s}$, which is, consequently, analytic for $\sigma > 1$ (by 3.9 and 3.11).

Definition 1 (Riemann).   The function defined for $\sigma > 1$ by $\sum_{n=1}^{\infty} n^{-s}$ is denoted, following Riemann, by $\zeta(s)$.

REMARK 1. If $s > 1$, then $\sum_{n=1}^{k} n^{-s} > \displaystyle\int_{1}^{k} x^{-s}\, dx = \dfrac{1}{1-s}(k^{1-s} - 1) =$

$(1 - k^{1-s})/(s - 1))$; hence, it follows that $\zeta(s) = \lim\limits_{k \to \infty} \sum_{n=1}^{k} n^{-s} \geq \dfrac{1}{s-1}$.

If we now let s approach 1 from the right, along the real axis, in symbols $s \to 1^{+}$, then $\dfrac{1}{s-1} \to +\infty$. Hence, $\zeta(s)$ does *not* stay bounded as $s \to 1^{+}$; the series $\sum_{n=1}^{\infty} n^{-s}$ diverges for $s = 1$ and Theorem 1 cannot be improved even to state the convergence of the series $\sum_{n=1}^{\infty} n^{-s}$ for $\sigma \geq 1$.

Euler, while considering only real values of s, proved the following Theorem, equally valid for complex s.

Theorem 2.   *For $\sigma > 1$, $\zeta(s) = \prod_{p} (1 - p^{-s})^{-1}$.*

Here and in what follows, the letter p under the symbol for sum or product means that the corresponding sum or product is extended over all primes.

PROOF. We consider the finite product $P_k(s) = \prod_{p \leq k} (1 - p^{-s})^{-1} = \prod_{p \leq k} (1 + 1/p^{s} + \cdots + 1/p^{ns} + \cdots)$. Multiplying out, the right-hand side is of the form

$\sum^1 n^{-s}$. All, and only those integers n occur in this sum, that contain no prime divisor larger than k. Also, on account of the uniqueness of factorization, each such integer occurs exactly once. Hence, $\sum^1 n^{-s} = \sum_{n=1}^{\infty} n^{-s} - \sum^2 n^{-s}$, where the sum $\sum^2 n^{-s}$ is extended over all integers n, containing at least one prime factor $p > k$. For $\sigma > 1$, however, $|\sum^2 n^{-s}| \le \sum^2 n^{-\sigma} < \sum_{n=k+1}^{\infty} n^{-\sigma}$ and, as $k \to \infty$, this sum approaches zero, because the series $\sum_{n=1}^{\infty} n^{-\sigma}$ converges. Hence, $\prod_p (1 - p^{-s})^{-1} = \lim_{k \to \infty} P_k(s) = \lim_{k \to \infty} \prod_{p \le k} (1 - p^{-s})^{-1}$
$= \zeta(s) - \lim_{k \to \infty} \sum^2 n^{-s} = \zeta(s)$, proving the Theorem.

Corollary 2.1 (Euler).   *There exist infinitely many primes.*

PROOF. We saw that for $s \to 1^+$, $\prod_p (1 - p^{-s})^{-1} = \zeta(s)$ does not stay bounded, while, if the number of primes would be finite, $\lim_{s \to 1^+} \prod_p (1 - p^{-s})^{-1} = \prod_p (1 - p^{-1})^{-1}$ would be a finite, actually even a rational number.

Corollary 2.2.   *The sum $\sum \dfrac{1}{p}$ extended over all primes diverges.*

PROOF. Let $x \ge 3$ and observe that just like in the proof of Theorem 2, $\sum_{n \le x} 1/n < \prod_{p \le x} (1 - (1/p))^{-1}$; hence,

$$\log \sum_{n \le x} \frac{1}{n} < -\log \prod_{p \le x} \left(1 - \frac{1}{p}\right) = -\sum_{p \le x} \log \left(1 - \frac{1}{p}\right) = \sum_{p \le x} \left(\frac{1}{p} + \sum_{m=2}^{\infty} \frac{1}{mp^m}\right)$$

$$= \sum_{p \le x} \frac{1}{p} + R(x),$$

with

$$0 < R(x) = \sum_{p \le x} \sum_{m=2}^{\infty} \frac{1}{mp^m} < \sum_{p \le x} \sum_{m=2}^{\infty} \frac{1}{p^m} = \sum_{p \le x} \frac{1}{p^2 - p} < 2 \sum_{p \le x} \frac{1}{p^2}$$

$$< 2 \sum_{n \le x} \frac{1}{n^2} < 2 \sum_{n=1}^{\infty} \frac{1}{n^2} = 2\zeta(2)$$

$(= \dfrac{\pi^2}{3}$ by 3.31, but the exact value of this constant is, of course, irrelevant). It follows that $\sum_{p \le x} (1/p) > \log \sum_{n \le x} 1/n - 2\zeta(2)$ and the result now follows from the divergence of the harmonic series $\sum_{n=1}^{\infty} 1/n$.

Corollary 2.3. $\zeta(s) \ne 0$ *for* $\sigma > 1$.

PROOF. For real $s > 0$, $\log(1 - p^{-s})$ is real and negative. For $\sigma > 0$, $|p^{-s}| = p^{-\sigma} < 1$; hence $1 - p^{-s} \ne 0$ and, therefore, we can define (see

3.27) a single valued branch of the function $\log(1 - p^{-s})$ in $\sigma > 0$, *a fortiori* in $\sigma > 1$. Expanding, $\log(1 - p^{-s})^{-1} = -\log(1 - p^{-s}) = p^{-s} + p^{-2s}/2 + \cdots + (p^{-ms}/m) + \cdots$ and

$$|\log(1 - p^{-s})^{-1}| = |\sum_{m=1}^{\infty} p^{-sm} m^{-1}| \le$$

$$\sum_{m=1}^{\infty} p^{-\sigma m} = p^{-\sigma}(1 - p^{-\sigma})^{-1} = (p^{\sigma} - 1)^{-1} < 2p^{-\sigma}$$

because $p \ge 2$ and $\sigma > 1$. Hence

$$|\log \prod_{p \le x} (1 - p^{-s})^{-1}| = |\sum_{p \le x} \log(1 - p^{-s})^{-1}| < 2 \sum_{p \le x} p^{-\sigma} < 2 \sum_{n=1}^{\infty} n^{-\sigma}$$

$$= 2\zeta(\sigma) = A,$$

say, (A being some constant), because the series converges by Theorem 1. Taking the limit for $x \to \infty$, the infinite product on the left converges to $\zeta(s)$, on account of Theorem 2 (because $\sigma > 1$). We conclude that $|\log \zeta(s)| < A$; hence, $\log|\zeta(s)| = $ Real part of $\log \zeta(s) > -A$, so that $|\zeta(s)| > e^{-A} > 0$, as asserted.

$\star$ALTERNATIVE PROOF. For $\sigma > 1$, $\zeta(s) \neq 0$ as convergent infinite product of nonvanishing factors.

5. THE ZETA FUNCTION AND $\pi(x)$

Before we continue with the study of the zeta function, it might be of interest to stop for a moment in order to show the close connection that $\zeta(s)$ has with the function $\pi(x)$; this is illustrated by the following theorem.

Theorem 3. *For* $\sigma > 1$, $\log \zeta(s) = s \int_{2}^{\infty} \frac{\pi(x)}{x(x^s - 1)} dx$.

PROOF. For $\sigma > 1$, $\zeta(s) \neq 0$ by Corollary 2.3, and, for real $s > 1$, $\zeta(s) > 1$. Hence, by 3.27 we can define a branch of $\log \zeta(s)$, real and positive for $s > 1$ and single valued for $\sigma > 1$.

Then, by Theorem 2,

$$\log \zeta(s) = -\sum_{p} \log(1 - p^{-s}) = -\lim_{k \to \infty} \sum_{n=2}^{k} (\pi(n) - \pi(n-1)) \log(1 - n^{-s}).$$

By *partial summation* (that is, by a regrouping of the finitely many terms of the sum; for detailed example see Section 6),

$$\log \zeta(s) = -\lim_{k \to \infty} \left\{ \sum_{n=2}^{k} \pi(n)[\log(1 - n^{-s}) - \log(1 - (n+1)^{-s})] \right.$$

$$\left. - \pi(1)\log(1 - 2^{-s}) + \pi(k)\log(1 - (k+1)^{-s}) \right\}$$

$$= \lim_{k \to \infty} \left\{ \sum_{n=2}^{k} \pi(n)[\log(1 - (n+1)^{-s}) - \log(1 - n^{-s})] \right\}$$

$$+ \lim_{k \to \infty} \pi(k)\log(1 - (k+1)^{-s}).$$

For $k \to \infty$, the last term is less than

$$\left| k \left\{ \frac{1}{(k+1)^s} + \frac{1}{2(k+1)^{2s}} + \cdots \right\} \right| < \frac{2k}{|(k+1)^s|} \to 0,$$

because $\sigma > 1$. Hence,

$$\log \zeta(s) = \sum_{n=2}^{\infty} \pi(n) \int_{n}^{n+1} \frac{d}{dx} \log(1 - x^{-s}) \, dx$$

$$= \sum_{n=2}^{\infty} \pi(n) \int_{n}^{n+1} \frac{s}{x(x^s - 1)} \, dx = s \sum_{n=2}^{\infty} \int_{n}^{n+1} \frac{\pi(x)}{x(x^s - 1)} \, dx$$

$$= s \int_{2}^{\infty} \frac{\pi(x)}{x(x^s - 1)} \, dx$$

and the Theorem is proven.

The PNT may now be obtained by "inverting" the relation given by Theorem 3, that is, by "solving" the equation of Theorem 3 for $\pi(x)$ (compare this situation with that in 3.30). Then $\pi(x)$ appears as an integral over $(\log \zeta(s))/s$; this integral is somewhat difficult to evaluate and, before we attempt this calculation we have to return to the study of the ζ-function.

6. FURTHER THEORY OF THE ZETA FUNCTION

Several interesting theorems concerning the zeta function may be obtained as particular cases of the following simple lemma, which is concerned only with finite sums:

Lemma 1.   *Let m and k be positive integers, while $s = \sigma + it$ is a complex number. Let $S = S(s; m, k) = \sum_{n=m+1}^{k} n^{-s}$. Then*

$$S = -s \int_{m}^{k} \frac{x - [x]}{x^{s+1}} \, dx + \frac{1}{s-1}(m^{1-s} - k^{1-s}).$$

PROOF. By partial summation we have

$$S = \frac{(m + 1) - m}{(m + 1)^s} + \frac{(m + 2) - (m + 1)}{(m + 2)^s} + \cdots$$

$$+ \frac{(m + a) - (m + a - 1)}{(m + a)^s} + \frac{(m + a + 1) - (m + a)}{(m + a + 1)^s} + \cdots$$

$$+ \frac{k - (k - 1)}{k^s} = \frac{-m}{(m + 1)^s} + (m + 1)\left(\frac{1}{(m + 1)^s} - \frac{1}{(m + 2)^s}\right) + \cdots$$

$$+ (m + a)\left(\frac{1}{(m + a)^s} - \frac{1}{(m + a + 1)^s}\right) + \cdots$$

$$+ (k - 1)\left(\frac{1}{(k - 1)^s} - \frac{1}{k^s}\right) + \frac{k}{k^s}$$

$$= \sum_{n=m+1}^{k-1} n\left(\frac{1}{n^s} - \frac{1}{(n + 1)^s}\right) - \frac{m}{(m + 1)^s} + \frac{k}{k^s}$$

$$= \sum_{n=m}^{k-1} n\left(\frac{1}{n^s} - \frac{1}{(n + 1)^s}\right) - m^{1-s} + k^{1-s}.$$

As in the proof of Theorem 3, we observe that the general term

$$n\left(\frac{1}{n^s} - \frac{1}{(n + 1)^s}\right) = sn\int_n^{n+1} \frac{dx}{x^{s+1}} = s\int_n^{n+1} \frac{[x]}{x^{s+1}}\, dx$$

and the sum on n becomes a sum of abutting integrals; hence, it can be written as a single integral, $s\int_m^k \frac{[x]}{x^{s+1}}\, dx$, and

$$S = s\int_m^k \frac{[x]}{x^{s-1}}\, dx - m^{1-s} + k^{1-s}. \tag{1}$$

In some cases, in order to improve the convergence, it is desirable to have a smaller numerator under the integral sign; we, therefore, subtract

$$s\int_m^k \frac{x}{x^{s+1}}\, dx = s\int_m^k x^{-s}\, dx = \frac{s}{1 - s}(k^{1-s} - m^{1-s})$$

and then add back the same quantity, obtaining

$$S = s\int_{m+1}^k \frac{[x] - x}{x^{s+1}}\, dx + \frac{1}{1 - s}(k^{1-s} - m^{1-s}),$$

which is precisely the Lemma.

Theorem 4. *For $\sigma > 1$, $\zeta(s)$ is regular analytic and has the representation*

$$\zeta(s) = s \int_1^\infty \frac{[x]}{x^{s+1}} \, dx. \tag{2}$$

PROOF. Take $m = 1$ and let $k \to \infty$ in (1); then, for $\sigma > 1$,

$$\lim_{k \to \infty} S = \zeta(s) - 1, \; m^{1-s} = 1, \; \lim_{k \to \infty} |k^{1-s}| = \lim_{k \to \infty} k^{1-\sigma} = 0$$

and the improper integral in (1) converges for $\sigma > 1$.

Theorem 5. *For $\sigma > 0$ $\zeta(s)$ is regular analytic, except for a pole of first order at $s = 1$, with residue $a_{-1} = 1$ and has the representation*

$$\zeta(s) = \frac{1}{s-1} + 1 - s \int_1^\infty \frac{x - [x]}{x^{s+1}} \, dx. \tag{3}$$

PROOF. Take $m = 1$ and let $k \to \infty$ in Lemma 1. Then the term k^{1-s} vanishes for $\sigma > 1$ and $k \to \infty$ and we obtain (3) formally. This representation holds, therefore, at least for $\sigma > 1$. However, the integral converges already for $\sigma > 0$ (because $x - [x]$ stays bounded), and uniformly so for $\sigma \geq \varepsilon$ ($\varepsilon > 0$, arbitrarily small). Consequently, for $\sigma > 0$, by 3.3, we can find the derivative of the definite integral in (3), by differentiating under the integral sign and, by 3.9 and 3.11, $-s \int_1^\infty (x - [x]) x^{-s-1} \, dx$ is an analytic function of s at least in the half-plane $\sigma > 0$. This function coincides there with $f(s) = \zeta(s) - \dfrac{1}{s-1} - 1$; it, therefore, represents the analytic continuation of $f(s)$ for $\sigma > 0$ (see 3.23). The assertion concerning the pole of $\zeta(s)$ at $s = 1$ can now be read off from (3).

Actually, we can do still better. If in (3) we introduce also the term $-\frac{1}{2}$ in the numerator of the integrand, the integral becomes $\int_1^\infty ((x)) x^{-s-1} \, dx$. To compensate for the change, we have to subtract $\frac{1}{2}s \int_1^\infty x^{-s-1} \, dx = \frac{1}{2}$ and then we obtain from (3)

Theorem 6. *For $\sigma > -1$, $\zeta(s)$ admits the representation*

$$\zeta(s) = \frac{1}{s-1} + \frac{1}{2} - s \int_1^\infty \frac{((x))}{x^{s+1}} \, dx. \tag{4}$$

PROOF. We already know that (4) holds for $\sigma > 0$. In order to prove Theorem 6, all we have still to show is that the integral converges for $\sigma > -1$. Indeed, let $y = \int_1^x ((t)) \, dt$; then $y(1) = 0$ and (see Theorem 6.3(6)) $|y(x)| \leq 1/8$ for all x. Hence, integrating by parts,

$$\int_1^\infty \frac{((x))}{x^{s+1}} \, dx = y(x) x^{-s-1} \Big|_1^\infty + (s+1) \int_1^\infty \frac{y(x)}{x^{s+2}} \, dx.$$

For $\sigma > -1$ the first term vanishes and the last integral converges, because $y(x)$ is bounded.

Corollary 6.1. $\lim_{s \to 1} (s-1)\zeta(s) = 1.$

PROOF is obvious from (4).

Corollary 6.2. *For* $\sigma > 0$, $\zeta(s) = \dfrac{1}{s-1} + \gamma + O(s-1)$, *where* $\gamma = \lim_{k \to \infty} \left(\sum_{n=1}^k \dfrac{1}{n} - \log k \right)$ *is the Euler-Mascheroni constant.*

PROOF.

$$\int_1^k \frac{x - [x]}{x^2} \, dx = \int_1^k \frac{dx}{x} - \sum_{n=1}^{k-1} n \int_n^{n+1} \frac{dx}{x^2}$$

$$= \log k - \sum_{n=1}^{k-1} n \left(\frac{1}{n} - \frac{1}{n+1} \right)$$

$$= \log k - \sum_{n=1}^{k-1} \frac{1}{n+1} = 1 - \left(\sum_{n=1}^k \frac{1}{n} - \log k \right).$$

For $k \to \infty$, the bracket has the finite limit denoted by γ; hence, (3) may be written as $\zeta(s) = (s-1)^{-1} + \gamma + \int_1^\infty (x - [x])(x^{-2} - sx^{-s-1}) \, dx$ and it only remains to show that the integral is $O(s-1)$. This is indeed the case, as can be seen by writing it in the form

$$\int_1^\infty \frac{x - [x]}{x^{s-1}} (x^{s-1} - s) \, dx = (s-1) \int_1^\infty \frac{x - [x]}{x^{s+1}} \frac{x^{s-1} - s}{s-1} \, dx = (s-1)I(s).$$

It is easy to see (see Problem 5) that for s bounded away from 1, $I(s)$ is bounded.

The proof of Corollary 6.2 will be complete, if we show that $I(s)$ stays bounded also for $s \to 1$. To see that, let $s = 1 + \varepsilon$, where ε is a complex number that we shall eventually let approach zero. To avoid trivial difficulties, we might even assume from the start that $|\varepsilon| < \frac{1}{3}$, so that $|\varepsilon| \log 1/|\varepsilon| < \frac{1}{3} \log 3$. For given ε, set $X = |\varepsilon|^{-1-2|\varepsilon|}$. Then

$$I(s) = \int_1^X + \int_X^\infty (x - [x])(x^\varepsilon - 1 - \varepsilon) x^{-s-1} \varepsilon^{-1} \, dx$$

The second integral is less, in absolute value, than

$$\left| \int_x^\infty \frac{1}{x^2} \frac{1 - (1 + \varepsilon)x^{-\varepsilon}}{\varepsilon} \, dx \right| < \frac{1}{|\varepsilon|} \int_x^\infty 3x^{|\varepsilon|-2} \, dx$$

$$= \frac{3X^{|\varepsilon|-1}}{|\varepsilon|(1-|\varepsilon|)} < \frac{6}{|\varepsilon|} X^{|\varepsilon|-1}$$

$$= 6|\varepsilon|^{-1} \cdot |\varepsilon|^{(1+2|\varepsilon|)(1-|\varepsilon|)}$$

$$= 6|\varepsilon|^{-1+1+|\varepsilon|-2|\varepsilon|^2}$$

$$< 6.$$

Next, one has $x^\varepsilon = 1 + \varepsilon \log x + \varepsilon^2 (\log x)^2/2! + \cdots$ so that

$$|x^\varepsilon - 1 - \varepsilon \log x| < \tfrac{1}{2}|\varepsilon|^2 \log^2 x(1 + \tfrac{1}{3}|\varepsilon| \log x + (\tfrac{1}{3}|\varepsilon| \log x)^2 + \cdots$$

$$= \tfrac{1}{2}|\varepsilon|^2 \log^2 x \cdot \frac{1}{1 - \tfrac{1}{3}|\varepsilon| \log x}.$$

By $x < X$ and the choice of X,

$$\tfrac{1}{3}|\varepsilon| \log x < \tfrac{1}{3}|\varepsilon|(1 + 2|\varepsilon|) \log \frac{1}{|\varepsilon|} < \tfrac{2}{3}|\varepsilon| \log \frac{1}{|\varepsilon|} \leq \tfrac{2}{3} \cdot \tfrac{1}{3} \log 3 < \tfrac{1}{4},$$

so that $x^\varepsilon = 1 + \varepsilon \log x + \theta|\varepsilon|^2 \log^2 x$ with $|\theta| < 1$. Consequently, the first integral may be written as

$$\int_1^X \frac{x - [x]}{x^{2+\varepsilon}} \frac{1 + \varepsilon \log x + \theta|\varepsilon|^2 \log^2 x - 1 - \varepsilon}{\varepsilon} \, dx$$

$$= \int_1^X \frac{x - [x]}{x^{2+\varepsilon}} (\log x - 1 + \theta|\varepsilon| \log^2 x) \, dx$$

and is less, in absolute value than

$$\int_1^X \frac{\log x + 1}{x^{2-1/3}} \, dx + |\varepsilon| \int_1^X \frac{\log^2 x}{x^{2-1/3}} \, dx$$

$$\leq \int_1^X \frac{\log x + 1}{x^{5/3}} \, dx + \frac{1}{3} \int_1^X \frac{\log^2 x}{x^{5/3}} \, dx < \int_1^\infty \frac{1 + \log x + \tfrac{1}{3} \log^2 x}{x^{5/3}} \, dx = A,$$

an absolute constant†. It follows that for $|s - 1| < \tfrac{1}{3}$, $|I(s)| < A + 6$, is bounded and this finishes the proof of the Corollary.

7. *THE FUNCTIONAL EQUATION

Let us look back for a moment, to see what we have accomplished: Starting with the representation $\zeta(s) = \sum_{n=1}^\infty n^{-s}$, valid only for $\sigma > 1$, we

† The value of the constant is 6, as an elementary computation shows.

obtained first the representation $\zeta(s) = \dfrac{1}{s-1} + 1 - s\displaystyle\int_1^\infty \dfrac{x - [x]}{x^{s+1}}\,dx$, which

extends the domain of definition of $\zeta(s)$ from $\sigma > 1$ to $\sigma > 0$; next, going

one step further, we proved $\zeta(s) = \dfrac{1}{s-1} + \tfrac{1}{2} - s\displaystyle\int_1^\infty \dfrac{((x))}{x^{s+1}}\,dx$ which extends

the domain of definition of $\zeta(s)$ still further, to $\sigma > -1$. It is possible to
continue step by step and it can be proven that we may continue doing
this indefinitely, with the result that $\zeta(s)$ can be defined in the whole plane
of the complex variable $s = \sigma + it$, and is analytic everywhere, except at
$s = 1$, where it has a pole of first order. However, instead of doing this
piecemeal, it is both easier and more elegant, to do it at one stroke, by
proving the justly celebrated functional equation of Riemann (which, however, will not be needed in the proof of the PNT).

Theorem 7 (Riemann).   *The zeta function satisfies the functional equation*

$$\zeta(s) = 2^s \pi^{s-1} \zeta(1-s)\Gamma(1-s)\sin\frac{\pi s}{2}. \tag{5}$$

SKETCH OF A PROOF. For $\sigma < 0$, $s\displaystyle\int_0^1 ((x))x^{-s-1}\,dx$ converges and has the
value

$$s\int_0^1 \frac{x - \tfrac{1}{2}}{x^{s+1}}\,dx = s\left\{\frac{x^{1-s}}{1-s} + \tfrac{1}{2}\frac{x^{-s}}{s}\right\}_0^1 = s\left(\frac{1}{1-s} + \frac{1}{2s}\right)$$

$$= \frac{s}{1-s} + \frac{1}{2} = \frac{1}{1-s} - 1 + \frac{1}{2} = -\frac{1}{s-1} - \frac{1}{2}.$$

Hence, by (4), for $-1 < \sigma < 0$,

$$\zeta(s) = -s\int_0^1 \frac{((x))}{x^{s+1}}\,dx - s\int_1^\infty \frac{((x))}{x^{s+1}}\,dx = -s\int_0^\infty \frac{((x))}{x^{s+1}}\,dx.$$

Here we replace $((x))$ by its Fourier series (see 3.29), integrate termwise (a
non-trivial justification is called for, because the series is *not* uniformly
convergent; it is mainly because we suppress here this justification that the
present section is entitled "sketch of a proof," rather than "proof") and
obtain, successively:

$$\zeta(s) = -s\int_0^\infty x^{-s-1}\left\{-\frac{1}{\pi}\sum_{n=1}^\infty \frac{\sin(2\pi nx)}{n}\right\}dx$$

$$= \frac{s}{\pi}\sum_{n=1}^\infty \frac{1}{n}\int_0^\infty x^{-s-1}\sin(2\pi nx)\,dx.$$

We make the change of variables $y = 2\pi nx$ and obtain

$$\zeta(s) = \frac{s}{\pi} \sum_{n=1}^{\infty} \frac{(2\pi n)^s}{n} \int_0^{\infty} y^{-s-1} \sin y \, dy$$

$$= \frac{s}{\pi} (2\pi)^s \sum_{n=1}^{\infty} n^{-(1-s)} \int_0^{\infty} y^{-s-1} \sin y \, dy.$$

On account of $\sigma < 0$, the convergence of the infinite series is guaranteed and its value is, by Definition 1, $\zeta(1 - s)$. The integral converges at least for $-1 < \sigma < 0$; remembering (see 3.7) that, for $0 < \operatorname{Re} z < 1$,

$$\int_0^{\infty} y^{z-1} \sin y \, dy = \sin (\pi z/2)\Gamma(z),$$

we have with $s = -z$, for $-1 < \sigma = \operatorname{Re} s < 0$, that

$$\int_0^{\infty} y^{-s-1} \sin y \, dy = -\sin (\pi s/2) \, \Gamma(-s).$$

Hence, $\zeta(s) = (s/\pi) (2\pi)^s \zeta(1 - s)(-\Gamma(-s))\sin (\pi s/2)$. Observing that (see 3.5) $s(-\Gamma(-s)) = (-s) \, \Gamma(-s) = \Gamma(1-s)$, we finally obtain (5). While the formula has been established only for $-1 < \sigma < 0$, it now appears that the right hand side is well defined and analytic for all s with $\sigma < 0$; hence, by 3.23, $\zeta(s)$ is now also defined (by (5)) for all s with $\sigma < 0$. Knowing some of the properties of the Γ-function and of $\sin(\pi s/2)$, we can read off the formula (5) many interesting properties of $\zeta(s)$. So, for instance, it is clear that the factor $2^s \pi^{s-1}\Gamma(1 - s)\zeta(1 - s)$ is analytic and different from zero for $\sigma < 0$. Hence, any zero, or singularity of $\zeta(s)$ for $\sigma < 0$, must come from $\sin(\pi s/2)$. But $\sin(\pi s/2)$ has no singularities and all its zeros s with $\sigma < 0$, are the even, negative integers $-2, -4, \cdots$. It follows that $\zeta(s)$ is analytic for $\sigma < 0$, and that $\zeta(s) = 0$ has the roots $s = -2n(n \in Z^+)$. These roots are usually called the "trivial roots" of the zeta function, in order to distinguish them from some other, harder to come by, roots, located in the strip $0 < \sigma < 1$. Next, we use (5), in order to show how one can compute, for instance, $\zeta(0)$. We have $2^0 \pi^{0-1}\Gamma(1 - 0) = 1/\pi$; hence,

$$\zeta(0) = \lim_{s \to 0} 2^s \pi^{s-1}\Gamma(1 - s)\zeta(1 - s) \sin \frac{\pi s}{2} = \frac{1}{\pi} \lim_{s \to 0} (-s)\zeta(1 - s) \frac{\sin (\pi s/2)}{-s}$$

$$= -\tfrac{1}{2} \cdot \lim_{s \to 0} \frac{\sin (\pi s/2)}{\pi s/2}$$

by Corollary 6.1. Therefore, finally, $\zeta(0) = -\tfrac{1}{2}$.

8. THE ZETA FUNCTION AND ITS DERIVATIVES FOR σ CLOSE TO 1

Theorem 8. *For $\sigma > 1$,*

$$\zeta'(s) = -\sum_{n=1}^{\infty} \frac{\log n}{n^s}, \tag{6}$$

and

$$\frac{\zeta'(s)}{\zeta(s)} = -\sum_{n=1}^{\infty} \frac{\Lambda(n)}{n^s} \tag{7}$$

and, if $\varepsilon > 0$, both series converge uniformly for $\sigma \geq 1 + \varepsilon$.

PROOF. The uniform convergence of both series follows, by observing that $\Lambda(n) \leq \log n < n^{\varepsilon/2}$ for sufficiently large n; hence, the terms of both series are less in absolute value than $n^{-(\sigma - \varepsilon/2)} \leq n^{-(1+\varepsilon/2)}$ and the series converge by Theorem 1. On account of the uniform convergence of (6), this formal derivative of the series defining the zeta-function is actually its derivative for $\sigma > 1$ (see 3.1). Next, observe that $\sum_{d|n} \Lambda(d) = \sum_{p|n} \sum_{p^m|n} \log p = \log n$. Hence,

$$\zeta(s) \sum_{n=1}^{\infty} \frac{\Lambda(n)}{n^s} = \sum_{m=1}^{\infty} \frac{1}{m^s} \sum_{d=1}^{\infty} \frac{\Lambda(d)}{d^s} = \sum_{n=1}^{\infty} \frac{1}{n^s} \sum_{d|n} \Lambda(n) = \sum_{n=1}^{\infty} \frac{\log n}{n^s} = -\zeta'(s)$$

and, because $\zeta(s) \neq 0$, when $\sigma > 1$, we may divide by $\zeta(s)$ and obtain (7).

★ALTERNATIVE PROOF. For $\sigma > 1$, $\zeta(s) \neq 0$; hence, a single valued branch of $\log \zeta(s)$ can be defined, real and positive for $s > 1$ (where $\zeta(s) > 1$). For this branch, $\log \zeta(s) = -\sum_p \log(1 - p^{-s}) = \sum_p \sum_{m \geq 1} p^{-ms}/m$; differentiating,

$$\zeta'(s)/\zeta(s) = -\sum_p \sum_{m \geq 1} p^{-ms} \log p = -\sum_{n=1}^{\infty} \Lambda(n)/n^{-s}.$$

Theorem 9 (Hadamard-de la Vallée-Poussin).

$$\zeta(1 + it) \neq 0.$$

PROOF. For $\sigma > 1$,

$$\log \zeta(s) = -\sum_p \log(1 - p^{-s}) = \sum_p \sum_{m \geq 1} \frac{p^{-ms}}{m}$$

$$= \sum_p \sum_{m \geq 1} \frac{1}{m} e^{-ms \log p} = \sum_{p,m} \frac{1}{m} e^{-m(\sigma + it) \log p}$$

$$= \sum_{p,m} \frac{1}{m} e^{-m\sigma \log p} e^{-mit \log p}$$

$$= \sum_{p,m} \frac{1}{m} e^{-m\sigma \log p} \{\cos(mt \log p) - i \sin(mt \log p)\}.$$

Hence,

$$\log |\zeta(s)| = \text{Re} \log \zeta(s) = \sum_{p,m} \frac{1}{m} e^{-m\sigma \log p} \cos (mt \log p) = \sum_{p,m} \frac{\cos (mt \log p)}{m p^{m\sigma}}.$$

Consider now the positive expression $S = |\zeta^3(\sigma)\zeta^4(\sigma + it)\zeta(\sigma + 2it)|$. Using above result for $\log |\zeta(s)|$, we easily obtain that

$$\log S = 3 \log |\zeta(\sigma)| + 4 \log |\zeta(\sigma + it)| + \log |\zeta(\sigma + 2it)|$$

$$= \sum_{m,p} \frac{1}{m p^{m\sigma}} (3 + 4 \cos (mt \log p) + \cos (2mt \log p)).$$

However, for every angle α, one has that

$$3 + 4 \cos \alpha + \cos 2\alpha = 3 + 4 \cos \alpha + 2 \cos^2 \alpha - 1 = 2(\cos \alpha + 1)^2 \geq 0;$$

hence, as a sum of positive quantities, $\log S \geq 0$ and $S \geq 1$. If we now assume that $\zeta(1 + it) = 0$ for some real t, we shall reach a contradiction. Indeed, considering $\zeta(\sigma + it) = f(\sigma)$ as a function of σ, the assumption reads $f(1) = 0$; hence, if $\sigma = 1$ is a zero of order $n(\geq 1)$, then (see 3.20) $(\sigma - 1)^n$ is a factor of $f(\sigma)$, that is, of $\zeta(\sigma + it)$ and, as $\sigma \to 1^+$, $|\zeta(\sigma + it)| < A(\sigma - 1)^n \leq A(\sigma - 1)$ for some constant A. Next, it follows from Corollary 6.1 that, as $\sigma \to 1^+$, $(\sigma - 1)\zeta(\sigma) \to 1$; hence, $|\zeta(\sigma)| < 2/(\sigma - 1)$. Finally, from Theorem 6 it follows that $|\zeta(1 + 2it)| = C$, some finite constant.

Consequently, $S < (2/(\sigma - 1))^3(A(\sigma - 1))^4 C = 8A^4 C(\sigma - 1)$ and, for $\sigma \to 1^+$, $S \to 0$. But this contradicts the inequality $S \geq 1$, which we just proved; hence, the assumption $\zeta(1 + it) = 0$ is not tenable and Theorem 9 is proven.

Corollary 9.1.   *The principal branch of the function $F(s) = \log \zeta(s)$, defined for real $s > 1$ by $F(s) = -\sum_p \log (1 - p^{-s})$ (see Theorem 2) and well defined for arbitrary complex s with $\sigma > 1$ by Corollary 2.3, may be continued also for $s = 1 + it(t \neq 0)$.*

PROOF.   By Theorem 5, $\zeta(\sigma + it)$ is analytic for $t \neq 0$, $\sigma \geq 1$, and $\zeta(1 + it) \neq 0$ by Theorem 9; hence, the result follows from 3.27.

Theorem 10.   *Let C be an arbitrary constant; then there exists a t_0 which depends only on C such that in the region $\mathscr{R}$ defined by $1 - C/(\log t) \leq \sigma \leq 2$, and $t \geq t_0$, $|\zeta(s)| = O(\log t)$ holds uniformly in σ.*

The exact meaning of this statement is that, given an arbitrary constant C, we can find t_0 and C_1 (both depending only on C) such that, for $1 - C/(\log t) \leq \sigma \leq 2$ and $t \geq t_0$, one has $|\zeta(s)| \leq C_1 \log t$.

REMARK 2. From the boundedness of $\zeta(s)$ on every bounded, closed set not containing $s = 1$, it follows that one may always take $t_0 = 1$, by increasing, if necessary, the constant C_1.

PROOF. In Lemma 1, if $\sigma > 1$, we may let $k \to \infty$; then the last term vanishes and the integral converges. Also, $\lim_{k \to \infty} S(s; m, k) = \sum_{n=m+1}^{\infty} n^{-s} = \zeta(s) - \sum_{n=1}^{m} n^{-s}$, so that

$$\zeta(s) = \sum_{n=1}^{m} n^{-s} - s \int_{m}^{\infty} \frac{x - [x]}{x^{s+1}} \, dx + \frac{m^{1-s}}{s - 1}. \tag{7}$$

This representation remains valid, as long as the integral converges, that is, for $\sigma > 0$. In fact, in $\mathscr{R}$, for, say, $t \geq 2$,

$$|s| \leq 2t, \quad \left| \int_{m}^{\infty} \frac{x - [x]}{x^{s+1}} \, dx \right| < \int_{m}^{\infty} \frac{dx}{x^{\sigma+1}} = \frac{1}{\sigma m^{\sigma}} \quad \text{and} \quad \left| \frac{m^{1-s}}{s - 1} \right| \leq \frac{m^{1-\sigma}}{t}.$$

Finally, in $\mathscr{R}$, $|n^{-s}| = n^{-\sigma} = e^{-\sigma \log n} \leq \exp\{-(1 - C/(\log t)) \log n\}$. So far, m has been an arbitrary integer. Now, if a (large) value of t is given, we select $m = [t]$, so that $m - 1 < t \leq m$. Then, for every $n \leq m$, $|n^{-s}| \leq \exp\{-\log n + C(\log n/\log t)\} \leq n^{-1} e^{C}$ and

$$\left| \sum_{n=1}^{m} n^{-s} \right| \leq \sum_{n=1}^{m} n^{-\sigma} \leq e^{C} \sum_{n=1}^{m} n^{-1} < e^{C} (\log m + 1) \leq e^{C} (\log t + 1).$$

Consequently,

$$|\zeta(s)| \leq \frac{2t}{\sigma m^{\sigma}} + \frac{m^{1-\sigma}}{t} + e^{C} (\log t + 1)$$

$$\leq \frac{2t}{\sigma(t - 1)^{\sigma}} + \frac{1}{t^{\sigma}} \left(\frac{t}{m} \right)^{\sigma - 1} + e^{C} \log t + e^{C}$$

$$\leq \frac{2}{\sigma} \frac{t^{1-\sigma}}{(1 - t^{-1})^{\sigma}} + \frac{3}{2t^{\sigma}} + e^{C} + e^{C} \log t,$$

because $(t/m)^{\sigma-1} \leq 3/2$ for $t \geq 2$, s in $\mathscr{R}$. For $t \geq 2$ and $\sigma \leq 2$, also $1 - t^{-1} \geq \frac{1}{2}$, and $(1 - t^{-1})^{\sigma} \geq \frac{1}{4}$, so that $|\zeta(s)| \leq (8/\sigma)t^{1-\sigma} + (3/2)t^{-\sigma} + e^{C} + e^{C} \log t$. For the given C, we now select t_0 so large that $1 - C/(\log t_0) > \frac{1}{2}$ and $t_0 \geq 2$ both hold. Then, if $1 - C/(\log t) \leq \sigma \leq 2$,

$$\frac{8}{\sigma} t^{1-\sigma} + \frac{3}{2} t^{-\sigma} \leq 16 t^{C/\log t} + \frac{3}{2} t^{-1/2} = 16 e^{C} + \frac{3}{2} t^{-1/2} < 16 e^{C} + 2$$

and

$$|\zeta(s)| \le 2 + 17e^C + e^C \log t = e^C \log t \left(1 + \frac{17 + 2e^{-C}}{\log t}\right).$$

If necessary, we may now increase t_0 once more, to insure that

$$(17 + 2e^{-C})/(\log t_0)^{-1} < 1;$$

then $|\zeta(s)| \le 2e^C \log t$ and the Theorem (actually, slightly more) is proven.

Corollary 10.1. $\zeta(1 + it) = O(\log t)$.

PROOF follows from Theorem 10, because $1 + it \in \mathcal{R}$.

Theorem 11. *In $\mathcal{R}$, $\zeta'(s) = O(\log^2 t)$ holds uniformly.*

PROOF. Differentiating (8), $\zeta'(s) = -\sum_{n=1}^{m} n^{-s} \log n$

$$-\int_m^\infty \frac{x - [x]}{x^{s+1}} dx + s \int_m^\infty \frac{(x - [x]) \log x}{x^{s+1}} dx - \frac{m^{1-s}}{(s-1)^2} - \frac{m^{1-s} \log m}{s-1}.$$

The first sum is estimated as in Theorem 11 and each term only has the extra factor $\log n \le \log m \le \log t$; the same holds for the last term. Next,

$$\left|\int_m^\infty \frac{x - [x]}{x^{s+1}} dx\right| \le \int_m^\infty \frac{dx}{x^{\sigma+1}} = \frac{1}{\sigma m^\sigma} \le \frac{1}{\sigma t^\sigma} \to 0 \qquad \text{for} \quad t \to \infty;$$

also

$$\left|\frac{m^{1-s}}{(s-1)^2}\right| = O(t^{-2} t^{1-\sigma}) = O(t^{-1-\sigma}) \to 0 \qquad \text{for} \quad t \to \infty$$

and only the term $s \int_m^\infty ((x - [x]) \log x) x^{-s-1} dx$ remains to be investigated.

One has

$$\left|\int_m^\infty \frac{(x - [x]) \log x}{x^{s+1}} dx\right| \le \int_m^\infty \frac{\log x}{x^{\sigma+1}} dx = \frac{\log m}{\sigma m^\sigma}\left(\frac{1}{\sigma \log m} + 1\right) < \frac{2 \log m}{\sigma m^\sigma},$$

again as in Theorem 11, except for the extra factor $\log m \le \log t$. Hence, besides terms that decrease to zero as $t \to \infty$, $\zeta'(s)$ contains only summands that essentially occur already in $\zeta(s)$, with at most an additional factor $\log t$; therefore, all terms are at most of order $O(\log^2 t)$ and the Theorem is proven.

Corollary 11.1. $\zeta'(1 + it) = O(\log^2 t)$.

PROOF. Evident.

Theorem 12. $$\frac{\zeta'}{\zeta}(1 + it) = O(\log^9 t).$$

PROOF. In the proof of Theorem 9 we saw that for $\sigma > 1$,

$$|\zeta^3(\sigma)\zeta^4(\sigma + it)\zeta(\sigma + 2it)| \geq 1;$$

hence,

$$|\zeta(\sigma + it)|^{-1} \leq |\zeta(\sigma)|^{3/4}|\zeta(\sigma + 2it)|^{1/4}$$

and, using Corollaries 6.1 and 6.2 and Theorem 10 we see that there exists some constant A such that, as $t \to \infty$ for fixed $\sigma > 1$,

$$\frac{1}{|\zeta(\sigma + it)|} < \frac{A \log^{1/4} t}{(\sigma - 1)^{3/4}} \quad \text{or} \quad |\zeta(\sigma + it)| > A\frac{(\sigma - 1)^{3/4}}{\log^{1/4} t}.$$

Also, integrating along a parallel to the real axis, for $\sigma > 1$,

$$\int_1^\sigma \zeta'(x + it)\, dx = \zeta(\sigma + it) - \zeta(1 + it);$$

hence,

$$\zeta(1 + it) = \zeta(\sigma + it) - \int_1^\sigma \zeta'(x + it)\, dx > A\frac{(\sigma - 1)^{3/4}}{\log^{1/4} t} - \left|\int_1^\sigma \zeta'(x + it)\, dx\right|.$$

By Theorem 11, the last term is less than $B \cdot \log^2 t \int_1^\sigma dx = B(\sigma - 1)\log^2 t$, for some constant B. Hence,

$$\zeta(1 + it) > A(\sigma - 1)^{3/4} \log^{-1/4} t - B(\sigma - 1) \log^2 t = f(\sigma - 1, t).$$

This result is valid for every $\sigma > 1$. We now select $\sigma - 1$ so as to maximize $f(\sigma - 1, t)$. Proceeding as in elementary calculus, it is an easy matter to show that the extremum of $f(\sigma - 1, t)$ is reached for $\sigma = 1 + (3A/4B)^4\log^{-9} t$ and that this is a maximum equal to $(3/B)^3(A/4)^4 \log^{-7} t$. Consequently, setting $(3/B)^3(A/4)^4 = C$,

$$|\zeta(1 + it)| > C \log^{-7} t \qquad\qquad (9)$$

and $|\zeta(1 + it)|^{-1} < (1/C) \log^7 t$. This, together with Corollary 11.1 finally leads to $|\zeta'(1 + it)/\zeta(1 + it)| \leq K \log^9 t$, which finishes the proof.

Corollary 12.1. $\zeta'(\sigma + it)/\zeta(\sigma + it) = O(\log^9 t)$ *holds not only for* $\sigma \geq 1$, *but actually for* $\sigma \geq 1 - C_2 \log^{-9} t$, *with some positive constant* C_2.

PROOF. Let $\sigma + it \in \mathcal{R}, \sigma < 1$; then, using Theorem 11,

$$|\zeta(1 + it) - \zeta(\sigma + it)| = \left|\int_\sigma^1 \zeta'(x + it)\, dx\right| \leq C_1 \log^2 t \cdot (1 - \sigma),$$

with some finite positive constant C_1. Hence, for any σ satisfying

$1 - C_2 \log^{-9} t \leq \sigma \leq 1$ one obtains, using also (9):

$$|\zeta(\sigma + it)| \geq |\zeta(1 + it)| - C_1(1 - \sigma) \log^2 t > C \log^{-7} t$$

$$- C_1 \log^2 t \cdot C_2 \log^{-9} t = (C - C_1 C_2) \log^{-7} t = K \log^{-7} t.$$

If we select $C_2 < C/C_1$, then $K > 0$ and the Corollary is proven.

Corollary 12.2. $\zeta(s) \neq 0$ for $\sigma > 1 - C_2 \log^{-9} t$.

PROOF follows almost trivially from Corollary 12.1.

Corollary 12.3. *The function* $g(s) = \zeta'(s)/\zeta(s) + (s - 1)^{-1}$ *is analytic for* $\sigma \geq 1$.

PROOF. For $\sigma > 1$ this is a consequence of Corollary 2.3 from which follows that $(s - 1)\zeta(s)$ is analytic and different from zero for $\sigma > 1$. Hence, $f(s) = \log (s - 1) + \log \zeta(s)$ has a single valued branch, real for real $s > 1$, which is analytic and has an analytic derivative; this is precisely $g(s)$. For $\sigma = 1$, $s \neq 1$, the same conclusion follows from Theorem 9 and for $s = 1$ from Theorem 9, Theorem 5 and Corollary 6.1 (see Problem 8).

Corollary 12.4. *For* $\sigma \geq 1$, $|\log \zeta(s)| = O(\log^9 t)$.

PROOF For $\sigma \geq 2$, $|\zeta(s)| \leq \zeta(2)$ (why?) Also

$$\text{Re } \zeta(s) \geq 1 - \sum_{n=2}^{\infty} n^{-\sigma} \geq 2 - \zeta(2) > 1/3;$$

hence, if we plot all values of $\zeta(\sigma + it)$ for $\sigma \geq 2$, all image points are in the right half plane and $|\arg \zeta(2 + it)| < \pi/2$. Consequently,

$$|\log \zeta(2 + it)| \leq \pi/2 + \log \zeta(2).$$

Also, for $\sigma > 1 - C_2 \log^9 t$, and using Corollary 12.1,

$$|\log \zeta(\sigma + it) - \log (2 + it)| = \left| \int_{2+it}^{\sigma+it} \frac{\zeta'}{\zeta}(\sigma + it) \, ds \right|$$

$$\leq \int_{\sigma}^{2} \left| \frac{\zeta'}{\zeta}(\sigma + it) \right| d\sigma$$

$$\leq \max_{\sigma \leq \sigma_1 \leq 2} \frac{\zeta'}{\zeta}(\sigma_1 + it) < K \log^9 t;$$

Corollary 12.4 now follows trivially.

9. COMMENTS ON THE ZETA FUNCTION

We have now obtained a certain amount of information concerning the function $\zeta(s)$. Our study may not have seemed to be too systematic; but it had as purpose, at least partly, to establish those properties that we want to use in the proof of the PNT. However, I shall have no quarrel with any reader who prefers, instead, the study of, say, the functional equation, although this has no direct bearing on the proof of the PNT to be presented. I actually want to urge the interested reader to pursure the study of this fascinating ζ-function for its own sake (see, e.g. [21]). Numerous, rich rewards in number theory (e.g. improved error term in the PNT), general theory of integration and differentiation (see, e.g. [12]) and other fields of mathematics are in store for any substantial improvement of our still fragmentary knowledge of the behavior of the zeta function. At this point, it is not possible to remain silent on what is probably the most intriguing unsolved problem in the theory of the zeta function and actually in all of number theory—and most likely even one of the most important unsolved problems in contemporary mathematics, namely the famous Riemann hypothesis. This is one among several unproven conjectures, found implicitly, or explicitly in Riemann's already mentioned memoir from 1859. All but one of these conjectures have since been settled (always in the sense expected by Riemann), through the work of Hadamard (1893 and 1896), de la Vallée-Poussin (1896) and von Mangoldt (1895; also 1905). The last, still unsolved problem has to do with the zeros of the zeta function. We easily could prove: (i) if $\sigma > 1$, then $\zeta(s) \neq 0$; (ii) if $\sigma < 0$, then $\zeta(s) = 0$ only for $s = -2n(n = 1, 2, 3, \cdots)$. But the functional equation—probably our most powerful tool, so far—does not give us much information on what happens for $0 < \sigma < 1$, in the so-called "critical strip". The ease with which we proved that $\zeta(s) \neq 0$ for $\sigma > 1$ (Corollary 2.3) should be contrasted with the rather difficult proof that the inequality $\sigma > 1$ can actually be improved to $\sigma \geq 1$ (Theorem 9). This situation is characteristic of all attempts to penetrate into the critical strip (or even to touch it!) Now, certain general considerations show that the equation $\zeta(s) = 0$ *does* have solutions, even infinitely many solutions, other than the even, negative integers, (which we called "trivial" roots). As we know, these other roots can be found only inside the critical strip. Riemann conjectured (and *this* is the statement known as the Riemann hypothesis) that all these "nontrivial" zeros of the zeta-function are at points $s = \frac{1}{2} + it$, of the complex plane, that is, that they all have the real part equal to $\frac{1}{2}$ so that they are located on the "critical line" $\sigma = \frac{1}{2}$. Some progress has has been made in this direction as follows: Gram [6], Backlund [2], and Hutchinson [8] computed several of the nontrivial zeros and found them all, as Riemann had expected, on the critical line; Hardy [7] proved that there are infinitely many zeros on the critical line; Selberg [16] proved a Theorem, which in nontechnical terms means essentially, that if not all, then at least a sizeable fraction of all nontrivial zeros of the zeta function lie on the critical line; finally, Lehmer [10] and [11] proved that the first few tens of thousands of the nontrivial roots all lie on the critical line. Still, the problem is open and fascinates and teases the best contemporary minds.

PROBLEMS

1. Give a proof that there are infinitely many primes, using the fact that $\pi^2/6$ is not rational.
(*Hint:* By 3.31, $\zeta(2) = \pi^2/6$).

2. Use partial summation to prove that for $\sigma > 1$,

$$-\frac{\zeta'(s)}{\zeta(s)} = s \int_1^\infty \psi(x) x^{-s-1}\, dx.$$

(*Hint:* By Theorem 8 and Definition 6.10 (3),

$$-\frac{\zeta'(s)}{\zeta(s)} = \sum_{n=1}^\infty \frac{\Lambda(n)}{n^s} = \sum_{n=2}^\infty \frac{\psi(n) - \psi(n-1)}{n^s}\Bigg).$$

3. (i) Use partial summation in order to show that, for $\sigma > 1$,

$$\frac{1}{\zeta(s)} = \sum_{n=1}^\infty \frac{\mu(n)}{n^s} = s \int_1^\infty \frac{M(x)}{x^{s+1}}\, dx.$$

(ii) Let A be such that $M(x) = O(x^A)$ for $x \to \infty$; show that the integral converges for $\sigma > A$ and uniformly so for $\sigma \geq A + \varepsilon (\varepsilon > 0,$ arbitrarily small).

(iii) Use parts (i) and (ii) in order to show that $M(x) = 0(x^A) \Rightarrow \zeta(s) \neq 0$ for $\sigma > A$.

4. Prove: For $\sigma \geq 2$, $|\zeta(s)| \leq \zeta(2)$.

5. Prove that

$$I(s) = \int_1^\infty \frac{x - [x]}{x^{s-1}} \frac{x^{s-1} - s}{s - 1}\, dx$$

stays uniformly bounded for $|s - 1| \geq \frac{1}{3}$, $\sigma \geq \varepsilon (>0)$.

(*Hints:* Let $\sigma > 0$; then

$$\left| \frac{x - [x]}{x^{s+1}} \frac{x^{s-1} - s}{s - 1} \right| \le \frac{1}{x^{\sigma+1}} \frac{x^{\sigma-1} + |s|}{|s - 1|}$$

and the integral is less than $|s - 1|^{-1} \int_1^\infty x^{-2} \, dx + |s/(s - 1)| \int_1^\infty x^{-\sigma-1} \, dx$.

Show (you may want to use a geometric argument) that under the stated conditions $|s/(s - 1)|$ attains its maximum for $s = 3/2$ and infer that $|I(s)| \le 2 + 3/\varepsilon$).

*6. Set $\chi(s) = \frac{1}{2}s(s - 1)\pi^{-s/2}\Gamma(s/2)\zeta(s)$.

(i) Show that $\chi(s)$ is analytic for every complex s, in other words, that it has no singular points.

(*Hint:* $\zeta(-2n) = 0$ for $n \in \mathbf{Z}^+$; also, it follows from 3.5 that $\lim_{z \to -n} (z + n)\Gamma(z) = (-1)^n/n!$. Study carefully the cases $s = 0$ and $s = 1$).

(ii) Prove that $\chi(s)$ satisfies the functional equation $\chi(s) = \chi(1 - s)$ (*Hint:* Use Theorem 7).

(iii) Use part (i) in order to find directly $\chi(0)$, $\chi(1)$, and $\chi(2)$; check that $\chi(0) = \chi(1)$. (What is the common value?) as required by part (ii) and find $\chi(-1)$ without further computations.

7. Make a sketch, showing the "critical strip" $0 \le \sigma \le 1$, the "critical line" $\sigma = \frac{1}{2}$, and the zero-free region guaranteed by Corollary 12.2 and Theorem 7.

8. Write out in detail the proof of Corollary 12.3 for $s = 1$.

BIBLIOGRAPHY

1. T. M. Apostol, *Mathematical Analysis*. Reading, Mass.: Addison-Wesley Publishing Co., 1957.

2. R. J. Backlund, "Sur les zéros de la fonction $\zeta(s)$ de Riemann," *Comptes Rendus de l'Acad. Sci.* (Paris), **158**, 1914, pp. 1979–1981.

3. M. B. Barban, *Doklady Akademii Nauk UzSSr*, **8** 1961, pp. 9–11.

4. V. Brun, "Le crible d'Eratosthène et le théorème de Goldbach," *Norske Videnskaps–selskapets Skrifter I*, No. 3. Kristiania (Oslo), 1920.

5. V. Brun, "La série $\frac{1}{5} + \frac{1}{7} + \frac{1}{11} + \frac{1}{13} + \cdots$ est convergente ou finie," *Bull. des Sciences Math.* (2), Vol. **43**, 1919, pp. 100–104, 124–128.

6. J. P. Gram, "Note sur les zéros de la fonction $\zeta(s)$ de Riemann," *Acta Math.*, **27**, 1903, pp. 289–304.

7. G. H. Hardy, "Sur les zéros de la fonction $\zeta(s)$ de Riemann," *Comptes Rendus de l'Acad. des Sci.* (Paris), **158**, 1914, pp. 1012–1014.

8.   J. I. Hutchinson "On the Zeros of the Riemann Zeta Function," *Transactions of the Amer. Math. Soc.*, **27**, 1925, pp. 49–60.

9.   D. Jackson, *Fourier series and Orthogonal Polynomials*, *Carus Monograph*, No. 6. Menasha, Wisc.: G. Banta Publishing Co., 1941.

10.   D. H. Lehmer, "On the roots of the Riemann Zeta Function," *Acta Mathem.*, **95**, 1956, pp. 291–298.

11.   D. H. Lehmer, "Extended Computation of the Riemann Zeta Function," *Mathematika*, **3**, 1956, pp. 102–108.

12.   M. Mikolás "Differentiation and Integration of Complex Order ...," *Acta Mathematica Acad. Sci. Hungar.* **10**, 1959, pp. 77–124.

13.   H. Rademacher, "Beiträge zur Viggo Brunschen Methode in der Zahlentheorie," *Abhandlungen aus dem Math. Seminar der Hamburger Univ.*, **3**, 1924, pp. 12–30.

14.   A. Rényi, "On the representation of even integers as sum of a prime and an almost prime," *Izvestia Akad. Nauk SSSR, Ser. Mat.* **12**, 1948, pp. 57–78; AMS Translation. Series 2, vol. 19 (1962), pp. 299–321.

15.   B. Riemann, *Collected Works of B. Riemann*, edited by H. Weber, 2nd ed. (1892/1902). New York: Dover Publishing, Inc., 1953.

16.   A. Selberg, "On the zeros of the Riemann Zeta Function on the critical line," *Arch. for Math. og Naturv.* **45**, 1942 pp. 101–114.

17.   A. Selberg, "On an elementary method in the Theory of primes," *Norske Vid. Selsk. Forh. Trondhjem*, No. 18, **19**, 1947, pp. 64–67.

18.   A. Selberg, "The general sieve method ... in prime number theory," *Proceedings of the International Congress of Mathematicians*, Cambridge, Mass., **1**, 1950, pp. 286–292.

19.   M. R. Spiegel, *Advanced Calculus*. New York: Schaum Publishing Co., 1963.

20.   E. C. Titchmarsh, *The Theory of Functions*, 2nd ed. Oxford: Clarendon Press, 1939.

21.   E. C. Titchmarsh, *The Theory of the Riemann Zeta Function*. Oxford: Clarendon Press, 1951.

22.   G. Valiron, *Théorie des Fonctions*, 2nd ed. Paris: Masson & Cie, 1948.

23.   Wang Yuan, Several papers on the representation of large integers as sum of a prime and an almost prime, in particular, *Acta Math. Sinica* 6(4), 1956, pp. 565–582; *Acta Math. Sinica* **10**(2), 1960, pp. 168–181; *Sciencia Sinica* **11**(8), 1962, pp. 1033–1054 (this is essentially an English translation of previous paper, plus a most interesting Appendix).

24.   D. V. Widder, *Advanced Calculus*, 2nd ed. Englewood Cliffs, N.J.: Prentice-Hall, Inc., 1961.

CHAPTER 8

The Prime Number Theorem

1. INTRODUCTION

As already mentioned in Section 1.4, a considerable part of the theory of functions of a complex variable owes its existence to the efforts made to prove the PNT. It was a resounding success when, at the end of the 19th century, these efforts were finally successful. Since then, sporadic attempts have been made to prove the PNT by purely arithmetic reasonings; in fact, the long and complicated analytic proofs of the simple†

Theorem 1. $\pi(x) \sim \dfrac{x}{\log x}$,

concerning the density of the set of primes, could not be considered satisfactory. However, shortly after Hadamard [5] and de la Vallée-Poussin [11] showed that (i) $\zeta(1 + it) \neq 0$; and that (ii) $\{\zeta(1 + it) \neq 0\} \Rightarrow \{\pi(x) \sim x/(\log x)\}$, it was proven that also the converse is true, namely, that $\{\pi(x) \sim x/(\log x)\} \Rightarrow \{\zeta(1 + it) \neq 0\}$. This fact, that the PNT implies the non-vanishing of the ζ-function on the line of abscissa $\sigma = 1$ was widely interpreted as meaning that it is futile to try to find an elementary proof of the PNT. Indeed, if $\zeta(1 + it) \neq 0$ were not true, neither would the PNT

† The reader is reminded (see p. 9; also p. 100) that $f(x) \sim g(x)$ means $\lim\limits_{x \to \infty} f(z)/g(x) = 1$.

141

hold; hence (so the reasoning went), one cannot hope to prove the PNT without using at some stage the fact that $\zeta(1 + it) \neq 0$—and this meant using the theory of functions of a complex variable, as applied to Riemann's zeta function.

It was, therefore, a great achievement, when, in 1949, Selberg [9] and Erdös [3] succeeded in proving the PNT by purely "elementary" arguments. Here "elementary" has to be understood in the technical sense of avoiding the use of complex variables, Fourier analysis and similar "non elementary" methods—but it should not be confused with "easy." In fact, the first published proofs were quite difficult. Since then these elementary proofs have been much improved. Several versions have appeared in books (see [6], pp. 359–367, [8], pp. 275–297, and [4], pp. 57–88) in highly polished, and very readable form. On the other hand, lately it has become possible to improve these "elementary" proofs also from another point of view. In their older version, they gave just the asymptotic equality $\pi(x) \sim x/(\log x)$, without any estimate of the so-called error term $E(x) = \pi(x) - x/(\log x)$. At present it is possible to give also estimates for $E(x)$, which approach in accuracy those obtainable by analytic methods (see [1], [2], [7], and [12]). It should be added, however, that these recent versions of "elementary" proofs, become again quite sophisticated and that the sharpest results, at present, are still obtained by analytic methods.

The proof of the PNT that follows has been selected among the numerous available ones, mainly because of its transparency. It seems to me that the basic idea of this proof is so simple that it will be grasped without difficulty by every reader who was able to reach the present chapter. Some details might be tedious—but even if some reader should not succeed to unravel every computation to his own entire satisfaction, he should still have a fairly clear idea of the general scheme of the proof. This scheme is due, presumably, to Titchmarsh, who published a proof based on it in his justly famous book on the Riemann zeta function [10].

2. SKETCH OF THE PROOF

We already saw in Section 7.5 that, for $\sigma > 1$,

$$\frac{\log \zeta(s)}{s} = \int_2^\infty \frac{\pi(x)}{x(x^s - 1)}\, dx. \tag{1}$$

The function $\log \zeta(s)$ is defined as the principal branch (real for real $s > 1$), and is a well defined, single valued analytic function for $\sigma \geq 1$, $s \neq 1$, by

Theorem 7.2 and Corollaries 7.2.3 and 7.9.1 (see also 7.3.27). For later use we recall that $\log \zeta(\sigma - it) = \overline{\log \zeta(\sigma + it)}$ (see 7.3.18).

The integral in (1) looks almost like the Mellin transform (see 7.3.30) $\int_2^\infty \pi(x)x^{-s-1} \, dx$ of $\pi(x)$; actually, we shall see that it is the Mellin transform not of $\pi(x)$, but of the closely related function

$$f(x) = \sum_{m=1}^\infty \frac{1}{m} \pi(x^{1/m}) = \pi(x) + \tfrac{1}{2}\pi(x^{1/2}) + \tfrac{1}{3}\pi(x^{1/3}) + \cdots .$$

Although this is formally an infinite series, it actually reduces to a finite sum, because if $q = [(\log x)/(\log 2)]$, then for $m > q$, $x^{1/m} < 2$ and $\pi(x^{1/m}) = 0$; hence, all but q terms of the series are zero. The difference between $f(x)$ and $\pi(x)$ is comparatively small; indeed,

$$f(x) - \pi(x) = \sum_{m=2}^q \frac{1}{m} \pi(x^{1/m}) \leq \sum_{m=2}^q \frac{1}{m} x^{1/m} \leq (q - 1) \cdot \tfrac{1}{2}x^{1/2}$$

$$< \frac{1}{2 \log 2} x^{1/2} \log x < x^{1/2}\log x.$$

We also note, for later use, that

$$f(x) = 0 \qquad \text{for } x < 2, \tag{2}$$

$$0 \leq f(x) < 2x, \tag{3}$$

$$\pi(x) = f(x) + O(x^{1/2} \log x). \tag{4}$$

Proofs of (2), (3), and (4) are left to the reader.

Once we show that $\int_2^\infty \{\pi(x)/x(x^s - 1)\} \, dx = F(s)$ is the Mellin transform of $f(x)$, i.e., that $F(s) = \int_1^\infty f(x)x^{-s-1} \, dx$, (1) becomes

$$\frac{\log \zeta(s)}{s} = \int_1^\infty f(x)x^{-s-1} \, dx \qquad (\sigma > 1). \tag{1'}$$

By 7.3.30, this equation may be inverted, that is, solved for $f(x)$, by the formula

$$f(x) = \frac{1}{2\pi i} \lim_{T \to \infty} \int_{c-iT}^{c+iT} \frac{x^s}{s} \log \zeta(s) \, ds, \tag{5}$$

with any $c > 1$. (Observe that s in 7.3.30 corresponds to $s + 1$ in (1') and (5)). Assuming that we can evaluate explicitly the integral in (5), our problem is completely solved by (4), with only an additional error term $O(x^{1/2} \log x)$.

One may attempt to compute the integral in (5) as follows: One first may select c to be arbitrarily close to one; then $s \cong 1 + it$ and it seems plausible that the major contribution to the integral comes from values of $t \cong 0$, that is, from $s \cong 1$. This suggests setting $h(s) = (s - 1)\zeta(s)$, so that $\log \zeta(s) = -\log (s - 1) + \log h(s)$, because $\log (s - 1)$ is a comparatively simple function and we know from Theorem 7.2, Corollary 7.2.3, Theorem 7.5, and Theorem 7.9 that $h(s)$ is analytic and different from zero for $\sigma \geq 1$, so that there (the principal branch of) $\log h(s)$ is a well defined single valued analytic function. Substituting this in (5), we obtain

$$f(x) = \frac{-1}{2\pi i} \lim_{T \to \infty} \int_{c-iT}^{c+iT} \frac{x^s}{s} \log (s - 1) \, ds$$

$$+ \frac{1}{2\pi i} \lim_{T \to \infty} \int_{c-iT}^{c+iT} \frac{x^s}{s} \log h(s) \, ds, \qquad (c > 1). \tag{5'}$$

The first integral can be computed explicitly (the operations parallel closely those we shall perform in Section 4) and we find as value of the first summand $x/(\log x) + o(x/(\log x))$; however, the second integral leads to difficulties.

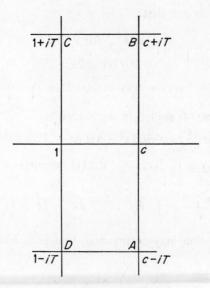

Figure 1

We may start by "moving" the line of integration from $\sigma = c > 1$ to $\sigma = 1$; this is legitimate, because inside the rectangular contour of vertices $1 \pm iT$, $c \pm iT$ the integrand is analytic and tends to zero along the horizontal lines, for $T \to \infty$.

By Cauchy's Theorem (7.3.17), $\int_{AB} + \int_{BC} + \int_{CD} + \int_{DA} = 0$ hence, $\int_{AB} = \int_{AD} + \int_{DC} + \int_{CB}$ and, for $T \to \infty$, $\int_{AD} \to 0$, $\int_{CB} \to 0$ so that $\lim\limits_{T \to \infty} \int_{c-iT}^{c+iT} = \lim\limits_{T \to \infty} \int_{1-iT}^{1+iT}$. Consequently, the second summand in (5′) equals

$$\frac{1}{2\pi i} \lim_{T \to \infty} \int_{-T}^{T} \frac{x^{1+it}}{1+it} \log h(1+it) d(1+it)$$

$$= \frac{x}{2\pi} \lim_{T \to \infty} \int_{-T}^{T} \frac{\log h(1+it)}{1+it} x^{it} dt.$$

We could now easily finish the proof, by using some form of the Riemann-Lebesgue Theorem (see Lemma 1 in Section 3), if we could show, for instance, that $\lim\limits_{T \to \infty} \int_{-T}^{T} |x^{it} (\log h(1+it))/(1+it)| \, dt$ exists and is finite. But actually

$$\log h(1+it) = \log \{it\zeta(1+it)\} = \log t + \log \zeta(1+it),$$

so that the last integral does *not* approach a finite limit for $T \to \infty$. It would be easy to handle the situation, if instead of s, we had s^2 in the denominator in (5′), because this would be sufficient to insure the absolute convergence of the integral. Therefore, we shall return for a moment to (1′) and rewrite it in a slightly modified form, which will give us the desired extra factor s in the denominator.

We define the function $g(x) = \int_{1}^{x} (f(u)/u) \, du$. One observes that $f(x)$ and $g(x)$ (which may be considered as some sort of average of the values of $f(x)$) have many features in common. So, for instance from $f(x) = 0$ for $x < 2$ it follows that also $g(x) = 0$ for $x < 2$. Also, an elementary consideration shows that if (as we hope) $f(x) \sim x/(\log x)$, then also $g(x) \sim x/(\log x)$. It is less immediate, but we shall prove it, that if $f(x)$ is *positive* and *nondecreasing* (as it actually is here) then also the converse holds and $g(x) \sim x/(\log x)$ can hold only if already $f(x) \sim x/(\log x)$. This is called a *Tauberian argument*. Using the definition of $g(x)$ and an integration by parts, the right-hand side of (1′) may be transformed as follows:

$$\int_{1}^{\infty} \frac{f(x)}{x} \cdot x^{-s} \, dx = \int_{1}^{\infty} g'(x) x^{-s} \, dx = g(x) x^{-s} \Big|_{1}^{\infty} + s \int_{1}^{\infty} g(x) x^{-s-1} \, dx.$$

The integrated part vanishes for $\sigma > 1$. Indeed, $g(1) = 0$ as seen; also, by (3), $g(x) \le \int_{1}^{x} (2u/u) \, du < 2x$, so that $\lim\limits_{x \to \infty} |g(x)x^{-s}| \le \lim\limits_{x \to \infty} 2x \cdot x^{-\sigma} = 0$ for

$\sigma > 1$. Hence, (1') may be written equivalently as $\log \zeta(s)/s = s \int_1^\infty g(x)x^{-s-1} \, dx$ or

$$\frac{\log \zeta(s)}{s^2} = \int_1^\infty g(x)x^{-s-1} \, dx \qquad \text{for } \sigma > 1. \tag{1''}$$

Just as we solved (1') for $f(x)$, we may now solve (1'') for $g(x)$ and obtain, by (7.3.30),

$$g(x) = \frac{1}{2\pi i} \lim_{T \to \infty} \int_{c-iT}^{c-iT} \frac{x^s}{s^2} \log \zeta(s) \, ds (c > 1). \tag{6}$$

The integral in (6) may be now evaluated just as outlined above, with the result that $g(x) = x/(\log x) + o(x/(\log x))$. From this we shall infer that also $f(x) \sim x/(\log x)$; finally, by (4) it then will follow that also $\pi(x) \sim x/(\log x)$, which is precisely the statement of the PNT.

3. SOME LEMMAS

Here we shall formulate with precision and prove two statements alluded to before (a version of the Riemann-Lebesgue Theorem and a simple Tauberian theorem); both are weak forms of more general Theorems, but are sufficient for our present purpose. We also prove, for later use, the uniform convergence of two series.

Lemma 1 (Riemann-Lebesgue). *Let $f(t)$ be differentiable on $(0, \infty)$ and be such that*

(i) *for any η_0, T_0 satisfying $0 < \eta_0 < T_0 < \infty$, $\int_{\eta_0}^{T_0} |f'(t)| \, dt$ exists and is finite; and*

(ii) $\lim_{\substack{\eta \to 0 \\ T \to \infty}} \int_\eta^T |f(t)| \, dt$ *exists and is finite.*

Then $G(y) = \lim_{\substack{\eta \to 0 \\ T \to \infty}} \int_\eta^T f(t)e^{ity} \, dt$ *exists for every real y and $G(y) = o(1)$ for $y \to \pm \infty$.*

PROOF. Given $\varepsilon > 0$, arbitrarily small, we determine constants η_0 and T_0 such that, for $0 < \eta_1 \leq \eta_2 \leq \eta_0$ and $T_0 \leq T_1 \leq T_2 < \infty$, one should have

$$\left| \int_{\eta_1}^{\eta_2} f(t)e^{ity} \, dt \right| \leq \int_{\eta_1}^{\eta_2} |f(t)| \, dt < \varepsilon/3$$

and

$$\left| \int_{T_1}^{T_2} f(t)e^{ity} \, dt \right| \leq \int_{T_1}^{T_2} |f(t)| \, dt < \varepsilon/3.$$

This is possible, because, by assumption, $\lim_{\substack{\eta \to 0 \\ T \to \infty}} \int_{\eta}^{T} |f(t)| \, dt$ exists; this proves the existence of $G(y)$.

Once η_0 and T_0 have been determined, we integrate by parts and find that

$$\left| \int_{\eta_0}^{T_0} f(t)e^{ity} \, dt \right| = \left| \frac{1}{iy} e^{ity} f(t) \Big|_{\eta_0}^{T_0} - \frac{1}{iy} \int_{\eta_0}^{T_0} f'(t)e^{ity} \, dt \right|$$

$$\leq \frac{1}{y} \left\{ |f(T_0)| + |f(\eta_0)| + \int_{\eta_0}^{T_0} |f'(t)| \, dt \right\}.$$

The bracket being independent of y, we may select $|y|$ so large that $|y|^{-1}\{ \cdots \} < \varepsilon/3$; hence,

$$|G(y)| = \left| \lim_{\substack{\eta \to 0 \\ T \to \infty}} \int_{\eta}^{T} f(t)e^{ity} \, dt \right|$$

$$\leq \lim_{\eta \to 0} \int_{\eta}^{\eta_0} |f(t)| \, dt + \left| \int_{\eta_0}^{T_0} f(t)e^{ity} \, dt \right| + \lim_{T \to \infty} \int_{T_0}^{T} |f(t)| \, dt < \varepsilon$$

and Lemma 1 is proven.

Lemma 2 (Tauberian). *Let $f(x)$ be positive and non-decreasing and set $g(x) = \int_{1}^{x} (f(u)/u) \, du$; if $g(x) \sim x/(\log x)$, then also $f(x) \sim x/(\log x)$.*

PROOF. Given any $\varepsilon > 0$, set $y = x(1 + \varepsilon)$, By the assumption on $g(x)$, for sufficiently large x,

$$(1 - \varepsilon^2)(x/(\log x)) < g(x) < (1 + \varepsilon^2)(x/(\log x)),$$

with similar inequalities for $g(y)$. Hence,

$$g(y) - g(x) < (1 + \varepsilon^2) \frac{y}{\log y} - (1 - \varepsilon^2) \frac{x}{\log x}$$

$$< \frac{1}{\log x} \{(1 + \varepsilon^2)y - (1 - \varepsilon^2)x\}$$

$$= \frac{x}{\log x} \{(1 + \varepsilon^2)(1 + \varepsilon) - 1 + \varepsilon^2\} = \frac{x}{\log x} \varepsilon(1 + \varepsilon)^2.$$

On the other hand, $f(x)$ does not decrease, so that

$$g(y) - g(x) = \int_x^y \frac{f(u)}{u}\, du \geq f(x) \int_x^y \frac{du}{u} = f(x) \log \frac{y}{x} = f(x) \log (1 + \varepsilon);$$

consequently,

$$f(x) \leq \frac{g(y) - g(x)}{\log (1 + \varepsilon)} \leq \frac{x}{\log x} \frac{\varepsilon(1 + \varepsilon)^2}{\log (1 + \varepsilon)} \leq \frac{x}{\log x} (1 + \varepsilon)^3.$$

In exactly the same way, considering $g(x) - g(z)$ with $z = x(1 - \varepsilon)$ one shows that $f(x) \geq (x/(\log x))(1 - \varepsilon)^3$, for arbitrarily small $\varepsilon > 0$, provided only that x is large enough. Both inequalities together show that $\lim_{x \to \infty} (\log x/x) f(x) = 1$ and the Lemma is proven.

Lemma 3.   *For constant $\sigma \geq 1$ and $2 \leq x < \infty$ the series $\sum_{m=1}^{\infty} \pi(x) x^{-ms-1}$ is uniformly convergent.*

PROOF. In absolute value, the terms of this series are less than $x \cdot x^{-m\sigma-1} = x^{-m\sigma} \leq (2^{-\sigma})^m \leq 2^{-m}$. The series $\sum_{m=1}^{\infty} 2^{-m}$ is convergent and independent of x and the Lemma is proven.

REMARK 1. The proof shows that the convergence of the series is uniform with respect to *both* variables, x and s; only the uniformity with respect to x will be used.

Lemma 4.   *For constant $\sigma \geq 1$ and $1 \leq x < \infty$, the series*

$$\sum_{m=1}^{\infty} m^{-1} \pi(x^{1/m}) x^{-s-1}$$

is uniformly convergent.

PROOF. We have to show that, given $\varepsilon > 0$ arbitrarily small, we can determine $M = M(\varepsilon)$, but independent of x, such that if $M_2 \geq M_1 \geq M$, then $R = |\sum_{M_1 < m \leq M_2} m^{-1} \pi(x^{1/m}) x^{-s-1}|$ satisfies $R < \varepsilon$. We shall show that it is actually sufficient to take $M = max\, (2, 1/\varepsilon)$.

Set $q = [(\log x)/(\log 2)]$; then all terms with $m > q$ vanish. Hence, if $M > q$, then $R = 0$; on the other hand, if $M \leq q$, then

$$R \leq \left| \sum_{M_1 < m \leq q} \frac{1}{m} x^{(1/m)-s-1} \right| \leq \sum_{M_1 < m \leq q} \frac{1}{m} x^{(1/m)-\sigma-1} \leq \sum_{M_1 < m \leq q} \frac{1}{M_1} x^{(1/M_1)-2}$$

$$= \frac{1}{M_1} x^{(1/M_1)-2}(q - M_1) < \frac{q}{M} x^{(1/M)-2} \leq \frac{\log x}{M \log 2} x^{-3/2}$$

$$= \frac{1}{M \log 2} G(x),$$

with $G(x) = x^{-3/2} \log x$, use having been made of the inequalities $\sigma \geq 1$ and $M_1 \geq M \geq 2$.

However, $\max\limits_{1 \leq x < \infty} G(x) = 2/3e$; hence,

$$R \leq \frac{2}{3e \log 2} \frac{1}{M} < \frac{1}{M} \leq \varepsilon,$$

because $2/(3e \log 2) < 1$ and $M \geq 1/\varepsilon$, and the Lemma is proven.

REMARK 2. It follows from this proof that the series converges uniformly in both variables, s and x, within the stated ranges. Only the uniformity of the convergence with respect to x will be needed in what follows.

4. PROOF OF THE PNT

We shall once more go over the complete proof, giving the justifications of those steps, that were skipped over in the sketch of the proof (Section 2). Equation (1) was proven in Section 7.5. In order to obtain (1') we have to present the

PROOF OF $F(s) = \int_1^\infty f(x)x^{-s-1}\,dx = \int_2^\infty \{\pi(x)/x(x^s - 1)\}\,dx$. By its definition, $F(s) = \int_1^\infty \left(\sum_{m=1}^\infty m^{-1}\pi(x^{1/m})x^{-s-1}\right)dx$. By Lemma 4, the series is uniformly convergent; hence (see 7.3.1), termwise integration is legitimate at least for real $s \geq 1$, when all terms are positive, and

$$F(s) = \sum_{m=1}^\infty \int_1^\infty m^{-1}\pi(x^{1/m})x^{-s-1}\,dx.$$

We now set $x^{1/m} = y$ and obtain

$$\int_1^\infty \frac{1}{m}\pi(x^{1/m})x^{-s-1}\,dx = \int_1^\infty \frac{1}{m}\pi(y)y^{-ms-m} \cdot my^{m-1}\,dy$$

$$= \int_1^\infty \pi(y)y^{-ms-1}\,dy,$$

so that $F(s) = \sum_{m=1}^\infty \int_1^\infty \pi(y)y^{-ms-1}\,dy = \sum_{m=1}^\infty \int_2^\infty \pi(x)x^{-ms-1}\,dx$, because the integrands vanish for $y < 2$ and because it is immaterial what symbol we use for the dummy variable of integration. On the other hand,

$$\int_2^\infty \frac{\pi(x)}{x(x^s-1)}\, dx = \int_2^\infty \frac{\pi(x)}{x^{s+1}} \frac{dx}{1-x^{-s}}$$

$$= \int_2^\infty \frac{\pi(x)}{x^{s+1}} \left(\sum_{m=0}^\infty x^{-ms} \right) dx = \int_2^\infty \left(\sum_{m=1}^\infty \pi(x) x^{-ms-1} \right) dx.$$

By Lemma 3, the series is uniformly convergent. Furthermore, for real s, all its terms are positive; hence, we may apply 7.3.1 and integrate termwise. Thus we obtain $\int_2^\infty \{\pi(x)/x(x^s-1)\}\, dx = \sum_{m=1}^\infty \int_2^\infty \pi(x) x^{-ms-1}\, dx = F(s)$, at least for real $s > 1$. We now observe that both sides of this equality are analytic functions of s, at least for $\sigma > 1$ and that they take on the same values at all points $s > 1$ of the real axis. By the principle of analytic continuation (see 7.3.23) it now follows that the equality holds for all $\sigma > 1$ and (1') is completely justified.

Next, in order to avoid the difficulties with non-absolutely convergent integrals, we set $g(x) = \int_1^x (g(u)/u)\, du$ and perform an integration by parts in the right-hand member of (1'), obtaining (1''), as already seen. Equation (1'') may be solved for $g(x)$, by using the inversion formula of (7.3.30) (s in 7.3.30 corresponds to $s + 1$ here) and we obtain (6). In (6) we set $\log \zeta(s) = -\log(s - 1) + \log h(s)$, where $h(s) = (s - 1)\zeta(s)$ is analytic and does not vanish for $\sigma \geq 1$. As already observed, the symbol "$\log$" stands in each case for the principal branch, real for real $s > 1$; this insures that $\log \zeta(s)$ and $-\log(s - 1) + \log h(s)$ have the same imaginary part (namely zero) when $s > 1$; by continuity, this equality persists as long as none of the functions involved vanishes, that is, at least for $\sigma \geq 1$, $s \neq 1$. Thus we obtain

$$g(x) = I_1(x) + I_2(x), \tag{6'}$$

with

$$I_1(x) = -\frac{1}{2\pi i} \lim_{T \to \infty} \int_{c-iT}^{c+iT} \frac{x^s}{s^2} \log(s - 1)\, ds,$$

and

$$I_2(x) = \frac{1}{2\pi i} \lim_{T \to \infty} \int_{c-iT}^{c-iT} \frac{x^s}{s^2} \log h(s)\, ds,$$

valid for any real $c > 1$.

We now show successively that $I_2(x) = o(x/(\log x))$ and that

$$I_1(x) = \frac{x}{\log x} + o\left(\frac{x}{\log x} \right).$$

PROOF THAT $I_2(x) = o(x/(\log x))$. The integrand $x^s s^{-2} \log h(s)$ is analytic for $\sigma \geq 1$; also, for $|t| \to \infty$,

$$\left| \frac{x^s}{s^2} \log h(s) \right| = \left| \frac{x^{\sigma+it}}{(\sigma + it)^2} \log \{(s - 1)\zeta(s)\} \right|$$

$$\leq \frac{x^\sigma}{|t|^2} (\log |t| + |\log \zeta(s)|)$$

$$< \frac{x^\sigma}{|t|^2} \cdot K \log^9 |t|$$

by Corollary 7.12.4. Using Cauchy's Theorem (7.3.17), the integral around the rectangle of vertices $1 \pm iT$, $c \pm iT$ vanishes, and, by 7.3.16, the two integrals along the horizontal segments contribute together less than

$$2(c - 1) \max_{1 \leq \sigma \leq c} \left| \frac{x^{\sigma+iT}}{(\sigma + iT)^2} \log h(\sigma + iT) \right| \leq 2K(c - 1) \frac{x^c}{T^2} \log^9 T,$$

which is arbitrarily small if T is taken sufficiently large; hence,

$$I_2(x) = \frac{1}{2\pi i} \lim_{T \to \infty} \int_{1-iT}^{1+iT} \frac{x^s}{s^2} \log h(s) \, ds$$

$$= \frac{1}{2\pi} \lim_{T \to \infty} \int_{-T}^{T} \frac{x^{1+it}}{(1 + it)^2} \log h(1 + it) \, dt = \frac{x}{2\pi} I_3(\log x),$$

with

$$I_3(y) = \lim_{T \to \infty} \int_{-T}^{T} \frac{\log h(1 + it)}{(1 + it)^2} e^{iyt} \, dt.$$

Integrating by parts,

$$\int_{-T}^{T} \frac{\log h(1 + it)}{(1 + it)^2} e^{iyt} \, dt$$

$$= \frac{e^{iyt}}{iy} \frac{\log h(1 + it)}{(1 + it)^2} \bigg|_{-T}^{T}$$

$$- \frac{1}{iy} \int_{-T}^{T} \frac{\{i(1 + it) \dfrac{h'(1 + it)}{h(1 + it)} - 2i \log h(1 + it)\} e^{ity} \, dt}{(1 + it)^3} .$$

As we already recalled, $|\log h(1 + it)| = O(\log^9 t)$; hence, taking the limit for $T \to \infty$, the integrated term vanishes. Also, by Theorem 7.12,

$$\frac{h'}{h}(s) = \frac{d}{ds} \log h(s) = \frac{1}{s - 1} + \frac{\zeta'}{\zeta}(s) = O(\log^9 t)$$

for $s = 1 + it$ and t sufficiently large, say $t \geq t_0$. However, for $\sigma \geq 1$, $\dfrac{1}{s-1} + \dfrac{\zeta'}{\zeta}(s)$ is analytic (see Corollary 7.12.3) so that $\left| \dfrac{1}{s-1} + \dfrac{\zeta'}{\zeta}(s) \right|$ is actually bounded by some constant if $s = 1 + it$, $|t| \leq t_0$. Consequently, the numerator in the last integral is $O(t \log^9 t)$, the integral satisfies the conditions of Lemma 1 and

$$\lim_{T \to \infty} \int_{-T}^{T} \cdots dt = o(1); \quad \text{hence} \quad \frac{1}{-iy} \lim_{T \to \infty} \int_{-T}^{T} \cdots dt = o\left(\frac{1}{y}\right).$$

It follows that $I_3(y) = o(1/y)$, $I_3(\log x) = o(1/(\log x))$ and $I_2(x) = (x/2\pi)I_3(\log x) = o(x/(\log x))$ as claimed.

EVALUATION OF $I_1(x)$. In a certain sense, this is the crux of the proof and yields the principal term. Once more we would like to move the line of integration from $\sigma = c > 1$ to $\sigma = 1$. But now we have to be careful,

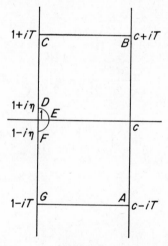

Figure 2

because $\log(s - 1)$ is not analytic at $s = 1$. Hence, we consider the contour $ABCDEFG$, consisting of a rectangle, with a small semicircular indentation (DEF in Fig. 2), around $s = 1$. Inside this contour the integrand $s^{-2}x^s \log(s - 1)$ is analytic; hence, by Cauchy's Theorem (7.3.17) the integral along the contour vanishes:

$$\int_{AB} + \int_{BC} + \int_{CD} + \int_{DEF} + \int_{FG} + \int_{GA} = 0,$$

or

$$\int_{c-iT}^{c+iT} = \int_{c-iT}^{1-iT} + \int_{1-iT}^{1-i\eta} + \int_{FED} + \int_{1+i\eta}^{1+iT} + \int_{1+iT}^{c+iT}.$$

For $T \to \infty$, the integrals $\int_{c-iT}^{1-iT}$ and $\int_{1+iT}^{c+iT}$ along AG and CB, respectively, go to zero as in the evaluation of $I_2(x)$. Therefore,

$$\lim_{T \to \infty} \int_{c-iT}^{c+iT} = \lim_{T \to \infty} \left\{ \int_{1-,T}^{1-i\eta} + \int_{FED} + \int_{1+i\eta}^{1+iT} \right\}. \tag{7}$$

We claim that $J = \left| \int_{FED} \right| \to 0$ for $\eta \to 0$. Indeed,

$$J = \left| \int_{-\pi/2}^{\pi/2} \frac{x^{1+\eta e^{i\theta}}}{(1 + \eta e^{i\theta})^2} \log(\eta e^{i\theta}) \cdot \eta i e^{i\theta} \, d\theta \right|$$

$$\leq \frac{x^{1+\eta}}{(1-\eta)^2} \cdot \eta \int_{-\pi/2}^{\pi/2} |\log(\eta e^{i\theta})| \, d\theta$$

$$< \frac{x^{1+\eta}}{(1-\eta)^2} \eta \int_{-\pi/2}^{\pi/2} \left(\log \frac{1}{\eta} + |\theta| \right) d\theta = \frac{x^{1+\eta}}{(1-\eta)^2} \eta \left(\pi \log \frac{1}{\eta} + \frac{\pi^2}{4} \right),$$

which can be made arbitrarily small, because $\lim_{\eta \to 0} \eta \log(1/\eta) = 0$. Consequently, by (7),

$$\lim_{T \to \infty} \int_{c-iT}^{c+iT} \frac{x^s}{s^2} \log(s-1) \, ds = \lim_{\eta \to 0} \lim_{T \to \infty} \left\{ \int_{1-iT}^{1-i\eta} + \int_{1+i\eta}^{1+iT} \frac{x^s}{s^2} \log(s-1) \, ds \right\}$$

$$= i \lim_{\eta \to 0} \lim_{T \to \infty} \left\{ \int_{-T}^{-\eta} + \int_{\eta}^{T} \frac{x^{1+it}}{(1+it)^2} \log(it) \, dt \right\}$$

and

$$I_1(x) = -\frac{x}{2\pi} I_4(x), \quad \text{with} \quad I_4(x) = \lim_{\eta \to 0} \lim_{T \to \infty} \left\{ \int_{-T}^{-\eta} + \int_{\eta}^{T} \frac{x^{it} \log(it)}{(1+it)^2} \, dt \right\}.$$

The first integral is the complex conjugate of the second. This follows, for instance, on account of 7.3.18, the integrand $(s^{-1} x^s \log(s-1))$ being real for real $s > 1$; or also directly, replacing t by $-t$ in the first integral. Consequently, it is sufficient to compute, say

$$I_5(y) = I_5(y; \eta) = \lim_{T \to \infty} \int_{\eta}^{T} \frac{x^{it} \log(it)}{(1+it)^2} \, dt = \lim_{T \to \infty} \int_{\eta}^{T} \frac{\log(it)}{(1+it)^2} e^{ity} \, dt$$

(where $y = \log x$), then take its complex conjugate and we obtain

$$I_4(x) = I_4(e^y) = \lim_{\eta \to 0} \{I_5(y) + \overline{I_5(y)}\}. \tag{8}$$

It remains to compute $I_5(y)$ and we do it integrating by parts; with $\log i = i\pi/2$, we obtain

$$\int_\eta^T \frac{\log t + i\pi/2}{(1 + it)^2} e^{ity} \, dt$$

$$= \frac{e^{ity}}{iy} \frac{\log t + i\pi/2}{(1 + it)^2} \bigg|_\eta^T - \frac{1}{iy} \int_\eta^T \frac{t^{-1}(1 + it) - 2i(\log t + i\pi/2)}{(1 + it)^3} e^{ity} \, dt$$

$$= -\frac{1}{iy} \left\{ \frac{(\log \eta + i\pi/2)e^{i\eta y}}{(1 + i\eta)^2} + O\left(\frac{\log T}{T^2}\right) \right.$$

$$\left. + \int_\eta^T \frac{e^{ity}}{t(1 + it)^3} \, dt + \int_\eta^T \frac{i + \pi - 2i\log t}{(1 + it)^3} e^{ity} \, dt \right\}.$$

Next,

$$\int_\eta^T \frac{e^{ity}}{t(1 + it)^3} \, dt = \int_\eta^T \frac{e^{ity}}{t} \, dt$$

$$+ 3\int_\eta^T \frac{i - t}{(1 + it)^3} e^{ity} \, dt - i\int_\eta^T \frac{t^2}{(1 + it)^3} e^{ity} \, dt.$$

The second integral can be handled by Lemma 1 and it will be easy to show that its contribution to $I_4(e^y)$ is negligible. However, Lemma 1 is not immediately applicable to the last integral. Therefore, we first transform it by one more integration by parts, obtaining

$$\int_\eta^T \frac{t^2}{(1 + it)^3} e^{ity} \, dt = \frac{t^2}{(1 + it)^3} \frac{e^{ity}}{iy} \bigg|_\eta^T - \frac{1}{iy} \int_\eta^T \frac{2t - it^2}{(1 + it)^4} e^{ity} \, dt$$

$$= O\left(\frac{1}{Ty}\right) + O\left(\frac{\eta^2}{y}\right) - \frac{1}{iy} \int_\eta^T \frac{2t - it^2}{(1 + it)^4} e^{ity} \, dt.$$

Putting these terms together and taking the limit for $T \to \infty$, we obtain

$$I_5(y) = -\frac{1}{iy} \left\{ \frac{\log \eta + \frac{1}{2}\pi i}{(1 + i\eta)^2} e^{i\eta y} + \int_\eta^\infty \frac{e^{ity}}{t} \, dt + 3\int_\eta^\infty \frac{i - t}{(1 + it)^3} e^{ity} \, dt \right.$$

$$\left. + \int_\eta^\infty \frac{i + \pi - 2i\log t}{(1 + it)^3} e^{ity} \, dt + \frac{1}{iy} \int_\eta^\infty \frac{2t - it^2}{(1 + it)^4} e^{ity} \, dt + O\left(\frac{\eta^2}{y}\right) \right\}.$$

When $\eta \to 0$, the term $O(\eta^2/y)$ vanishes and the last three integrals converge, to

$$\int_0^\infty \frac{i-t}{(1+it)^3} e^{ity}\, dt, \quad \int_0^\infty \frac{i+\pi-2i\log t}{(1+it)^3} e^{ity}\, dt \quad \text{and} \quad \int_0^\infty \frac{2t-it^2}{(1+it)^4} e^{ity}\, dt,$$

respectively; all three satisfy the conditions of Lemma 1 so that, for $y \to \infty$, they are all $o(1)$ and contribute to $I_4(e^y)$ terms that are at most $o(1/y)$, $o(1/y)$, and $o(1/y^2)$, respectively.

REMARK 3. Consideration of the second of these integrals should convince the reader that it had been essential to formulate Lemma 1 in the generality in which it was done, in particular, without restricting $f(t)$ to be bounded on $0 \le t < \infty$.

Adding now to $I_5(y)$ its complex conjugate and taking the limit for $\eta \to \infty$, we obtain by (8), successively

$$I_4(e^y) = \frac{1}{y} \lim_{\eta \to 0} \left\{ [i(\log \eta + i\pi/2)e^{i\eta y} - i(\log \eta - i\pi/2)e^{-i\eta y}](1 + O(\eta)) \right.$$

$$\left. - \int_\eta^\infty \frac{e^{ity} - e^{-ity}}{it}\, dt \right\} + o\left(\frac{1}{y}\right)$$

$$= \frac{1}{y} \lim_{\eta \to 0} \left\{ (-2\log \eta \sin \eta y - \pi \cos \eta y)(1 + O(\eta)) \right.$$

$$\left. - 2\int_\eta^\infty \frac{\sin ty}{t}\, dt \right\} + o\left(\frac{1}{y}\right)$$

$$= -\frac{1}{y} \left\{ \pi + 2\int_0^\infty \frac{\sin ty}{ty}\, d(ty) \right\} + o\left(\frac{1}{y}\right).$$

By 7.3.6, the integral equals $\pi/2$, so that

$$I_4(e^y) = -\frac{2\pi}{y} + o\left(\frac{1}{y}\right) \quad \text{or} \quad I_4(x) = -\frac{2\pi}{\log x} + o\left(\frac{1}{\log x}\right),$$

and, consequently,

$$I_1(x) = -\frac{x}{2\pi} I_4(x) = \frac{x}{\log x} + o\left(\frac{x}{\log x}\right).$$

COMPLETION OF THE PROOF. Going back to (6') we see that we have proven $g(x) = x/(\log x) + o(x/(\log x))$. By Lemma 2 we infer that $f(x) \sim x/(\log x)$. Finally, it follows from (4) that $\pi(x) = f(x) + O(x^{1/2} \log x) = x/(\log x) + o(x/(\log x)) + O(x^{1/2} \log x)$; however, $x^{1/2} \log x = o(x/(\log x))$, so that the last error term may be absorbed into the first and we have proven that $\pi(x) = x/(\log x) + o(x/(\log x))$, or what is the same, that $\pi(x) \sim x/(\log x)$, the PNT we had set out to prove.

PROBLEMS

1. Prove formally (2), (3), and (4).

2. Justify (5) and (6) by using 7.3.30, with the change of variable $s_1 = s + 1$.

3. Compute the first summand in (5′) explicitly, show that its value is $x/(\log x) + O(x/(\log^2 x))$. Show that if we know that the second summand in (5′) is $O(x/(\log^2 x))$, it follows, beyond the statement of the PNT, that $\pi(x) = x/(\log x) + O(x/(\log^2 x))$.

   COMMENT. By working a little harder, we could have shown similarly that $I_1(x) = x/(\log x) + O(x/(\log^2 x))$, but there was no point in doing it, because

   (i) we were unable to estimate $I_2(x)$ sharper than $o(x/(\log x))$; and
   (ii) even if we knew that $g(x) = (x/(\log x)) + O(x/(\log^2 x))$, Lemma 2 does not allow us to infer for $f(x)$ anything better than $f(x) = x/(\log x) + o(x/(\log x))$.

4. Prove that $g(x) = \int_1^x (f(u)/u)\, du$ and $f(x) \sim x/(\log x)$ without any further conditions on $f(x)$ imply that $g(x) \sim x/(\log x)$.

5. Prove the following Tauberian theorem: $g(x) = \int_1^x (f(u)/u)\, du \sim x$ and $f(x) > 0$, nondecreasing $\Rightarrow f(x) \sim x$.

6. Justify the inequality $\varepsilon(1 + \varepsilon)^2/\log(1 + \varepsilon) \le (1 + \varepsilon)^3$ used in the proof of Lemma 2. Within what range of ε does the inequality hold?

7. In the proof of Lemma 2, show that for every $\varepsilon > 0$, $((\log x)/x)\, f(x) > (1 - \varepsilon)^3$ if x is sufficiently large.

8. In the evaluation of $I_1(x)$, provide a proof that the integrals along the two horizontal segments are less, in absolute value than any pre-assigned $\varepsilon > 0$, if the ordinate T is sufficiently large.

9. Prove: $\underset{1 \le x \le \infty}{\text{Max}}\; x^{-3/2} \log x = 2/3e$.

10. Justify among all possible values of $\log i$ the selection $\log i = \pi i/2$ used in the computation of $I_5(y)$.

11. Investigate which of the following limits exist.

   (a) $\displaystyle \lim_{T \to \infty} \int_\eta^T \frac{e^{ity}}{t}\, dt$;

(b) $\displaystyle \lim_{\eta \to 0} \lim_{T \to \infty} \int_{\eta}^{T} \frac{e^{ity}}{t} \, dt;$

(c) $\displaystyle \lim_{\eta \to 0} \lim_{T \to \infty} \int_{\eta}^{T} \frac{e^{ity} - e^{-ity}}{t} \, dt;$

(d) $\displaystyle \lim_{\eta \to 0} \lim_{T \to \infty} \int_{\eta}^{T} \frac{e^{ity} + e^{-ity}}{t} \, dt.$

BIBLIOGRAPHY

1. S. A. Amitsur, *Canad. J. Math.*, **13**, 1961, pp. 83–109.
2. E. Bombieri, "Maggiorazione del resto nel 'Primzahlsatz' col metodo di Erdös-Selberg". *Ist. Lombardo Acad. Sci. Lett. Rend. A.*, **96**, 1962, pp. 343–350.
3. P. Erdös, *Proc. Nat. Ac. Sc.*, **35**, 1949, pp. 374–384.
4. I. S. Gál, *Lectures on Number Theory*. Minneapolis: Jones Letter Service, 1961.
5. J. Hadamard, *Bull. Soc. Math. France*, **24**, 1896, pp. 199–220.
6. G. H. Hardy, and E. M. Wright, *An Introduction to the Theory of Numbers*, 3rd ed. The Clarendon Press, Oxford: 1951.
7. W. B. Jurkat, *Abstracts of Short Communications, International Congress of Mathematicians*, Stockholm, 1962, p. 35.
8. T. Nagell, *Introduction to Number Theory*. New York: John Wiley & Sons, Inc., 1951.
9. A. Selberg, "An elementary proof of the prime-number theorem". *Annals of Mathematics*, **50**, 1949, pp. 305–313.
10. E. C. Titchmarsh, *The Theory of the Riemann Zeta Function*. Oxford: The Clarendon Press, 1951.
11. C. de la Vallée-Poussin, *Annales de la Soc. Sciences Bruxelles*, **20**, 1896, pp. 183–256 and pp. 281–297.
12. E. Wirsing, "Elementare Beweise des Primzahlsatzes mit Restglied I and II" *Journal für die reine u. angw. Mathematik*, **211**, 1962, pp. 205–214; **214/215**, 1964, pp. 1–18.

CHAPTER 9

Diophantine Equations and
Fermat's Conjecture

1. INTRODUCTION

In Chapter 4 we considered linear congruences, or, equivalently, linear Diophantine equations and found that the questions one may be interested to ask have, in general, simple, straightforward answers. Therefore, it may come as something of a surprise to the reader, that for non-linear Diophantine equations hardly any general results were known even 40–50 years ago. Actually, even today, we are reduced in most cases to study individual equations, rather than classes of equations and one can hardly consider the results very satisfactory.

As a matter of fact, we do not have a general method by which to decide whether a given Diophantine equation has any solutions, or how many solutions. Partial answers to some of these questions are contained in theorems first proven by mathematicians that are still very active. So, for instance, there exists a set of results due to A. Thue, A. Ostrowski, E. Landau, C. L. Siegel (see [6], pp. 52–60) of which a typical theorem reads as follows: Let $a, b, c, d, n \in \mathbf{Z}$, $ad \neq 0$, $b^2 - 4ac \neq 0$, $n \geq 3$; then $ay^2 + by + c = dx^n$ has only finitely many solutions.

The determination of the number of solutions of the equation $\sum_{j=0}^{r} a_j x_j^{n_j} = b$ over a finite field (this contains as a particular case that of a congruence of the same form mod p—why?) is the object of a beautiful paper by A. Weil (see [22]; weaker results, found earlier, are also quoted in [22]). L. J. Mordell proved many important results concerning the number of integral and rational solutions of Diophantine equations, but a famous conjecture of his (which will not even by quoted, because it involves the concept of genus of an algebraic curve, not defined in this book) has not yet been proven in its full generality. H. Hasse has shown that a certain type of Diophantine equations will have solutions, unless this is "obviously" impossible, either on account of the fact that the two sides of the equation cannot even be congruent modulo some prime, or else on account of some sign condition (e.g. a sum of squares set equal to a negative number). Many other mathematicians have contributed to increase our knowledge of Diophantine equations. An excellent account, at least of the work done before 1938 may be found in T. Skolem's monograph [19]. However, just to illustrate the general situation as it is today, let it be said that such simple looking Diophantine equations like $y^2 - k = x^3$ or $2^y - k = x^2 (k \in \mathbf{Z})$ are the object of current investigations (see Ramanujan [16] p. 327 for a conjecture proven by Skolem, Chowla and Lewis [9] p. 241–244), or Ljunggren [11]).

2. FERMAT'S EQUATION

Of all non-linear Diophantine equations, by far the most famous is Fermat's equation

$$x^n + y^n = z^n. \tag{1}$$

The case $n = 2$ had been completely understood already during the Greek antiquity (our Theorem 1 is due to Diophantus himself, weaker results were known long before—possibly even by Pythagoras), but it was not until some 1400 years later that the next progress was made, by Fermat, Leibniz (1646–1716) and Euler, who gave independent proofs of our Theorem 2 and Corollary 2.1, stating that (1) has no solutions with x, y, $z \in \mathbf{Z}$, $x \cdot y \cdot z \neq 0$, for $n = 4$.

It has often been told, but bears repeating, that on Fermat's copy of Diophantus' work (edited by Bachet), one finds a marginal note (presumably from 1637) to the effect that Fermat had found a "truly marvelous proof" of the statement: "(1) is not solvable in non-vanishing integers x, y, z for any integral $n \geq 3$." He added that the proof was too long for insertion in the free space available on that page of Diophantus. We shall refer to this statement as the *Fermat Conjecture*, or the *FC*.

Since the 17th century, many among the foremost mathematicians have tried, in vain, to reconstruct the proof that Fermat claimed to possess (or to find another one). The likelihood that Fermat really had a proof may be a tantalizing—but hardly profitable—subject for speculation; those interested in it may want to consult Mordell's beautiful booklet [14].

If the exponent $n > 2$ is not a prime, then it is either a power of 2, or else it is divisible by some odd prime p. In the first case, $n = 4k$ and (1) may be written as $(x^k)^4 + (y^k)^4 = (z^k)^4$. As already mentioned, we have a proof going back to Fermat himself, of the fact that the sum of two fourth powers cannot be a fourth power (actually, it cannot be even a perfect square, as we shall see). In the second case, $n = pk$ and (1) becomes $(x^k)^p + (y^k)^p = (z^k)^p$. Hence, in order to prove that (1) is not solvable for arbitrary integral powers n, it is sufficient to prove that it is not solvable when $n = p$, an odd prime.

We can simplify the problem still further, by observing that if x, y, z are integers satisfying (1) and any two of them are divisible by an integer d, then d divides also the third one and, writing $x = dx_1$, $y = dy_1$, $t = dz_1$, (1) shows that also $x_1^n + y_1^n = z_1^n$. Hence, it is sufficient to look only for solutions of (1) in integers x, y, z that are coprime in pairs; such solutions are called *primitive solutions*. Finally, in order to obtain a more symmetric formulation, we observe that if p is an odd prime, $(-z)^p = -z^p$. This leads us to reformulate the problem as follows:

To prove that if p is an odd prime, then

$$x^p + y^p + z^p = 0 \qquad (1')$$

has no solutions in rational integers x, y, z, which are pairwise coprime and with $x \cdot y \cdot z \neq 0$.

It will soon turn out that it is convenient to distinguish between the following two cases

Case I: $p \nmid x \cdot y \cdot z$;

and

Case II: $p \mid x \cdot y \cdot z$.

From $(x, y) = (y, z) = (z, x) = 1$ it follows that in Case II, p divides exactly one of the three integers x, y, or z. It also will appear soon that Case I is the much easier one to deal with—and we can dispose of it almost trivially for small primes.

Not surprisingly, the first case considered successfully was $p = 3$. Incorrect proofs of the insolvability of (1') for $p = 3$ seem to have been proposed already before 1000 A.D. (see [2], Chapter XXI). The first essentially correct (although incomplete) proof for $p = 3$ is due to Euler (1753), while the first complete proof is due to Legendre (after 1800; see [7]). Using ideas similar to those that worked for $p = 3$, Legendre disposed also of the case $p = 5$ (in 1823). This result was obtained also by Dirichlet almost at the same time (see [4]). After that, several other particular cases could be settled, but at the price of increasingly complicated reasonings and it became clear that different methods were called for if the general case was to be settled.

About 1843 Kummer believed to have the proof of the FC in the general case—but Dirichlet, no newcomer to this problem, observed that at one point the argument had a gap, essentially the same one as in Euler's proof for $p = 3$. This can be expressed succintly by stating that in these proofs the uniqueness of factorization of "integers" of a special kind was taken for granted without a proof. A few years later, Cauchy, who also had thought for a moment that he had proved the FC, showed that not only were the alleged proofs incomplete, but that the case $p = 23$ actually furnished a counterexample to the hoped for uniqueness of factorization.

As a result of these failures, Kummer undertook the study of the arithmetic in special (so-called cyclotomic) number fields. He devised a method to re-establish uniqueness of factorization—not quite within the set of "integers" under consideration, but in a larger set, obtained by adjoining to those concrete integers some others, which Kummer called "ideal numbers" and which, in a sense, fill the gaps responsible for the lack of the uniqueness of factorization (see Chapter 3, Section 3). In this way Kummer was able to prove the FC for a large number of primes p—but not for all, not even for infinitely many! Indeed, the machinery needed to deal with the problem increased its complexity and new conditions had to be satisfied. In particular, in order to permit the reasoning to go through, a special condition comes up, which Kummer called "regularity" of the prime (see Chapter 11). While it is not easy to decide directly the regularity of a given prime p, Kummer also discovered a simple criterion of regularity, involving a curious relation between this property and the numerators of certain rational numbers B_n, called Bernoulli numbers. These may be defined in various ways, for instance, by the expansion

$$\cotg z = z^{-1} + \sum_{n=2}^{\infty} (-1)^n (2^n B_n/n!) z^{n-1}.$$

Other necessary conditions for the solvability of (1') were discovered and outstanding contributions to the problem were made, by Wieferich [24], Mirimanoff [12] and [13], Libri [10], Sophie Germain [7], Dickson [3], Vandiver [20], Hecke [5], and many others. In the last few years, high-speed computers were also used and, by a combination of deep theoretical work, ingenuity and high-speed computers, Rosser (see [17]) and the Lehmers (see [8]) showed that the FC holds in Case I at least up to $p = 253{,}747{,}889$, while, as already mentioned, Selfridge, Vandiver, and Nicol proved (see [18]) the FC in Case II (i.e. unconditionally) at least up to $p = 4001$.

In Section 3 we shall easily solve (1) in case $n = 2$. In Section 4 we shall (also easily) dispose of the case $n = 4$. In order to avoid later interruptions, Section 5 will contain a list of definitions, theorems, corollaries, and so on, numbered consecutively and without proofs. These cover essentially material well known to Dirichlet and Kummer before ideals were introduced by the latter. The case $p = 3$ of $(1')$ will be the object of Section 6, and Case I for $p = 5$ is discussed in Section 7. For general p, Case I is treated, as far as this is possible without the theory of ideals, in Section 8. There we shall arrive at a dead end. To overcome the basic difficulties of the situation, Chapter 10 is devoted to an elementary study of the theory of ideals in number fields. Next, the general case is taken up once more in Chapter 11, now with the powerful tool of ideal theory.

3. SOLUTION OF FERMAT'S EQUATION FOR $n = 2$

Clearly, (1) is not solvable in Case I, because if x, y, z are all odd, $x^2 + y^2$ is even, while z^2 is odd, Considering next Case II, $2 \mid x \cdot y \cdot z$, but $(x, y) = (y, z) = (z, x) = 1$, because we are only interested in primitive solutions; this implies that at most one (hence, exactly one) of the three integers x, y, z is even, the other two being odd. Also, if $x = 2m + 1$, $y = 2n + 1$, $z = 2k$, then $x^2 + y^2 \equiv 2 \,(\mathrm{mod}\, 4)$, $z^2 \equiv 0 \,(\mathrm{mod}\, 4)$, which is impossible. Therefore, the even one is either x or y and, without loss of generality, we may assume that $x = 2q$, y and z being odd. This makes $z + y$ and $z - y$ even, say $z + y = 2m$, $z - y = 2n$. Equation (1) may now be written as $x^2 = z^2 - y^2 = (z + y)(z - y)$ or $4q^2 = 2m \cdot 2n$, so that $q^2 = m \cdot n$. The integers $m = \frac{1}{2}(z + y)$ and $n = \frac{1}{2}(z - y)$ are coprime; otherwise if $(m, n) = d > 1$, then $d \mid m + n = z$, $d \mid m - n = y$, contrary to the assumption $(y, z) = 1$. The integers m and n are coprime and their product is a perfect square; hence, each of them is a perfect square (the reader is invited to prove this), $m = a^2$, $n = b^2$. From $(m, n) = 1$ follows of course that also $(a, b) = 1$. We have obtained so far that $z = m + n = a^2 + b^2$, $y = m - n = a^2 - b^2$ and $x^2 = 4q^2 = 4mn = 4a^2b^2$ or $x = 2ab$, with $(a, b) = 1$. From $(a, b) = 1$ it is clear that a and b cannot both be even, but they cannot both be odd either, because a and b odd would force y and z to be even, which is false. Hence, exactly one of a and b is even, the other is odd. We therefore proved: Every primitive solution of (1) with $n = 2$, is necessarily of the form $x = 2ab$, $y = a^2 - b^2$, $z = a^2 + b^2$, with $(a, b) = 1$, $a \cdot b \equiv$

2 (mod 4), except for the possibility of interchanging x and y. Conversely, if x, y, z are of this form, one obviously has $x^2 + y^2 = 4a^2b^2 + (a^2 - b^2)^2 = a^4 + 2a^2a^2 + b^4 = (a^2 + b^2)^2 = z^2$ and (1) holds. This completes the proof of

Theorem 1. *All primitive solutions of equation* (1) *with $n = 2$ are of the form $x = 2ab$, $y = a^2 - b^2$, $z = a^2 + b^2$ or $x = a^2 - b^2$, $y = 2ab$, $z = a^2 + b^2$ with $(a, b) = 1$, $a \cdot b \equiv 2 \,(\text{mod } 4)$.*

While it is true that the FC has neither been proven, nor disproven, it should be observed that $n = 2$ is the only exponent for which solutions are known.

4. PROOF OF THE FC FOR $n = 4$

Fermat proved a statement which is slightly stronger than and implies the truth of the FC for $n = 4$, namely.

Theorem 2. *The Diophantine equation*

$$x^4 + y^4 = z^2 \tag{2}$$

has no solution in integers.

The proof of Fermat is based on the "method of descent," which he invented and used successfully also in other problems. In order to disprove the existence of solutions, we assume the contrary, namely, that a solution exists; next, we show that from a given solution we can construct another one, with a smaller value of some integral parameter, which, however, has to stay positive. This, of course, is a self-contradictory statement, because, starting from a given positive value, in a finite number of descending steps, every integral valued parameter reaches the value zero, or becomes negative. This proves the desired result, namely, that it was false in the first place to assume the existence of a solution.

Before proving Theorem 2, let us observe that it implies

Theorem 2'. *Equation* (1) *has no solutions for $n = 4$.*

PROOF. If $x^4 + y^4 = z^4$, then, setting $z^2 = z_1$, $x^4 + y^4 = z_1^2$, contrary to Theorem 2.

PROOF OF THEOREM 2. As already observed, it is sufficient to find a primitive solution, that is, a solution with x, y, z coprime in pairs; this will be tacitly understood throughout this chapter, without further mention.

Let us then assume that there exists a primitive solution x, y, z of (2).

As in the case $n = 2$, either x or y (but not both) must be even, and z is odd. Let x be even. From Section 3 it follows that if $(x^2)^2 + (y^2)^2 = z^2$ and x is even, then $x^2 = 2ab$, $y^2 = a^2 - b^2$, $z = a^2 + b^2$ with $(a, b) = 1$, $a \cdot b \equiv 2 \pmod 4$. Actually, here it is easy to decide that a is odd and b even, which leads to $y^2 = a^2 - b^2 \equiv 1 \pmod 4$, while a even, b odd would lead to $y^2 \equiv 3 \pmod 4$, which is impossible. Hence, set $b = 2c$, $(a, c) = 1$ so that $x^2 = 4ac$ and, as in Section 3 we conclude that $a = z_1^2$, $c = e^2$, $(z_1, e) = 1$. It follows that $y^2 = a^2 - b^2 = z_1^4 - 4e^4$ or $(2e^2)^2 + y^2 = (z_1^2)^2$, with $2e$, y, z_1 coprime in pairs. This equation is of the same form as (1) with $n = 2$; hence, according to Theorem 1, $2e^2 = 2ml$, $z_1^2 = m^2 + l^2$, $y^2 = m^2 - l^2$, $(m, l) = 1$, $m \cdot l \equiv 2 \pmod 4$. From $e^2 = ml$ and $(m, l) = 1$ follows that $l = x_1^2$, $m = y_1^2$, so that $z_1^2 = l^2 + m^2 = x_1^4 + y_1^4$. Consequently, assuming that a primitive solution x, y, z of (2) exists, we have constructed another primitive solution x_1, y_1, z_1. (Why is x_1, y_1, z_1 a *primitive* solution?) But, clearly, $z > a^2 = z_1^4 \geq z_1$; hence, from any given primitive solution x, y, z, we can construct another one, x_1, y_1, z_1 with $z_1 < z$. After a finite number of steps, $z_1 \leq 0$; yet $z_1^2 = x_1^4 + y_1^4 > 0$, unless $x_1 = y_1 = 0$, which is contrary to, say, $(x_1, y_1) = 1$. This contradiction finishes the proof of Theorem 2.

5. NUMBER FIELDS AND RINGS

This section, just as Section 3 in Chapter 7, lists definitions, theorems, corollaries, and so on, needed in the following sections of this chapter. They are numbered consecutively and no proofs are given. Some of the proofs may be found sketched in Appendix B, but all this material is, of course, classical and may be found in detail in such well-known, easily available texts as the books by Van der Waerden [21], Pollard [15], Landau [6] or Weyl [23]. References to at least one of these texts are given for each statement.

Concerning notations, lower-case latin letters a, b, c, ... will continue to stand for rational integers, for instance, $a \in \mathbf{Z}$; rationals (not necessarily integers) will be denoted by capitals, A, B, C, ..., so that $A \in \mathbf{Q}$, say. Finally, we shall use lower-case Greek letters to denote elements of other number fields, for instance, $\alpha \in \mathbf{K}$. If these are integers, this fact will either be stated explicitly, often, by the symbol $\alpha \in \mathbf{I}$, (see [34]) or be unambiguously clear from the context (e.g. if one speaks about divisibility).

1. A set of real or complex numbers, closed under addition, subtraction, multiplication and division, except division by zero (which is not defined), is called a number *field*. A field in general is defined in the same way, except

that the elements are not required to be numbers and one postulates commutativity and the distributive law, (see [15], p. 22 and [21], p. 37) also
Appendix B, Section 2(a)).

2. The rationals $\mathbf{Q}$ and reals $\mathbf{R}$ form fields; the integers $\mathbf{Z}$ do not form
a field. If $\omega = e^{2\pi i/m} = \cos(2\pi/m) + i\sin(2\pi/m)$, then the set $\mathbf{K} = \mathbf{Q}(\omega) = \{A_0 + A_1\omega + \cdots + A_{m-2}\omega^{m-2} \mid A_j \in \mathbf{Q}, \ 0 \le j \le m - 2\}$ is a field and is
called a *cyclotomic field* (see [15], p. 55 and [6], p. 218–227, also Appendix
B, Section 6).

3. Let $f(x) = a_0 x^m + a_1 x^{m-1} + \cdots + a_m (a_j \in \mathbf{Z})$ be a polynomial irreducible over $\mathbf{Q}$ (that is, $f(x) = g(x)h(x)$ is not possible with non-constant
polynomials $g(x)$ and $h(x)$ with rational coefficients; see [21]) and let θ be
one of its roots, $f(\theta) = 0$. Then θ is said to be an *algebraic number* and $\mathbf{K} = \mathbf{Q}(\theta) = \{\sum_{j=0}^{m-1} A_j \theta^j \mid A_j \in \mathbf{Q}\}$ is a field said to be generated by θ. If m is the
degree of $f(x)$, then $\mathbf{K}$ is said to be of degree m (see [15], p. 37 and [21],
p. 106; also Appendix B, Section 4).

4. The set of rational fractions in an indeterminate x with coefficients in
$\mathbf{Q}$ is a field (but not a number field), usually denoted by $\mathbf{Q}(x)$ (see [21],
p. 94).

5. A set of real or complex numbers, closed under addition, subtraction
and multiplication, is called a *ring* of numbers (see [15], p. 60 and [21],
p. 32; also Appendix B, Section 5). More generally if operations of "addition,"
"subtraction" (that is, the inverse of addition) and "multiplication" are
defined on a set whose elements are not necessarily numbers and if the distributive law holds then we say that the set is a ring.

6. $\mathbf{Z}$ is a ring and so are the sets $\{a + b\sqrt{3} \mid a, b \in \mathbf{Z}\}$ and (less trivially)
$\{\frac{1}{2}(a + b\sqrt{5}) \mid a, b \in \mathbf{Z}, a \equiv b \pmod{2}\}$. The set of polynomials in an
indeterminate x with coefficients in $\mathbf{Q}$ is a ring, usually denoted by $\mathbf{Q}[x]$.
If $f(x) \in \mathbf{Q}[x]$ and if the polynomial $f(x)$ is considered as an element of the
ring, rather than as a function of x, we shall write f instead of $f(x)$ (see
[21], p. 46).

7. The set of polynomials $f(x) = a_0 x^n + a_1 x^{n-1} + \cdots + a_n$, with
$a_j \in \mathbf{Z}(0 \le j \le n)$ forms a ring but not a ring of numbers, denoted by $\mathbf{Z}[x]$.
If $a_0 = 1$, the polynomial is called a *monic* polynomial (see [15], p. 26;
also Appendix B, Section 3(a) and 3(b)).

8. An element of a ring with the property that also its (multiplicative)
inverse is in the ring is called a *unit* of the ring. $+1$ and -1 are the only
units of the ring $\mathbf{Z}$. $1 + \sqrt{2}$ is a unit of the ring $\{a + b\sqrt{2} \mid a, b \in \mathbf{Z}\}$. The
units of the ring $\mathbf{Q}[x]$ of polynomials in x are the constants $\neq 0$ (that is,
the elements ($\neq 0$) of $\mathbf{Q}$) (see [15], p. 71 or [21], p. 59; also Appendix B,
Section 2(b)).

9. If α, β, γ are elements of a ring and $\alpha = \beta \cdot \gamma$ with neither β, nor γ a unit, we say that α *splits* in the ring and that β and γ *divide* α. Elements which do not split are called *irreducible* or *prime* (see [21], p. 59 and [15], p. 25; also Appendix B, Section 3(c)).

10. Let $f, g \in \mathbf{Q}[x]$, neither f nor g being identically zero; denote by $\partial^\circ f$ the degree of f. Then $\exists q, r \in \mathbf{Q}[x]$, $\partial^\circ r < \partial^\circ g \ni f = gq + r$ (see [21], p. 57 and [15], p. 25; also Appendix B, Section 3(c)).

11. Let $f, g, h \in \mathbf{Q}[x]$, $(\partial^\circ g) \cdot (\partial^\circ h) \neq 0$, $f = h \cdot g$; then f is said *to factor* or *to split* over $\mathbf{Q}$, g, and h are said to be factors of f or to divide f. In symbols we write $g \mid f$ and $h \mid f$. If $f \in \mathbf{Q}[x]$ does not split over $\mathbf{Q}$, it is said to be *irreducible* over $\mathbf{Q}$. This terminology is consistent with that of item 9 (see [15], p. 23, or [21], p. 59; also Appendix B, Section 3(c)).

12. Let $f_1, f_2, g, h_1, h_2 \in \mathbf{Q}[x]$; if $f_1 = gh_1, f_2 = gh_2$, then g is said to be a common factor of f_1 and f_2. If the only common factors of f_1 and f_2 are the units of $\mathbf{Q}[x]$ (that is, elements of $\mathbf{Q}$; obviously, these common factors always exist) then f_1 and f_2 are said to be relatively prime or coprime (see [15] p. 24; also Appendix B, Section 3(c)).

13. (Existence of a greatest common divisor in $\mathbf{Q}[x]$).

$$f, g \in \mathbf{Q}[x] \Rightarrow \exists d \in \mathbf{Q}[x] \ni$$

(i) $d \mid f, d \mid g$;

(ii) $c \in \mathbf{Q}[x], c \mid f, c \mid g \Rightarrow c \mid d$;

(iii) $\exists h, k \in \mathbf{Q}[x] \ni hf + kg = d$.

This element is called a *greatest common divisor* of f and g and we write $(f, g) = d$. Clearly, d is unique only up to factors which are units of $\mathbf{Q}[x]$, that is, up to rational numbers (see [21], p. 56 and p. 83; also Appendix B, Section 3(c)).

14. In particular, if $f_1, f_2 \in \mathbf{Q}[x]$, and f_1, f_2 are coprime, then $\exists g_1, g_2 \in \mathbf{Q}[x] \ni f_1 g_1 + f_2 g_2 = 1$ and we write $(f_1, f_2) = 1$ (see [15], p. 25; also Appendix B, Section 3(c)).

15. If θ is a root of the irreducible polynomial equation $f(x) = 0$ and $g(\theta) = 0$, $g \in \mathbf{Q}[x]$, g not identically zero, then $f \mid g$ (see [15], p. 36; also Appendix B, Section 4(a)).

16. Except for units and order, in $\mathbf{Q}[x]$ the factorization into primes is unique (see [15], p. 24–26, or [21], p. 70; also Appendix B, Section 3(c)).

17. If $f(x) = \sum_{j=0}^{n} a_j x^{n-j} \in \mathbf{Z}[x]$, then $c = (a_0, a_1, ..., a_n)$, the greatest common divisor of the coefficients, is called the *content* of f. If $c = 1$, f is said to be *primitive*. It is important to remember that the coefficients of a primitive polynomial are rational integers (see [15], p. 27, or [21], pp. 71–73; also Appendix B, Section 4(b)).

18. If $g \in \mathbf{Q}[x]$, then $g = c \cdot f(x)$, where $0 < c \in \mathbf{Q}$ and $f(x)$ is primitive; this factorization is unique (see [15], p. 28; also Appendix B, Section 4(b)).

19. (Gauss' Lemma). The product of primitive polynomials is primitive (see [15], p. 27, or [21], p. 71; also Appendix B, Section 4(c)).

20. If $f \in \mathbf{Z}[x]$ and splits over $\mathbf{Q}$, then it already splits over $\mathbf{Z}$ (see [15], p. 27 or [21], p. 73; also Appendix B, Section 4(c)).

21. (Eisenstein's criterion of irreducibility). If $f(x) = \sum_{j=0}^{n} a_j x^{n-j} \in \mathbf{Z}[x]$ and if there exists a prime p such that $p \mid a_j$, $0 < j \le n$, $p \nmid a_0$, $p^2 \nmid a_n$, then $f(x)$ is irreducible over $\mathbf{Q}[x]$. (see [15], p. 29 or [21], p. 74; also Appendix B, Section 4(d)).

22. The cyclotomic polynomials $f_p(x) = \dfrac{x^p - 1}{x - 1} = x^{p-1} + x^{p-2} + \cdots$ $+ x + 1$ are irreducible over $\mathbf{Q}$ (see [15], p. 30 or [21], p. 75; also Appendix B, Section 4(e)).

23. The algebraic numbers that are zeros of monic polynomials are called *algebraic integers*. If $\alpha \in \mathbf{Q}(\theta)$ and is an algebraic integer, it is said to be an integer of $\mathbf{Q}(\theta)$ (see [15], p. 58, or [6], p. 32; also Appendix B, Section 5(e)).

24. The algebraic integers of a number field form a ring (see [15], pp. 58–59; also Appendix B, Section 5(f)).

25. Let $f(x) = x^n + A_1 x^{n-1} + \cdots + A_n (A_j \in \mathbf{Q})$, be irreducible over $\mathbf{Q}$. The n roots of $f(x) = 0$ are all distinct and will be denoted by $\theta = \theta^{(1)}$, $\theta^{(2)} \dots, \theta^{(n)}$. The algebraic numbers $\theta^{(j)}$ (not necessarily integers, because $A_j \in \mathbf{Q} \not\Rightarrow A_j \in \mathbf{Z}$) are called the *conjugates* of θ (see [15], p. 36, or [21], p. 97; also Appendix B, Section 5(b)). In general $\theta^{(i)} \notin \mathbf{Q}(\theta)$ for $i \ne 1$.

26. For the A_j in item 25, one has the following equalities.

$$- A_1 = \sum \theta^{(j)}, \; A_2 = \sum_{i \ne j} \theta^{(i)} \theta^{(j)}, \; \dots, \; (-1)^r A_r = \sum_{i_j \ne i_k} \theta^{(i_1)} \theta^{(i_2)} \cdots \theta^{(i_r)}, \; \dots,$$

$$(-1)^n A_n = \theta^{(1)} \theta^{(2)} \cdots \theta^{(n)}.$$

The sums of products in the right-hand members are called the *elementary symmetric functions* of the conjugates. $\sum \theta^{(j)}$ is called the *trace* of θ, often denoted by $S(\theta)$; $\theta^{(1)} \theta^{(2)} \cdots \theta^{(n)}$ is called the *norm* of θ, and is denoted by $N(\theta)$ (see [15], p. 72 or [21], p. 128; also Appendix B, Section 5(f)).

27. A function of n variables is called *symmetric*, if it stays unchanged under all permutations of the variables. A symmetric polynomial in n variables with coefficients in $\mathbf{Q}$ (or in any other field $\mathbf{K}$), can be written as a polynomial in the elementary symmetric functions, that is, in the A_j of item 25, with coefficients in $\mathbf{Q}$ (or in $\mathbf{K}$, respectively). A symmetric polynomial in n variables with coefficients in $\mathbf{Z}$, can be written as a polynomial in the A_j with coefficients in $\mathbf{Z}$ (see [15], p. 32, or [21], pp. 78–81).

28. If $\alpha \in \mathbf{Q}(\theta)$ and $\mathbf{Q}(\theta)$ is of degree n, then $\alpha = A_0 + A_1\theta + \cdots + A_{n-1}\theta^{n-1}$, $A_j \in \mathbf{Q}(0 \leq j \leq n - 1)$ and this representation is unique. If in this polynomial that represents α we replace θ successively by its conjugates, we obtain, by definition, the *field conjugates* of α (see [15], p. 53; also Appendix B, Section 5(a)). One may observe that, in general, not all conjugates of α are in $\mathbf{Q}(\theta)$.

29. If $\alpha \in \mathbf{Q}(\theta)$, then α satisfies an irreducible equation $g(x) = 0$, $g \in \mathbf{Q}[x]$ where the degree m of $g(x)$ is a divisor of n. The set of m conjugate of α according to item 25, each taken n/m times, coincides with the set of field conjugates of α as defined by 28; hence, it is not necessary to specify each time in what sense one considers the conjugates. In particular, if $\alpha = a \in \mathbf{Q}$, then $g(x) = x - a$ and the n conjugates of $\alpha = a$ are all equal to α (see [15], p. 53; also Appendix B, Section 5(b)).

30. If $\alpha_1, \alpha_2, ..., \alpha_m \in \mathbf{Q}(\theta)$ and there exists $A_1, A_2, ..., A_m \in \mathbf{Q}$ with at least one $A_j \neq 0$ and such that $\alpha_1 A_1 + \cdots + \alpha_m A_m = 0$, then the $\alpha_1, \alpha, ..., \alpha_m$ are said to be *linearly dependent over* $\mathbf{Q}$. If any relation $\alpha_1 A_1 + \alpha_2 A_2 + \cdots + \alpha_m A_m = 0$, with $A_1, A_2, ..., A_m \in \mathbf{Q}$ is possible only if $A_1 = A_2 = \cdots = A_m = 0$, then $\alpha_1, \alpha_2, ..., \alpha_m$ are said to be linearly independent over $\mathbf{Q}$. In a field of degree n over $\mathbf{Q}$ there can exist no sets of $n + 1$ or more elements, independent over $\mathbf{Q}$. If $\alpha_1, \alpha_2, ..., \alpha_n$ are n independent elements of $\mathbf{Q}(\theta)$, then every other element α is dependent on them; therefore, there exist $A_1, A_2, ..., A_n \in \mathbf{Q} \ni \alpha = A_1\alpha_1 + A_2\alpha_2 + \cdots + A_n\alpha_n$. This representation is unique. A set $\alpha_1, \alpha_2, ..., \alpha_n$ of n independent elements of $\mathbf{Q}(\theta)$ is called a *basis* for $\mathbf{Q}(\theta)$. As seen under item 27, $1, \theta, \theta^2, ..., \theta^{n-1}$ are a set with the required properties; hence bases always exist (see [15], p. 47; also Appendix B, Section 5(c)).

31. Let $f(x) = x^n + a_1 x^{n-1} + \cdots + a_n$, $a_j \in \mathbf{Z}$, $f(\alpha) = 0$. Then α, as well as the other roots of $f(x) = 0$ are algebraic integers and are said to be *conjugate* to each other. $S(\alpha) = \alpha^{(1)} + \alpha^{(2)} + \cdots + \alpha^{(n)} = -a_1$ and $N(\alpha) = \alpha^{(1)}\alpha^{(2)} \cdots \alpha^{(n)} = (-1)^n a_n$ are rational integers (see [15], p. 72, or [21], p. 128, or [6], p. 80).

32. α is a unit if and only if $N(\alpha) = \pm 1$ (see [15], p. 72 or [6] p. 87; also Appendix B, Section 5(g)).

33. $\alpha, \beta \in \mathbf{Q}(\theta) \Rightarrow S(\alpha + \beta) = S(\alpha) + S(\beta)$, $N(\alpha \cdot \beta) = N(\alpha) \cdot N(\beta)$. If, in particular, $\alpha = a \in \mathbf{Q}$, then it follows from items 28 and 29 that $Na = a^n$ (see [15], p. 72, or [21], p. 129; also Appendix B, Section 5(f)).

34. Let us denote the set of algebraic integers of $\mathbf{Q}(\theta)$ by $\mathbf{I}(\theta)$. If $\alpha, \beta, \gamma, \delta \in \mathbf{I}(\theta)$ and $\alpha = \beta \cdot \gamma$, then β and γ are said to *divide* α; in symbols $\beta \mid \alpha$ and $\gamma \mid \alpha$. If $\delta \mid \alpha$, $\delta \mid \beta$, then δ is said to be a *common factor* of α and β. If α and β have only units as common factors, they are called *relatively prime*, or

coprime. If $\alpha \mid \beta$ and $\beta \mid \alpha$ then $\alpha = \varepsilon\beta$ with ε a unit of $\mathbf{I}(\theta)$ and α and β are said to be *associates* (see [15], p. 82).

35. Let $\alpha, \beta, \gamma \in \mathbf{I}(\theta)$; if $\gamma \mid \alpha - \beta$ we say that α is *congruent to β modulo γ,* in symbols: $\alpha \equiv \beta \pmod{\gamma}$. Congruence mod γ is an equivalence relation, the corresponding equivalence classes are called *residue classes* mod γ (see [15], p. 12 and p. 103).

36. If $\alpha \in \mathbf{I}(\theta)$ but is not a unit of $\mathbf{I}(\theta)$ and $\alpha = \beta \cdot \gamma$, $\beta, \gamma \in \mathbf{I}(\theta) \Rightarrow \beta$ or γ is a unit of $\mathbf{I}(\theta)$, then α is said to be an *irreducible* or a *prime* of $\mathbf{I}(\theta)$. Otherwise, α is said to be *composite* (see [15], p. 71).

37. $\alpha \in \mathbf{I}(\theta)$, $N\alpha = p$, a rational prime $\Rightarrow \alpha = \pi$, a prime of $\mathbf{I}(\theta)$ (see [15], p. 72).

38. In every algebraic number field, one can factorize the integers into products of primes, but in general this factorization is not unique (see [15], pp. 71–78).

39. If the ring of integers $\mathbf{I}(\theta)$ in an algebraic number field $\mathbf{Q}(\theta)$ has the property that the factorization into primes is unique, except for order and units, then $\mathbf{I}(\theta)$ is said to be a *domain of unique factorization* (see [21] pp. 58–62 or [15], p. 98; also Appendix B, Section 7).

40. Let $\mathbf{I}(\theta)$ be a domain of unique factorization. If $\alpha, \beta, \gamma \in \mathbf{I}(\theta)$, $(\alpha, \beta) = 1$ and $\alpha\beta = \gamma^n$, then $\exists\ \phi, \psi \in \mathbf{I}(\theta) \ni \alpha = \phi^n\varepsilon_1$, $\beta = \psi^n\varepsilon_2$ where $\varepsilon_1, \varepsilon_2$ are units of $\mathbf{I}(\theta)$ (see [14], p. 10; see also Appendix B, Section 7 and Problem 1).

41. In a cyclotomic field $\mathbf{Q}(\omega)$, $\omega = e^{2\pi i/p}$ (p = rational prime), the integers are all represented by polynomials $a_0 + a_1\omega + \cdots + a_{p-2}\omega^{p-2}$ with $a_j \in \mathbf{Z}(0 \le j \le p - 2)$ and this representation is unique (see [6], p. 222 and [15], p. 70; also Appendix B, Section 6(b)).

42. Let $\omega_1, \omega_2, \ldots, \omega_{p-1}$ be a set with the property that $\sum_{j=1}^{p-1} a_j\omega_j$ represents all integers of $\mathbf{I}(\omega)$ uniquely as the a_j's run independently through the rational integers; then $\omega_1, \omega_2, \ldots, \omega_n$ is said to be an *integral basis* for $\mathbf{Q}(\omega)$. An integral basis exists for every $\mathbf{K} = \mathbf{Q}(\theta)$ and the number n of its elements equals the degree of $\mathbf{K}$. According to item 41, in the particular case of a cyclotomic field 1, $\omega, \ldots, \omega^{p-1}$ is an integral basis (see [6], p. 222, or [15], p. 70; also Appendix B, Section 5(h)).

6. PROOF OF THE FC FOR $p = 3$

Instead of proving the FC for $p = 3$ in the way we formulated it on p. 160, it turns out that it is actually easier to prove a stronger statement, namely,

Theorem 3. *Let* $\omega = e^{2\pi i/3} = \frac{1}{2}(-1 + i\sqrt{3})$ *and consider the field*

$\mathbf{K} = \mathbf{Q}(\omega) = \{A + B\omega \mid A, B \in \mathbf{Q}\}$, with the ring of integers $\mathbf{I} = \mathbf{I}(\omega) = \{a + b\omega \mid a, b \in \mathbf{Z}\}$. Then the equation

$$\xi^3 + \eta^3 + \zeta^3 = 0 \tag{3}$$

has no solution in integers $\xi, \eta, \zeta \in \mathbf{I}$, *with* $\xi \cdot \eta \cdot \zeta \neq 0$.

REMARK 1. $\mathbf{K}$ is a cyclotomic field because $\omega = e^{2\pi i/3}$, so that $\omega^3 = e^{2\pi i} = 1$. It is a field of degree 2. Indeed, ω satisfies the equation $x^3 - 1 = (x - 1)(x^2 + x + 1) = 0$; but $\omega \neq 1$, so that ω is one of the roots of the quadratic equation $\omega^2 + \omega + 1 = 0$, the other root being its complex conjugate $\bar{\omega} = \frac{1}{2}(-1 - i\sqrt{3})$. One also observes that $\omega^2 = \bar{\omega} = -(1 + \omega)$.

REMARK 2. The definition of $\mathbf{I}(\omega)$ in Theorem 3 is consistent with 5.41. The norm of $\alpha = a + b\omega$ is $N\alpha = (a + b\omega)(a + b\bar{\omega}) = a^2 + ab(\omega + \bar{\omega}) + b^2\omega\bar{\omega} = a^2 - ab + b^2$, where use has been made of $\omega + \bar{\omega} = \omega + \omega^2 = -1$ and of $\omega\bar{\omega} = \omega \cdot \omega^2 = \omega^3 = 1$.

It now follows from 5.32 that the units of $\mathbf{K}$ are the integers $\alpha = a + b\omega$ with $N\alpha = a^2 - ab + b^2 = \pm 1$. From $a^2 - ab + b^2 = (a - \frac{1}{2}b)^2 + \frac{3}{4}b^2 \geq \frac{3}{4}b^2$ follows that $|N\alpha| = 1 \Rightarrow N\alpha = 1 \Rightarrow \frac{3}{4}b^2 \leq 1$ or that $b = -1$, 0, or $+1$. Substituting these values and solving for a, one obtains

Lemma 1. *There are exactly six units in* $\mathbf{K}$, *namely,* ± 1, $\pm\omega$, *and* $\pm\omega^2$.

REMARK 3. All rational integers are also integers of $\mathbf{K}$ (because they are of the form $a + b\omega$ with $0 = b \in \mathbf{Z}$).

On account of Remark 3, Theorem 3, implies the

Corollary 3.1. *If* $p = 3$ *equation* (1') *has no solution in rational integers* x, y, z, *with* $x \cdot y \cdot z \neq 0$.

Before actually proving Theorem 3, it may be worthwhile to show that (1') has no solutions for $p = 3$ in Case I. Indeed, if $x \cdot y \cdot z \not\equiv 0 \pmod 3$, then x^3, y^3, and z^3 are all congruent to either $+1$ or to $-1 \pmod 9$. Hence, their sum is congruent to -3, -1, $+1$, or $+3 \pmod 9$, which is impossible if $x^3 + y^3 + z^3 = 0$. We have proven

Theorem 3'. *The FC holds for* $p = 3$ *in Case 1.*

In the proof of Theorem 3, we shall need a few Lemmas.

Lemma 2'. $\lambda = 1 - \omega$ *is a prime in* $\mathbf{K}$.

PROOF. By 5.31, $N\lambda = (1 - \omega)(1 - \bar{\omega}) = (1 - \omega)(1 - \omega^2) = 1 - (\omega + \omega^2) + \omega^3 = 3$; hence, λ is a prime by 5.37.

Lemma 3'. *There exist exactly three residue classes* mod λ *and* $-1, 0, +1$ *form a complete set of residues.*

PROOF. The fact that $-1, 0, +1$ are incongruent follows by verifying that λ does not divide any of their differences. Clearly, $\lambda \nmid \pm 1$, because λ is not a unit; also, $\lambda \nmid \pm 2$ because

$$\frac{2}{\lambda} = \frac{2}{1 - \omega}\frac{1 - \bar{\omega}}{1 - \bar{\omega}} = \tfrac{1}{3}(2 - 2\omega^2) = \tfrac{1}{3}(2 + 2 + 2\omega) = 1 + \tfrac{1}{3}(1 + 2\omega) \notin \mathbf{I}.$$

The fact that $-1, 0, +1$ actually forms a complete set of residues follows trivially from a general theorem that identifies the number of residue classes with the absolute value of the norm (here $N\lambda = 3$); not having further use here for this general theorem, we shall not prove it and proceed directly to verify Lemma 3′: If $\alpha \in \mathbf{I}$, then $\alpha = a + b\omega = a + b(1 - \lambda) \equiv a + b$ (mod λ). From $\lambda\bar{\lambda} = 3$ follows $\lambda \mid 3$; hence, if $\beta \equiv \gamma$ (mod 3), *a fortiori*, $\beta \equiv \gamma$ (mod λ). But $a + b$ may have only the three least residues $-1, 0,$ $+1$ (mod 3); consequently the same holds for α (mod λ), and, as these residues are incongruent (mod λ), they form a complete set of residues; the Lemma is proven.

Lemma 4′. $\alpha \in \mathbf{I}, \lambda \nmid \alpha \Rightarrow \alpha^3 \equiv \pm 1$ (mod λ^4).

PROOF. By Lemma 3′, $\lambda \nmid \alpha \Rightarrow \alpha \equiv \pm 1$ (mod λ). For concreteness, let $\alpha \equiv 1$ (mod λ), that is, $\alpha \equiv \beta\lambda + 1$. Then

$$
\begin{aligned}
\alpha^3 - 1 &= (\alpha - 1)(\alpha^2 + \alpha + 1) = (\alpha - 1)(\alpha - \omega)(\alpha - \omega^2) \\
&= \beta\lambda(\beta\lambda + 1 - \omega)(\beta\lambda + 1 - \omega^2) \\
&= \beta\lambda(\beta\lambda + \lambda)(\beta\lambda + (1 - \omega)(1 + \omega)) = \beta\lambda^2(\beta + 1)(\beta\lambda + \lambda(1 + \omega)) \\
&= \beta\lambda^3(\beta + 1)(\beta + 1 + \omega) = \beta\lambda^3(\beta + 1)(\beta + 2 - \lambda) \\
&= \lambda^3\beta(\beta + 1)(\beta - 1 + (3 - \lambda)).
\end{aligned}
$$

But $\lambda\bar{\lambda} = 3$ so that $\lambda \mid 3 - \lambda$ and $\beta - 1 + (3 - \lambda) \equiv \beta - 1$ (mod λ); hence, using Lemma 3′, the three factors $(\beta + 1)$, β, $(\beta - 1)$ being incongruent mod λ, are congruent in some order to $-1, 0,$ and $+1$; therefore, $\lambda \mid (\beta - 1)\beta(\beta + 1)$ and $\alpha^3 - 1 = \lambda^4\gamma$, $\gamma \in \mathbf{I}$, so that $\alpha^3 \equiv 1$ (mod λ^4). The proof that $\alpha \equiv -1$ (mod λ) $\Rightarrow \alpha^3 \equiv -1$ (mod λ^4) is similar.

Lemma 5. *Factorization in* **I** *is unique.*

This is the key to the success of the present proof of Theorem 3.

PROOF OF LEMMA 5. Let us assume that any two integers α, $\beta \in \mathbf{I}$ have a greatest common divisor δ (possibly a unit) in **I**, with the properties stated in Definitions 3 and 3′ of Chapter 3; then the proof of unique factorization in **I** is an exact repetition of the corresponding one in **Z** as presented in Chapter 3. For completeness, let us review the principal steps: If $\pi \in \mathbf{I}$ is a prime and $\pi \nmid \alpha(\in \mathbf{I})$, then $(\pi, \alpha) = \varepsilon$, a unit, and, by one of the properties of the g.c.d., $\exists \mu, \nu \in \mathbf{I} \ni \varepsilon = \mu\pi + \nu\alpha$, whence, for every $\beta \in \mathbf{I}$, $\varepsilon\beta = \mu\pi\beta + \nu\alpha\beta$. Assume now that $\pi \mid \alpha\beta$; then $\pi \mid \pi(\mu\beta) + \alpha\beta \cdot \nu = \varepsilon\beta$ and $\pi \mid \beta$ because ε is a unit. One now proves by induction on the number of factors that $\pi \mid \alpha_1\alpha_2 \cdots \alpha_r \Rightarrow \exists j(1 \le j \le r) \ni \pi \mid \alpha_j$. Finally, assuming that some integer has at least two essentially distinct factorization $\alpha = \varepsilon\pi_1 \cdots \pi_r = \varepsilon'\pi_1', \cdots \pi_s'(\varepsilon, \varepsilon'$ units), one makes a "descent" on the number of factors and, as this can always be reduced by one, yet can never reach zero, the ensuing contradiction proves the uniqueness of factorization. It, therefore, only remains to verify our assumption concerning the existence of a greatest common divisor. We shall do this by first proving

Lemma 6 (Euclidean algorithm in $\mathbf{I}$).

$$\alpha, \beta \in \mathbf{I} \Rightarrow \exists \gamma, \rho \in \mathbf{I} \ni \alpha = \beta\gamma + \rho, N\rho < N\beta.$$

PROOF.

$$\frac{\alpha}{\beta} = \frac{a_1 + a_2\omega}{b_1 + b_2\omega} = \frac{(a_1 + a_2\omega)(b_1 + b_2\overline{\omega})}{(b_1 + b_2\omega)(b_1 + b_2\overline{\omega})}$$

$$= \frac{a_1b_1 - a_1b_2 + a_2b_2 + \omega(a_2b_1 - a_1b_2)}{b_1^2 - b_1b_2 + b_2^2}$$

$$= C + D\omega, C, D \in Q, \qquad \text{because } a_1, a_2, b_1, b_2 \in \mathbf{Z}.$$

Let now c and d be rational integers closest to C and D, respectively, so that $C - c = F$, $D - d = G$, with

$$|F| \le \tfrac{1}{2}, \qquad |G| \le \tfrac{1}{2}. \tag{4}$$

Then $C + D\omega = c + d\omega + F + G\omega$. Clearly, $\gamma = c + d\omega \in \mathbf{I}$ and $F + G\omega \in \mathbf{K}$. Hence, $\alpha = \beta\gamma + \rho$, $\rho = \alpha - \beta\gamma$ is an integer and $\rho = \beta(F + G\omega)$. By 5.33, $N\rho = N\beta \cdot N(F + G\omega)$ and, by Remark 2 (equally valid, mutatis mutandis, for elements of $\mathbf{K}$ as for elements of $\mathbf{I}$), $0 \le N(F + G\omega) = F^2 - FG + G^2 \le F^2 + |FG| + G^2$. Hence, using (4), $0 \le N(F + G\omega) \le \tfrac{3}{4} < 1$ and $N\rho \le \tfrac{3}{4}N\beta < N\beta$; the Lemma is proven.

REMARK 4. All norms in $\mathbf{K}$ being non-negative, it is not necessary to consider the absolute values of these norms. Using Lemma 6 it is easy to prove.

Lemma 7. *Any two integers* $\alpha, \beta \in \mathbf{I}$ *have a greatest common divisor* $\delta = (\alpha, \beta)$, *unique up to multiplication by units.*

PROOF. By successive applications of Lemma 6 we determine a sequence of integers $\gamma_1, \gamma_2, \ldots, \gamma_k$ and $\rho_1, \rho_2, \ldots, \rho_k$ as follows:

$$\alpha = \beta\gamma_1 + \rho_1, \qquad\qquad N\beta > N\rho_1;$$

$$\beta = \rho_1\gamma_2 + \rho_2, \qquad\qquad N\rho_1 > N\rho_2;$$

$$\cdots\cdots\cdots\cdots\cdots\cdots\cdots\cdots\qquad\qquad \cdots\cdots\cdots\cdots\cdots\cdots$$

$$\rho_{j-1} = \rho_j\gamma_{j+1} + \rho_{j+1}, \qquad N\rho_j > N\rho_{j+1};$$

$$\cdots\cdots\cdots\cdots\cdots\cdots\cdots\cdots\qquad\qquad \cdots\cdots\cdots\cdots\cdots\cdots$$

$$\rho_{k-1} = \rho_k\gamma_{k+1} + \rho_{k+1}, \qquad N\rho_k > N\rho_{k+1}.$$

Setting $\alpha = \rho_{-1}$, $\beta = \rho_0$ this system may be written simply as $\rho_{j-1} = \rho_j\gamma_{j+1} + \rho_{j+1}$, $N\rho_j > N\rho_{j+1}(0 \le j \le k)$. After a finite number k of steps (it is easy to see that $k \le N\beta$), $N\rho_{k+1} \le 0$; in view of Remark 4, one actually has $N\rho_{k+1} = 0$ which implies $\rho_{k+1} = 0$. Hence $\rho_k \mid \rho_{k-1}$; also $\rho_k \mid \rho_k$. In general, if $\rho_k \mid \rho_j$ and $\rho_k \mid \rho_{j+1}$, it follows from $\rho_{j-1} = \rho_j\gamma_{j+1} + \rho_{j+1}$ that $\rho_k \mid \rho_{j-1}$; hence, by finite induction on j, $\rho_k \mid \rho_1, \rho_k \mid \rho_0 \Rightarrow \rho_k \mid \rho_{-1}$, that is, $\rho_k \mid \beta$ and $\rho_k \mid \alpha$ so that ρ_k is a common divisor of α and β.

Also, starting from $\rho_k = \rho_{k-2} - \gamma_k\rho_{k-1}$ and replacing each ρ_{j+1} by $\rho_{j-1} - \rho_j\gamma_{j+1}$, one obtains $\rho_k = \phi_j\rho_j + \phi_{j-1}\rho_{j-1}$ for every $0 \le j \le k$. In particular, for $j = 0$ one obtains $\rho_k = \mu\alpha + \nu\beta$ (where $\phi_{-1} = \mu$, $\phi_0 = \nu$ are integers in $\mathbf{I}$).

Let now $\gamma \mid \alpha$, $\gamma \mid \beta$; then $\gamma \mid \mu\alpha + \nu\beta = \rho_k$. This justifies calling ρ_k a greatest common divisor of α and β. Let δ be another greatest common divisor; then $\delta \mid \rho_k$ and $\rho_k \mid \delta$; hence, δ and ρ_k are associates, $\delta = \varepsilon\rho_k$ with ε one of the six units of $\mathbf{I}$. Lemma 7 is completely proven.

As already seen, the existence of $\delta = (\alpha, \beta)$ with the property that $\delta = \mu\alpha + \nu\beta$ implies the uniqueness of factorization and this finishes also the proof of Lemma 5.

We are now in a position to prove the following version of the fact that (3) has no solution in Case I, namely

Theorem 3″.   *Equation* (3) *has no solutions with* $\xi, \eta, \zeta \in \mathbf{I}$, *and* $\lambda \nmid \xi \cdot \eta \cdot \zeta$.

PROOF. It is sufficient to show that (3) has no primitive solutions of the stated kind. By Lemma 4, $\sigma = \xi^3 + \eta^3 + \zeta^3 \equiv \pm 1 \pm 1 \pm 1 \pmod{\lambda^4}$. If all signs are the same, $\sigma \equiv \pm 3 \pmod{\lambda^4}$, otherwise $\sigma \equiv \pm 1 \pmod{\lambda^4}$. If (3) holds, then $\sigma = 0$ so that either $\lambda^4 \mid 3$, or $\lambda^4 \mid 1$. The last alternative is obviously impossible, on account of 5.32, because λ is no unit. Also, $\lambda = 1 - \omega$, $\lambda^2 = 1 - 2\omega + \omega^2 = 1 + \omega + \omega^2 - 3\omega = -3\omega$, $\lambda^4 = 9\omega^2$ so that (remembering that ω^2 is a unit) λ^4 is associated with 9 and $\lambda^4 \mid 3 \Leftrightarrow 9 \mid 3$, which is clearly false; Theorem 3″ is proven.

We conclude, just as previously for $n = 2$, that it is sufficient to consider only Case II, which, for (3) means that $\lambda \mid \xi\eta\zeta$. Remembering also that we are looking only for a primitive solution, it follows that λ divides exactly one among the three integers ξ, η, ζ of **I**. By the symmetry of (3) it is immaterial which one we assume to be divisible by λ; therefore, we are free to let $\lambda \mid \xi$, which will permit us to keep up the analogy with case $n = 2$. If k is the highest power of λ which divides ξ, we may set $\xi = \lambda^k\alpha$, $(\alpha, \lambda) = 1$, and (3) becomes $\lambda^{3k}\alpha^3 + \eta^3 + \zeta^3 = 0$. Once more it turns out that it is easier to prove a slightly more general result (which, however, is in some sense a more natural one, as the experienced reader will presumably agree), namely

Theorem 4.   *The equation*

$$\varepsilon\lambda^{3k}\alpha^3 + \eta^3 + \zeta^3 = 0 \tag{5}$$

has no solutions with $\alpha, \eta, \zeta \in \mathbf{I}$, $\lambda \nmid \alpha \cdot \eta \cdot \zeta$, $1 \le k \in \mathbf{Z}$ *and* ε *a unit in* **I**.

A primitive solution of (5) (and this is, of course, the only kind we are interested in) which satisfies also the other conditions of Theorem 4 will be called simply an *admissible* solution. It is clear that Theorem 4 contains in particular Theorem 3 in Case II; hence, in view of Theorem 3″, the proof of Theorem 4 will complete also the proof of Theorem 3.

PROOF OF THEOREM 4. This proof gives us another opportunity to use Fermat's method of descent; this time, the descent will operate on the exponent k. More precisely, we shall show

(i) for every admissible solution of (5), $k \ge 2$; and

(ii) from every admissible solution of (5) with a $k = k_0 \ge 2$, we can construct another admissible solution with $k = k_0 - 1$. These two assertions are, of course, contradictory, because, starting with any integer k_0 after a finite number of steps, all possible by (ii), we end up with an admissible solution with $k \le 1$, and this is impossible by (i).

The assertion (i) is almost obvious; indeed, from $\lambda \nmid \eta \cdot \zeta$ and Lemma 4 it follows that $\varepsilon\lambda^{3k}\alpha^3 \equiv -\eta^3 - \zeta^3 \equiv \left\{ {-2 \atop 0 \atop +2} \right. \pmod{\lambda^4}$. The alternatives ± 2 are impossible even mod λ, because $\varepsilon\lambda^{3k}\alpha \equiv 0 \pmod{\lambda}$ and $\lambda \nmid 2$. Next, $\lambda \nmid \alpha^3$, so that $\varepsilon\lambda^{3k}\alpha^3 \equiv 0 \pmod{\lambda^4} \Rightarrow \lambda^4 \mid \lambda^{3k} \Rightarrow k \ge 4/3 \Rightarrow k \ge 2$, as claimed.

The hardest part is the proof of (ii). We may try to follow the successful pattern of the procedure for $n = 2$ and, assuming that there exists an admissible solution with $k \ge 2$, we write (5) in the form $-\varepsilon\lambda^{3k}\alpha^3 = \eta^3 + \zeta^3 = (\eta + \zeta)(\eta + \omega\zeta)(\eta + \omega^2\zeta)$. We have $\lambda = 1 - \omega$, so that $\omega \equiv 1 \pmod{\lambda}$

and also $\omega^2 \equiv 1 \pmod{\lambda}$. It follows that $\eta + \zeta \equiv \eta + \omega\zeta \equiv \eta + \omega^2\zeta \pmod{\lambda}$ and either all, or none of these three integers of **I** are divisible by λ; but their product is $-\varepsilon\lambda^{3k}\alpha^3$ $(k \geq 2)$, so that all three are divisible by λ. Therefore, $\phi = (\eta + \zeta)/\lambda$, $\psi = (\eta + \omega\zeta)/\lambda$, $\chi = (\eta + \omega^2\zeta)/\lambda$ are all integers in **I**. We claim that (ϕ, ψ), (ψ, χ) and (χ, ϕ) are all units. (The reader may reflect upon the fact that this statement and its proof rely heavily upon Lemma 7—or equivalently, Lemma 5. Otherwise even the symbols (ϕ, ψ), (χ, ϕ) and (χ, ψ) need not be well defined, or stand for elements of **I**). Indeed, assume, for instance, that $(\chi, \phi) = \delta$, δ not a unit. Then $\delta \mid \phi - \chi$; but $\phi - \chi = \zeta(1 - \omega^2)/\lambda = \zeta(1 + \omega) = -\omega^2\zeta$, so that $\delta \mid \zeta$. Also, $\delta \mid \omega^2\phi - \chi$ and $\omega^2\phi - \chi = \eta(\omega^2 - 1)/\lambda = -(\omega + 1)\eta = \omega^2 \eta$ and $\delta \mid \eta$. If δ is not a unit, then ζ and η are not coprime and the solution was not primitive, contrary to our assumption. In the same way one shows that (ϕ, ψ) and (ψ, χ) are units.

Equation (5) now reads $-\varepsilon\lambda^{3k}\alpha^3 = \lambda\phi \cdot \lambda\psi \cdot \lambda\chi$ or

$$-\varepsilon\lambda^{3(k-1)}\alpha^3 = \phi\psi\chi, \qquad (\phi, \psi) = (\psi, \chi) = (\chi, \phi) = 1. \tag{6}$$

From (6) and $k \geq 2$ follows that $\lambda \mid \phi\psi\chi$ and from the pairwise coprimality that λ divides exactly one of the three factors. Because of the symmetry in ϕ, ψ, χ, we may assume, for instance, that $\lambda \mid \phi$, $\lambda \nmid \psi\chi$. Then $\lambda^{3(k-1)} \mid \phi$, or $\phi = \lambda^{3(k-1)}\theta$, $\theta \in \mathbf{I}$ and (6) becomes

$$-\varepsilon\alpha^3 = \theta\psi\chi, \qquad (\theta, \psi) = (\psi, \chi) = (\chi, \theta) = 1. \tag{7}$$

On account of Lemma 5, it is possible to invoke 5.40, which states that θ, ψ and χ must each be associated with perfect cubes. It is worthwhile to stress the fact that if we had no Lemma 5 at our disposal, the last conclusion would not be warranted, and soon we shall be faced with the consequences of this distressing reality! But now we may proceed, and we know that we are permitted to write $\theta = \varepsilon_1\alpha_1^3$, $\psi = \varepsilon_2\beta^3$, $\chi = \varepsilon_3\zeta_1^3$, with $\alpha_1, \beta, \zeta_1 \in \mathbf{I}$ and $\varepsilon_1, \varepsilon_2, \varepsilon_3$ units of **I**. Substituting these values we obtain that $\eta + \zeta = \lambda\phi = \lambda \cdot \lambda^{3(k-1)}\theta = \lambda^{3k-2}\varepsilon_1\alpha_1^3$ and in the same way we compute $\eta + \omega\zeta$ and $\eta + \omega^2\zeta$, obtaining

$$\eta + \zeta = \varepsilon_1\lambda^{3(k-2)}\alpha_1^3, \eta + \omega\zeta = \varepsilon_2\lambda\beta^3, \eta + \omega^2\zeta = \varepsilon_3\lambda\zeta_1^3, \tag{8}$$

$$\lambda \nmid \alpha_1 \cdot \beta \cdot \zeta_1 \qquad (\alpha_1, \beta) = (\beta, \zeta_1) = (\zeta_1, \alpha_1) = 1,$$

$\varepsilon_1, \varepsilon_2, \varepsilon_3$ units of **I**.

Let us consider now the sum $\sigma = (\eta + \zeta) + \omega(\eta + \omega\zeta) + \omega^2(\eta + \omega^2\zeta)$; on the one hand, it is clear that $\sigma = \eta(1 + \omega + \omega^2) + \zeta(1 + \omega^2 + \omega^4) = 0$; on the other hand, replacing in σ the brackets by their values from (8) we obtain $\sigma = \varepsilon_1 \lambda^{3k-2} \alpha_1^3 + \omega \varepsilon_2 \lambda \beta^3 + \omega^2 \varepsilon_3 \lambda \zeta_1^3$. Equating these two values and dividing by $\varepsilon_3 \lambda (\neq 0)$, we obtain

$$\varepsilon_4 \lambda^{3(k-1)} \alpha_1^3 + \varepsilon_5 \beta^3 + \zeta_1^3 = 0, \qquad \text{with} \tag{5'}$$

$$(\alpha_1, \beta) = (\beta, \zeta_1) = (\zeta_1, \alpha_1) = 1,$$

ε_4 and ε_5 units of **I**. Equation (5') is almost of the same form as (5), with α_1, β, ζ_1 instead of α, η, ζ and with k replaced by $k - 1$. Were it not for the (so far not determined) unit ε_5, the proof of (ii)—and, hence, of Theorem 4—would be complete. It remains to show that we actually may take $\varepsilon_5 = 1$. Indeed, $k \geq 2$ so that $\lambda^3 \mid \lambda^{3(k-1)} \varepsilon_4 \alpha_1^3$. Also, $\lambda \nmid \beta \cdot \zeta_1$ so that, by Lemma 4, $\beta^3 \equiv \pm 1 \pmod{\lambda^4}$, $\zeta_1^3 \equiv \pm 1 \pmod{\lambda^4}$. Consequently, $\varepsilon_5 \beta^3 + \zeta_1^3 \equiv \pm \varepsilon_5 \pm 1 \pmod{\lambda^4}$ and the congruence holds, *a fortiori*, to the modulus λ^3. We obtain, therefore, that $0 \equiv -\lambda^{3(k-1)} \varepsilon_4 \alpha^3 \equiv \varepsilon_5 \beta^3 + \zeta_1^3 \equiv \pm \varepsilon_5 \pm 1 \pmod{\lambda^3}$. However, $\pm \omega \pm 1$ and $\pm \omega^2 \pm 1$ are not divisible by λ^3 (not even by λ^2; why?); hence, $0 \equiv \pm \varepsilon_5 \pm 1 \pmod{\lambda^3}$ is possible only if $\varepsilon_5 = \pm 1$ and (5') becomes $\varepsilon_4 \lambda^{3(k-1)} \alpha_1^3 + (\pm \beta)^3 + \zeta_1^3 = 0$, or, setting $\pm \beta = \eta_1$ $\varepsilon_4 \lambda^{3(k-1)} \alpha_1^3 + \eta_1^3 + \zeta_1^3 = 0$ with $\alpha_1, \eta_1, \zeta_1 \in \mathbf{I}$, $\lambda \nmid \alpha_1 \cdot \eta_1 \cdot \zeta_1$; $\alpha_1, \eta_1, \zeta_1$ coprime in pairs and ε_4 a unit of **I**.

In other words, starting with an admissible solution $\xi = \lambda^k \alpha, \eta, \zeta$, we have constructed another admissible solution $\xi_1 = \lambda^{k-1} \alpha_1, \eta_1, \zeta_1$, with a smaller exponent k. This finishes the proof of (ii), hence that of Theorem 4, hence that of Theorem 3.

7. CASE I FOR $p = 5$

While already the proof of the FC for $p = 3$ is not precisely trivial, the general case is still much more difficult. Therefore, in order to warm up, let us consider one last case that can be handled with elementary methods, namely, Case I for $p = 5$. We propose to prove.

Theorem 5.   *The equation*

$$\xi^5 + \eta^5 + \zeta^5 = 0 \tag{9}$$

has no solutions with ξ, η, ζ integers of the cyclotomic field $\mathbf{Q}(\omega)$, $\omega = e^{2\pi i/5}$, none of which is divisible by $\lambda = 1 - \omega$.

For simplicity in the present section we shall denote the field $\mathbf{Q}(e^{2\pi i/5})$ by $\mathbf{K}_5$ and its ring of integers by $\mathbf{I}_5$. Also, in the present section, a primitive solution of (9), satisfying all conditions of Theorem 5, will be called for short an *admissible solution*.

Lemma 2″. $\lambda = 1 - \omega$ *is a prime in* I_5.

PROOF. ω and its conjugates are the roots of the irreducible cyclotomic equation $(x^5 - 1)/(x - 1) = x^4 + x^3 + x^2 + x + 1 = 0$; hence, $\lambda = 1 - \omega$ satisfies the equation $(1 - \lambda)^4 + (1 - \lambda)^3 + (1 - \lambda)^2 + (1 - \lambda) + 1 = 0$ or, rearranging the terms, $\lambda^4 - 5\lambda^3 + 10\lambda^2 - 10\lambda + 5 = 0$. Hence, by 5.31, $N\lambda = \lambda^{(1)}\lambda^{(2)}\lambda^{(3)}\lambda^{(4)} = 5$ and it follows from 5.37 that λ is a prime.

Corollary 2″.1. $\lambda \mid 5$.

PROOF. Obvious.

Corollary 2″.2. λ^4 *and 5 are associates.*

PROOF. In the proof of Lemma 2″ we obtained that $\lambda^4 = 5(\lambda^3 - 2\lambda^2 + 2\lambda - 1)$. The result now follows by observing that the bracket is a unit (why?).

Corollary 2″.3. $x \in \mathbf{Z}$ *and* $\lambda \mid x \Rightarrow 5 \mid x$.

PROOF. $\lambda \mid x \Rightarrow \lambda^4 \mid x^4 \Rightarrow 5 \mid x^4$ by Corollary 2″.2. But $x \in \mathbf{Z}$ and 5 is a prime; hence, $5 \mid x$.

REMARK 5. It is clear (see e.g. 5.28 and 5.41) that $\mathbf{Z} \subset \mathbf{I}_5$; hence, Theorem 5 and Corollary 2″.1 have as consequence, (why?), that for $p = 5$, (1′) has no solutions $x, y, z \in \mathbf{Z}$ with $5 \nmid x \cdot y \cdot z$, so that for $p = 5$ the FC holds at least in Case I. It also is clear that $\lambda \nmid \xi \cdot \eta \cdot \zeta$ is the proper formulation of the Case I restriction, in the present, slightly more general setting.

Lemma 3″. *There exist exactly 5 residue classes* mod λ *and* $-2, -1, 0, 1, 2$ *form a complete set of residues* mod λ.

PROOF. By 5.41,

$$\alpha \in \mathbf{I}_5 \Rightarrow \alpha = a_0 + a_1\omega + a_2\omega^2 + a_3\omega^3 + a_4\omega^4 \qquad \text{with } a_m \in \mathbf{Z};$$

hence,

$$\alpha = a_0 + a_1(1 - \lambda) + \cdots + a_4(1 - \lambda)^4 \equiv a_0 + a_1 + \cdots + a_4 \,(\text{mod } \lambda).$$

However, $\sum_{j=0}^4 a_j \equiv \pm 2, \pm 1, 0 \,(\text{mod } 5)$ and hence, using Corollary 2″.1, the same holds *a fortiori* mod λ. The proof is completed as in the case $p = 3$, by checking that these five residues are incongruent not only mod 5, but also mod λ.

Lemma 4″. $\alpha, \beta \in \mathbf{I}_5$, $\alpha \equiv \beta \,(\text{mod } \lambda) \Rightarrow \alpha^5 \equiv \beta^5 \,(\text{mod } \lambda^5)$

PROOF. $\alpha^5 - \beta^5 = (\alpha - \beta)(\alpha - \omega\beta)(\alpha - \omega^2\beta)(\alpha - \omega^3\beta)(\alpha - \omega^4\beta)$; but $\omega \equiv 1 \,(\text{mod } \lambda) \Rightarrow \omega^k \equiv 1 \,(\text{mod } \lambda)$ so that $\alpha - \omega^k\beta \equiv \alpha - \beta \,(\text{mod } \lambda)$. Hence, if $\lambda \mid \alpha - \beta$, then $\lambda \mid \alpha - \omega^k \beta$, each of the 5 factors is divisible by λ and $\lambda^5 \mid \alpha^5 - \beta^5$ or $\alpha^5 \equiv \beta^5 \pmod{\lambda^5}$. We also could prove the analog of Lemma 5, stating that factorization into primes is unique in I_5, but we shall not need the result and omit the somewhat lengthy proof.

PROOF OF THEOREM 5. By assumption $\lambda \nmid \xi \cdot \eta \cdot \zeta$; hence, by Lemma 4″, if $\xi \equiv \pm 1 \pmod{\lambda}$, then $\xi^5 \equiv \pm 1 \pmod{\lambda^5}$; if $\xi \equiv \pm 2 \pmod{\lambda}$, then $\xi^5 \equiv \pm 32 \pmod{\lambda^5}$, and similarly for η and ζ. Consequently, $\xi^5 + \eta^5 + \zeta^5 \equiv a + b + c \pmod{\lambda^5}$, where each of a, b, and c may take only one of the four values ± 1, ± 32. If ξ, η, ζ are an admissible solution of (9) and $a + b + c = f$ then $0 = \xi^5 + \eta^5 + \zeta^5 \equiv f \pmod{\lambda^5}$. Using Corollaries 2″.2 and 2″.3, $f \equiv 0 \pmod{\lambda^5} \Leftrightarrow \lambda^5 \mid f \Leftrightarrow 5\lambda \mid f \Rightarrow \lambda \mid (f/5) \Rightarrow 5 \mid (f/5) \Rightarrow 5^2 \mid f$ so that $f \equiv 0 \pmod{25}$. If we now take for a, b, c any of the values ± 1 or ± 32 ($\equiv \pm 7 \pmod{25}$), no combination of three of them leads to zero (the sum with same signs is at most $\equiv 3 \cdot 7 \equiv 21 \pmod{25}$); hence, $f \equiv 0 \pmod{25}$ is impossible and Theorem 5 is proven.

8. CASE I FOR AN ARBITRARY PRIME *p*

Let us set $\omega = e^{2\pi i/p}$ and, for simplicity of writing, let us denote (throughout this section) by **K** the cyclotomic field $\mathbf{Q}(\omega)$ generated by ω (that is, the set $\sum_{j=0}^{p-2} A_j \omega^j$, $A_j \in \mathbf{Q}$) and by **I** the ring of integers of **K** (so that, by 5.41, $\mathbf{I} = \sum_{j=0}^{p-2} a_j \omega^j$, $a_j \in \mathbf{Z}$); let also $\lambda = 1 - \omega$. Exactly as in the cases $p = 3$ and $p = 5$ one has.

Lemma 2. $\lambda = 1 - \omega$ *is a prime in* **I** *and* $N\lambda = p$.

PROOF. Once we show that $N\lambda = p$, it follows by 5.37 that λ is a prime. To show that $N\lambda = p$ we consider the equation of degree $p - 1$ with integer coefficients satisfied by λ. From $\omega^{p-1} + \omega^{p-2} + \cdots + \omega + 1 = 0$ and $\omega = 1 - \lambda$ follows that $(1 - \lambda)^{p-1} + (1 - \lambda)^{p-2} + \cdots + (1 - \lambda) + 1 = 0$, or, rearranging, $\lambda^{p-1} + a_1 \lambda^{p-2} + \cdots + \underbrace{(1 + 1 + \cdots + 1)}_{p} = 0$; hence,

$N\lambda = \lambda^{(1)}\lambda^{(2)} \cdots \lambda^{(p-1)} = (-1)^{p-1}p = p$, as claimed.

Corollary 2.1. λ^{p-1} *and* p *are associates.*

PROOF. In $(x^p - 1)/(x - 1) = x^{p-1} + x^{p-2} + \cdots + x + 1 = \prod_{j=1}^{p-1} (x - \omega^j)$ set $x = 1$, obtaining $p = (1 - \omega)(1 - \omega^2) \cdots (1 - \omega^{p-1})$. For very $k \not\equiv 0e \pmod{p}$, $1 - \omega$ and $1 - \omega^k$ are associates. Indeed,

$$1 - \omega^k = (1 - \omega)(1 + \omega + \cdots + \omega^{k-1})$$

so that $1 - \omega \mid 1 - \omega^k$. Next, one can solve the congruence $km \equiv 1 \pmod{p}$, because $(k, p) = 1$; let m be the smallest positive solution. Then

$$1 - \omega^{km} = 1 - \omega^{np+1} = 1 - \omega;$$

also,

$$1 - \omega^{km} = (1 - \omega^k)(1 + \omega^k + \omega^{2k} + \cdots + \omega^{(m-1)k})$$

so that

$$1 - \omega = (1 - \omega^k)(1 + \omega^k + \omega^{2k} + \cdots + \omega^{(m-1)k})$$

and $1 - \omega^k \mid 1 - \omega$. Consequently, $1 - \omega$ and $1 - \omega^k$ are indeed associates, $(1 - \omega)(1 - \omega^2) \cdots (1 - \omega^{p-1}) = \varepsilon(1 - \omega)^{p-1} = \varepsilon\lambda^{p-1}$ and the Corollary is proven.

Corollary 2.2.   *If $(k, p) = 1$ and $mk \equiv 1 \pmod{p}$, then $1 + \omega^k + \omega^{2k} + \cdots + \omega^{(m-1)k}$ is a unit of* **I**.

PROOF. $1 - \omega$ and $1 - \omega^k$ are associates by Corollary 2.1; hence their ratio $\dfrac{1 - \omega}{1 - \omega^k} = \dfrac{1 - \omega^{mk}}{1 - \omega^k} = 1 + \omega^k + \cdots + \omega^{(m-1)k}$ is a unit.

Corollary 2.3.   *For every $m \not\equiv 0 \pmod{p}$, $1 + \omega + \omega^2 + \cdots + \omega^{m-1}$ is a unit.*

PROOF. For $p \nmid m$, $1 - \omega^m$ and $1 - \omega$ are associates and $(1 - \omega^m)/(1 - \omega) = 1 + \omega + \cdots + \omega^{m-1}$.

Lemma 3.   *There exist exactly p residue classes mod λ and $0, \pm 1, \pm 2, \ldots, \pm\frac{1}{2}(p - 1)$ form a complete set of residues.*

PROOF. Same (mutatis mutandis) as for $p = 3$, or $p = 5$.

Lemma 4. $\alpha, \beta \in \mathbf{I}, \alpha \equiv \beta \pmod{\lambda} \Rightarrow \alpha^p \equiv \beta^p \pmod{\lambda^p}$.

PROOF. Same (mutatis mutandis) as for $p = 5$.

One would now try to prove the generalization of Lemma 5. As will be seen presently, this would enable us to prove the FC easily, at least in Case I. However, the generalization of previous proof for $p = 3$, does not go through! It may be worthwhile to observe though that when one tries to prove the uniqueness of factorization for $\mathbf{Q}(e^{2\pi i/p})$ with $p = 5$, $p = 7$, and so on, one seems to succeed each time. Yet each time some new, specific reasoning, some trick that works just once, for that particular p, seems to be needed, and any attempt at a general proof fails. It is quite frustrating (and must have been so for Kummer) to prove uniqueness of factorization for one cyclotomic field after another and not to be able to prove it in general! The reason for this failure is, of course, that actually the factorization *is not unique,* in a general cyclotomic field—yet the first case of failure occurs only for $p = 23$ and, this was originally pointed out by Cauchy in 1847 (see [1]), as we already know.

Deprived of Lemma 5 in the general case, let us try, nevertheless, and see what we can achieve with only Lemmas 2, 3, and 4 at our disposal. Equation (1') may be written as

$$-x^p = y^p + z^p = (y + z)(y + \omega z) \cdots (y + \omega^{p-1}z),$$

with $\alpha_k = y + \omega^k z \in \mathbf{I}$, provided that $y, z \in \mathbf{Z}$. As until now, we are interested only in primitive solutions, with x, y, z coprime in pairs.

Restricting ourselves to Case I, that is, to solutions x, y, z such that $p \nmid x \cdot y \cdot z$, we claim that the factors α_k with different subscripts are coprime. Indeed if π is a prime, $\pi \mid y + \omega^k z$ and $\pi \mid y + \omega^m z$ with, say, $k > m$, then $\pi \mid (y + \omega^k z) - (y + \omega^m z) \Rightarrow \pi \mid \omega^k(1 - \omega^{m-k})z$ or $\pi \mid \lambda \varepsilon z$, with ε a unit of $\mathbf{I}$, by Corollary 2.3. If $\pi \mid \lambda$, then π and λ are associates; also, $\pi \mid y + \omega^k z \Rightarrow \pi \mid y^p + z^p \Rightarrow \pi \mid -x^p \Rightarrow \lambda \mid x^p \Rightarrow N\lambda \mid x \Rightarrow p \mid x$ contrary to our assumption, hence, $\pi \mid z$. This, together with $\pi \mid y + \omega^k z \Rightarrow \pi \mid y$; consequently, taking norms, we show that $N\pi \mid y$, $N\pi \mid z$, contrary to the assumption that y and z are coprime.

We can formulate the results obtained so far as follows: If x, y, z are a primitive solution of (1') with $p \nmid x \cdot y \cdot z$, then

$$-x^p = \alpha_0 \alpha_1 \cdots \alpha_{p-1} \qquad \text{with } \alpha_i \in \mathbf{I}(0 \le i \le p - 1), (\alpha_i, \alpha_j) = \varepsilon,$$

a unit of $\mathbf{I}$ if $i \ne j$. We would like to continue as in the particular case $p = 3$ and invoke 5.40 to the effect that each α_j is the associate of an exact p-th power, that is, $\alpha_j = \varepsilon_j \xi_j^p$, ε_j a unit, ξ_j an integer of $\mathbf{I}$. But this conclusion is warranted only if $\mathbf{I}$ is a domain of unique factorization. Let us assume for a moment that this is the case.

In order to continue our reasoning, we still need some more Lemmas, which, however, have nothing to do with the uniqueness of factorization.

Lemma 8. *If ε is a unit of $\mathbf{I}$, then there exists an exponent $k(\in \mathbf{Z})$ such that $\varepsilon = \omega^k \eta$, with real η.*

REMARK 6. $\eta = \varepsilon \omega^{-k}$ is a unit because ε and ω^{-k} are units.

The *Proof of Lemma* 8 is long, but otherwise rather routine. It may be found in [6], pp. 225–227, or in [15], pp. 118–120 and will not be reproduced here. It seems worthwhile to mention, that the proof of Lemma 8 is based on the following Lemma, of independent interest.

Lemma 9. $\gamma \in \mathbf{I} \Rightarrow \gamma^p \equiv a(\mathrm{mod}\ \gamma^p)$ *for some $a \in \mathbf{Z}$.*

PROOF. By Lemma 3, each residue class mod λ contains some $c \in \mathbf{Z}$ (even some c with $|c| \leq \frac{1}{2}(p - 1)$); hence, $\gamma \in \mathbf{I} \Rightarrow \exists c \in \mathbf{Z} \ni \gamma \equiv c \pmod{\lambda}$. Using Lemma 4, $\gamma^p \equiv c^p (\mathrm{mod}\ \lambda^p)$ and the Lemma is proven with $a = c^p$ (which is somewhat more than claimed).

Corollary 9.1. $\gamma \in \mathbf{I} \Rightarrow \exists a \in \mathbf{Z} \ni \gamma^p \equiv a \pmod{p}$.

PROOF. By Lemma 9, there exists an integer $a \in \mathbf{Z}$ such that $\lambda^p \mid \gamma^p - a$; *a fortiori*, $\lambda^{p-1} \mid \gamma^p - a$. Yet, by Corollary 2.1, $p = \varepsilon\lambda^{p-1}$ and the result follows.

Returning now to $\alpha = \alpha_1 = y + \omega z$, we assume that 5.40 is applicable; hence, that $\alpha = \varepsilon\xi^p$. Using Lemma 8, we may replace ε by $\omega^r\eta$ (η real), so that $\alpha = \eta\omega^r\xi^p$; next, by Corollary 9.1, we can determine $a \in \mathbf{Z} \ni \xi^p \equiv a$ $(\mathrm{mod}\ p)$ and obtain $\alpha \equiv \eta\omega_r a \pmod{p}$, or, setting $\eta a = b$, $\alpha \equiv b\omega^r \pmod{p}$ with real $b \in \mathbf{I}$. Hence, $b = \omega^{-r}\alpha \pmod{p}$; being real, $b = \bar{b}$, its complex conjugate, that is, $b = \bar{b} \equiv \omega^r\bar{\alpha} \pmod{p}$. We conclude that $\omega^r\bar{\alpha} \equiv \omega^{-r}\alpha \pmod{p}$. Replacing α by $y + \omega z$ and $\bar{\alpha}$ by $y + \bar{\omega}z$, the last congruence becomes

$$y\omega^{-r} + z\omega^{1-r} - y\omega^r - z\omega^{r-1} \equiv 0 \pmod{p}. \qquad (10)$$

If $r \equiv 0 \pmod{p}$ then (10) reduces to $y + z\omega - y - z\omega^{-1} \equiv 0 \pmod{p}$; but $p \nmid z$; hence, $p \mid \omega - \omega^{-1}$ or $p \mid 1 - \omega^2$, that is, $\lambda^{p-1} \mid (1 - \omega)(1 + \omega)$ or $\lambda^{p-2} \mid 1 + \omega$ which is false, because $p \geq 3$ and $1 + \omega$ is a unit. If $r \equiv 1 \pmod{p}$ one similarly obtains $y\omega^{-1} + z - y\omega - z \equiv 0 \pmod{p}$, with the same conclusion, because $p \nmid y$. Consequently, $r \not\equiv 0$, $r \not\equiv 1 \pmod{p}$ and (10) is equivalent to an equation of the form

$$y\omega^{2r} + z\omega^{2r-1} - z\omega - y + pf(\omega) = 0. \qquad (10')$$

with $f(\omega) \in \mathbf{Z}[\omega]$, and where $2r$ may be taken less than p (because $\omega^p = 1$). There are two possibilities: The first is that the terms in (10) mutually cancel out, and then (10') holds with $f(\omega)$ identically zero; in the other alternative, by 5.15, (10') must be a multiple of the irreducible (cyclotomic) polynomial

$$\omega^{p-1} + \omega^{p-2} + \cdots + \omega + 1. \qquad (11)$$

A glance at (10') shows that this is not possible. Indeed, discarding the cases $p = 3$ and $p = 5$ (for which Case I has been settled), (11) contains at least 7 terms; hence if the polynomial in (10') is a multiple of (11), $f(\omega)$ does not vanish identically. The coefficients of all terms of $f(\omega)$ are multiples of p; hence if the polynomial in (10') is a multiple of (11), also the other coefficients in (10'), namely, y and z have to be multiples of p, contrary to the assumption $p \nmid x \cdot y \cdot z$. It follows that the first alternative holds. Clearly, $2r \equiv 2r - 1 \pmod{p}$ is not possible and $2r \equiv 0 \pmod{p}$ has been ruled out.

The only possibility for mutual cancellation of the 4 terms in (10) is, there-fore, $2r \equiv 1 \pmod{p}$ and (10) becomes

$$\omega^{-r}(y + z\omega - y\omega^{2r} - z\omega^{2r-1}) = \omega^{-r}(y + z\omega - y\omega - z) \equiv 0 \pmod{p},$$

or, ω being a unit, $y(1 - \omega) + z(\omega - 1) = (y - z)(1 - \omega) = \lambda(y - z) \equiv 0$ $\pmod{p}$. p being associated with λ^{p-1}, $\lambda^{p-2} \mid y - z$; hence, as already seen several times, $p \mid y - z$. By symmetry, starting in (1') from $-z^p = x^p + y^p$, it follows in exactly the same way that $p \mid x - y$. Hence, $x \equiv y \equiv z$ $\pmod{p}$, $x^p + y^p + x^p \equiv 3x^p \pmod{p}$. If x, y, z are a solution of (1'), the left-hand sum vanishes, so that $p \mid 3x^p$. For $p > 3$ this means $p \mid x$, which contradicts the condition $p \nmid x \cdot y \cdot z$ of Case I. We may state the result obtained as our last result in this chapter, namely;

Theorem 6.   *If for some p the cyclotomic field $\mathbf{K} = \mathbf{Q}(e^{2\pi i/p})$ has the pro-perty of uniqueness of factorization of its integers, then there exists no solution of* (1') *in integers x, y, $z \in \mathbf{Z}$, with $p \nmid x \cdot y \cdot z$.*

PROBLEMS

1.   Prove: m, n, $q \in \mathbf{Z}$, $(m, n) = 1$, $m \cdot n = q^2 \Rightarrow \exists a$, $b \in \mathbf{Z} \ni m = a^2$, $n = b^2$.

2.   Show that the "solution" x_1, y_1, z_1 constructed in the proof of Theo-rem 2 is primitive.

3.   Prove: In $\mathbf{Q}(e^{2\pi i/3})$ all norms are non-negative and $N\alpha = 0 \Leftrightarrow \alpha = 0$.

4.   If α, $\beta \in \mathbf{I}(e^{2\pi i/3})$ and $N\beta = m$, show that the total number k of steps in the Euclidean algorithm starting with $\alpha = \beta\gamma_1 + \rho_1$, satisfies $k \leq m$.

5.   In (8), compute $\eta + \omega\zeta$ and $\eta + \omega^2\zeta$ as functions of α_1, β, ζ_1.

6.   Show that in (8) α_1, β, ζ_1 are coprime in pairs.

7.   If $\omega = e^{2\pi i/3}$ show that
$$1 + \omega^r + \omega^{2r} = \begin{cases} 3 & \text{if } r \equiv 0 \pmod 3, \\ 0 & \text{otherwise.} \end{cases}$$

8.   Generalize the result of Problem 7 to $\omega = e^{2\pi i/p}$.

9.   Let $\lambda = 1 - \omega$, $\omega = e^{2\pi i/3}$; prove that $\lambda^2 \nmid \omega \pm 1$ and $\lambda^2 \nmid \omega^2 \pm 1$.

10.   Prove that the equation satisfied by λ in the proof of Lemma 2'' is irreducible over $\mathbf{Q}$. (*Hint:*   Use 5.22.)

11.   Prove that $\lambda^3 - 2\lambda^2 + 2\lambda - 1 (\lambda = 1 - e^{2\pi i/5})$ is a unit in $\mathbf{I}_5$.

12.   Prove that ± 2, ± 1, 0 are incongruent mod λ $(\lambda = 1 - e^{2\pi i/5})$.

13.   Can Lemma 4 be strengthened to $\alpha \equiv \beta \pmod{\lambda} \Rightarrow \alpha^p \equiv \beta^p \pmod{\lambda^{p+1}}$, so that it should generalize Lemma 4' and reduce to it for $p = 3$, $\lambda \nmid \alpha$?

14. Let $\omega = e^{2\pi i/p}$, $\lambda = 1 - \omega$; prove that $N\lambda = p$.

15. Give the details of the proof of Lemma 3.

16. Give the details of the proof of Lemma 4.

17. Let π be a prime in $I(e^{2\pi i/p})$, let $a \in Z$ and assume that $\pi \mid a$; show that there exists a rational prime q, uniquely defined by π and such that $q \mid a$. (*Hint:* $N\pi = q^k$, $1 \leq k \leq p - 1$.)

BIBLIOGRAPHY

1. A. L. Cauchy, *Comptes Rendus Ac. Sciences* (Paris), **24**, 1847, pp. 578–584.

2. L. E. Dickson, *History of the Theory of Numbers*, Vol. 2, *Diophantine Analysis*. New York: Chelsea Publishing Co., 1952.

3. L. E. Dickson, *Quarterly Journal of Math.*, **40**, 1908, pp. 27–45.

4. G. L. Dirichlet, Mémoire read at the Royal Acad. of Sciences, Paris, (Institut de France) on July 11, 1825, but not published until 1828 in the *Journal f. d. reine u. angw. Mathem.*, **3**, 1828, pp. 354–375; Werke, **1**, pp. 21–46.

5. E. Hecke, *Nachrichten der Akad. Wissenschaften Göttingen* II. *Mathem.*, *Physik. Klasse*, 1910, pp. 420–424.

6. E. Landau, *Vorlesungen über Zahlentheorie*, Vol. 3. Leipzig: S. Hirzel 1927.

7. A. M. Legendre, *Essai sur la Théorie des Nombres*. Paris: Duprat 1808 (gives credit for many results to Sophie Germain).

8. D. H. Lehmer and E. Lehmer, *Bulletin of the Amer. Math. Soc.*, **47**, 1941, pp. 139–142.

9. D. J. Lewis, *Report on the Institute in the Theory of Numbers*. Boulder, Colo.: Univ. of Colorado, 1959.

10. G. Libri, *Journal f. d. reine u. angw. Mathem.*, **9**, 1832, pp. 270–275.

11. W. Ljunggren, *Acta Arithm.* **8**, (1962/1963), pp. 451–463.

12. D. Mirimanoff, *L'Enseignement Mathématique*, **11**, 1909, pp. 49–51.

13. D. Mirimanoff, *Comptes Rendus Ac. Sci.* (Paris), **150**, 1910, pp. 204–206.

14. L. J. Mordell, *Three Lectures on Fermat's Last Theorem*. Cambridge: The University Press, 1921.

15. H. Pollard, *The Theory of Algebraic Numbers* (Carus Monograph No. 9). New York: J. Wiley & Sons, 1950.

16. S. Ramanujan, *Collected Papers*, edited by G. H. Hardy, P. V. Sashu Aiyar, and B. M. Wilson. Cambridge: Cambridge University Press, 1927.

17. J. B. Rosser, *Bulletin of the Amer. Math. Soc.*, **46**, 1940, pp. 299–304 and **47**, 1941, pp. 109–110.

18. J. L. Selfridge, H. S. Vandiver, C. A. Nicol, *Proceedings National Acad. Sciences* (U.S.A.), **41**, 1955, pp. 970–963.

19. T. Skolem, *Diophantische Gleichungen*, Ergebnisse der Math. und ihrer Grenzgebiete, **5**. Berlin: Springer, 1938.

20. H. S. Vandiver, a large number of papers, most of which are quoted in the bibliography of his survey article in the *American Mathematical Monthly*, **53**, 1946, pp. 555–578.

21. B. L. Van der Waerden, *Modern Algebra*, Vol. 1. New York: F. Ungar Publ. Co., 1953.

22. A. Weil, *Bulletin of the Amer. Math. Soc.*, **55**, 1949, pp. 497–508.

23. H. Weyl, *Algebraic Theory of Numbers* (Annals of Math. Studies, No. 1), Princeton, N.J.: Princeton Univ. Press, 1940.

24. A. Wieferich, *Journal f. d. reine u. angw. Math.*, **136**, 1909, pp. 293–302.

CHAPTER 10

Ideal Theory

1. INTRODUCTION

Theorem 9.6 can hardly be considered satisfactory. The many hedges and restrictions are a far cry from Fermat's original conjecture. The principal hurdle that stands in the way of a less restrictive result is the requirement of unique factorization. Indeed, we already know that, in general, the factorization of integers of a given field into indecomposable (that is, "prime") integers of the same field *is not unique*. And we also have at least an intuitive, heuristic understanding for the reason of this difficulty. In some sense, there are not enough elements in the ring of integers; in particular, given any two integers α and β of that ring, there is, in general, no integer δ in the same ring which has all the necessary properties to qualify as the greatest common divisor of α and β. We also saw in Chapter 3 how one could approach the problem, in order to overcome this difficulty. Given α, β in a ring $\mathbf{I}$, one could form the set $\{\mu\alpha + \nu\beta\}$, with μ and ν ranging independently over all elements of the ring. If the ring was $\mathbf{Z}$, this set was nothing but a module, consisting precisely of all the multiples of the g.c.d. of α and β. In the more general case which we now consider, this set, called an *ideal*, may, or may not, consist of all (and only) the multiples of an integer $\delta \in \mathbf{I}$. If it does, δ is actually a g.c.d. of α and β and we say that the ideal is a *principal ideal*. It may be shown:

(i) There is a one-to-one correspondence between the integers of $\mathbf{I}$ and the set of principal ideals.

(ii) In the cases where for given α, $\beta \in \mathbf{I}$ there exists no integer δ in $\mathbf{I}$ such that its multiples $\{\lambda\delta \mid \lambda \in \mathbf{I}\}$ are precisely the integers $\mathfrak{a} = \{\mu\alpha + \nu\beta \mid \mu, \nu \in \mathbf{I}\}$ one can still find an integer δ, belonging not to the field $\mathbf{K}$, but to another field $\mathbf{K}_1 \supset \mathbf{K}$, such that the set of all those multiples of δ that belong to $\mathbf{K}$ coincides with $\mathfrak{a}$. In this extended sense, therefore, a g.c.d. always exist and we may hope to recapture somehow the uniqueness of factorization. In view of the fact that all multiples of δ which we can reach within $\mathbf{K}$ are represented by $\mathfrak{a}$ we may try to study δ (which is not within our reach in $\mathbf{K}$) by studying the ideal $\mathfrak{a}$. This attempt turns out to be successful and leads to the result:

(iii) Ideals can be *factored* into "*prime*" ideals and this factorization is unique.

After this preparation, one can return to the FC with a new and powerful tool. This heuristic discussion should be sufficient to motivate the development of some elements of the theory of ideals, which follows. Throughout this chapter, $\mathbf{K}$ stands for a field of algebraic numbers, $\mathbf{K} = \mathbf{Q}(\theta)$, and $\mathbf{I}$ for the ring of integers of $\mathbf{K}$. Concerning notations, we shall continue to denote rational integers, arbitrary rationals, and elements of $\mathbf{K}$, by lower-case letters, capitals, and Greek (lower-case) letters, respectively. So, for instance, we write $a \in \mathbf{Z}$, $A \in \mathbf{Q}$, $\alpha \in \mathbf{K}$. Concerning ideals, we ought to use **heavy print**, because they are sets; however, on the one hand they do occur very frequently, and, on the other hand, we know that they are really stand-ins for numbers; therefore, we shall follow the general custom and denote them by German script—as we already did, as a matter of fact! Also, in what follows, certain sets, or classes of ideals will occur. We shall denote them by capital German letters.

2. DEFINITIONS AND ELEMENTARY PROPERTIES OF IDEALS

Definition 1.   Let $\mathbf{I}$ be a ring of algebraic integers in some number field $\mathbf{K}$ of degree n over $\mathbf{Q}$, and let $\alpha_j \in \mathbf{I}(1 \leq j \leq k)$. The set $\mathfrak{a} = \{\lambda_1\alpha_1 + \cdots + \lambda_k\alpha_k\}$ obtained when the λ_j's range independently over $\mathbf{I}$ is said to be an *ideal*. $\alpha_1, \alpha_2, ..., \alpha_k$ are called the *generators* of $\mathfrak{a}$, in symbols, $\mathfrak{a} = (\alpha_1, \alpha_2, ..., \alpha_k)$. Two ideals are identical, $\mathfrak{a} = \mathfrak{b}$, if they consist of the same integers.

REMARK 1. The set $\{0\}$ consisting of the only element zero is an ideal, according to Definition 1. It will be denoted by $\mathfrak{o}$, but, unless specific mention is made to the contrary, we shall always assume tacitly that any ideal $\mathfrak{a}$ under consideration is not $\mathfrak{o}$. Also the whole ring $\mathbf{I}$ is clearly an ideal. For uniformity of notation we shall denote it by $\mathfrak{i}$ when we want to consider it as an ideal.

REMARK 2. If $\alpha_j = a_j \in \mathbf{Z}$, then $\mathfrak{a} = \{kd\}$, where $d = (\alpha_1, ..., \alpha_k)$. Hence, although conceptually, considered as the g.c.d., $(\alpha_1, ..., \alpha_k) = d$ is a number and not a set, there will be no real danger of confusion (and there will be some important advantages) if we use the same symbol, $(\alpha_1, \alpha_2, ..., \alpha_k)$ to stand also for the ideal generated by $\alpha_1, \alpha_2, ..., \alpha_k$.

Theorem 1. *If $\alpha \in \mathfrak{a}$, $\beta \in \mathfrak{a}$, $\lambda \in \mathbf{I}$ then $\alpha \pm \beta \in \mathfrak{a}$, $\lambda \alpha \in \mathfrak{a}$.*

PROOF left to the reader.

REMARK 3. The generators of a given ideal are by no means unique. In particular, one may suppress among them or add to them any integer, α_0, say, which is not "linearly independent" of the others, that is, which can be represented as a sum $\alpha_0 = \sum_i \lambda_i \alpha_i$ with α_i generators of $\mathfrak{a}$, $\lambda_i \in \mathbf{I}$. Also, without changing the ideal one may add, or subtract from any generator, products of any other generator by integers of the ring.

Definition 2. An ideal $\mathfrak{a} = (\alpha)$, that can be generated by a single generator is called a *principal ideal*.

Theorem 2. *Two principal ideals $\mathfrak{a} = (\alpha)$ and $\mathfrak{b} = (\beta)$ are equal if and only if the generators α and β are associates.*

PROOF. $\mathfrak{a} = \mathfrak{b} \Leftrightarrow \alpha \mid \beta$ and $\beta \mid \alpha$.

Theorem 3. *In $\mathbf{Z}$ all ideals are principal.*

PROOF left to the reader.

REMARK 4. The ideal (1) is identical with the ring $\mathbf{I}$ or by Remark 1, $(1) = \mathfrak{i}$; conversely, it follows from Theorem 2 that if $(\alpha) = \mathfrak{i}$, then α is a unit.

Definition 3. Given the ideals $\mathfrak{a} = (\alpha_1, \alpha_2, ..., \alpha_m)$ and $\mathfrak{b} = (\beta_1, \beta_2, ..., \beta_k)$ we call *product* of $\mathfrak{a}$ and $\mathfrak{b}$ the ideal $\mathfrak{c}$ generated by all products $\alpha_i \beta_j$.

REMARK 5. $\mathfrak{c}$ depends only on $\mathfrak{a}$ and $\mathfrak{b}$, not on the particular set of generators (why?).

Theorem 4. *The multiplication of ideals is commutative and associative.*

PROOF. This follows from the corresponding properties of the multiplication of integers.

NOTATION. We shall denote products of ideals by themselves as powers. For instance, $\mathfrak{a} \cdot \mathfrak{a} = \mathfrak{a}^2$, $\mathfrak{a} \cdots\cdots \mathfrak{a} = \mathfrak{a}^m$, $\mathfrak{a}^0 = (1) = \mathfrak{i} = \mathbf{I}$.

Definition 4. If $\mathfrak{a} = \mathfrak{b} \cdot \mathfrak{c}$, we say that $\mathfrak{a}$ has the *factors* $\mathfrak{b}$ and $\mathfrak{c}$ and that $\mathfrak{b}$ and $\mathfrak{c}$ *divide* $\mathfrak{a}$; in symbols, $\mathfrak{b} \mid \mathfrak{a}$, $\mathfrak{c} \mid \mathfrak{a}$.

The statements of the following theorem are immediate consequences of the definitions and their proofs are left to the reader.

Theorem 5. *If* $\mathfrak{a} = (\alpha)$ *and* $\mathfrak{b} = (\beta)$ *are principal ideals, then*

(1) $\mathfrak{b} \mid \mathfrak{a} \Leftrightarrow \beta \mid \alpha$; *for all ideals* $\mathfrak{a}, \mathfrak{b}, \mathfrak{c}, \mathfrak{d}$ *one has*

(2) $\mathfrak{a} \mid \mathfrak{b}, \mathfrak{b} \mid \mathfrak{c} \Rightarrow \mathfrak{a} \mid \mathfrak{c}$;

(3) $\mathfrak{a} \mid \mathfrak{b} \Rightarrow \mathfrak{a}\mathfrak{d} \mid \mathfrak{b}\mathfrak{d}$;

(4) $\mathfrak{i} \mid \mathfrak{a}$;

(5) $\mathfrak{a} \mid \mathfrak{a}$.

Definition 5. We say that $\alpha(\in I)$ is divisible by an ideal $\mathfrak{a}$ if and only if the principal ideal (α) is divisible by $\mathfrak{a}$, that is, if and only if $\mathfrak{a} \mid (\alpha)$.

Theorem 6. $\mathfrak{a} \mid \mathfrak{b} \Rightarrow \mathfrak{a} \supset \mathfrak{b}$ (*that is, each integer of* $\mathfrak{b}$ *belongs to* $\mathfrak{a}$).

PROOF. Follows from Definition 3.

Corollary 6.1. $\mathfrak{a} \mid \mathfrak{i} \Rightarrow \mathfrak{a} = \mathfrak{i}$.

PROOF left to the reader.

Definition 6. An ideal $\mathfrak{p} \neq \mathfrak{i}$ is said to be a prime ideal if it has no other factors except $\mathfrak{p}$ itself and $\mathfrak{i}$.

Definition 7. A set $\alpha_1, \ldots, \alpha_k \in \mathfrak{a}$ is said to form a *basis* for $\mathfrak{a}$ if every integer $\alpha \in \mathfrak{a}$ has exactly one representation of the form $\alpha = a_1\alpha_1 + \cdots + a_k\alpha_k$, with $a_j \in \mathbf{Z}(1 \leq j \leq k)$.

Theorem 7. *Every ideal* $\mathfrak{a}(\neq \mathfrak{o})$ *has a basis.*

PROOFS may be found in [4], pp. 78–79 or [1], pp. 116–117 but will not be given here, because the theorem itself, quoted for its intrinsic interest, will not be used.

Theorem 8. *There exist only finitely many ideals containing a given integer* $a \in \mathbf{Z}$.

PROOF. Let $\mathfrak{a} = (\alpha_1, \alpha_2, \ldots, \alpha_m)$ contain $a \in \mathbf{Z}$. Then, by Remark 3, $\mathfrak{a} = (\alpha_1, \ldots, \alpha_m, a)$. If $(\omega_1, \ldots, \omega_n)$ is an integral basis (one always exists; see 9.5.42), then $\alpha_j = a_{j1}\omega_1 + \cdots + a_{jn}\omega_n(a_{jk} \in \mathbf{Z})$. Clearly, there exist $q_{jk} \in \mathbf{Z}$, $r_{jk} \in \mathbf{Z}$ such that $a_{jk} = aq_{jk} + r_{jk}$, with $0 \leq r_{jk} < a$. Hence, if we set $\sum_{k=1}^{n} r_{jk}\omega_k = \beta_j$ and use Remark 3 once more, we obtain $\mathfrak{a} = (\beta_1, \beta_2, \ldots, \beta_m, a)$. Here a is fixed and the β_j each may take only finitely many values, namely, those of the sums $\sum_{k=1}^{n} r_{jk}\omega_k$ with $0 \leq r_{jk} \leq a - 1$. Also, by Remark 3 we know that we need to keep only independent elements as generators and it follows from 9.5.42 that there can exist at most n such elements, if the degree of the field is n. Hence, $m \le n$ and the total number of ideals $\mathfrak{a} = (\beta_1, \beta_2, ..., \beta_m, a)$ that may contain $a \in \mathbf{Z}$ is indeed finite.

3. DIVISIBILITY PROPERTIES OF IDEALS

Theorem 9.   *An ideal $\mathfrak{a}$ has only a finite number of factors.*

PROOF. First we recall, that by Theorem 6, $\mathfrak{b} \mid \mathfrak{a} \Leftrightarrow \mathfrak{b} \supset \mathfrak{a}$. Next, by Theorem 1, $\alpha \in \mathfrak{a}, \lambda \in \mathbf{I} \Rightarrow \lambda\alpha \in \mathfrak{a}$. Taking in particular λ as product of all conjugates of α (Why is λ an integer? Why is λ in $\mathbf{K}$?), $\lambda\alpha = N\alpha \in \mathfrak{a}$; hence, if $\mathfrak{b} \mid \mathfrak{a}$, then $N\alpha = a(\in \mathbf{Z})$ belongs also to $\mathfrak{b}$. However, by Theorem 8, the number of ideals containing a given $a(\in \mathbf{Z})$ is finite and the Theorem is proven.

Theorem 10.   *Given an ideal $\mathfrak{a}$, there exists an ideal $\mathfrak{b}$ such that $\mathfrak{a} \cdot \mathfrak{b} = (a), a \in \mathbf{Z}^+$, that is, such that the product is a principal ideal, generated by a positive rational integer.*

In view of the great importance of this theorem, it is recommended that the reader make the necessary effort to understand thoroughly the not very simple proof.

PROOF OF THEOREM 10. Let $\mathfrak{a} = (\alpha_0, \alpha_1, ..., \alpha_m)$ and consider the polynomial $f(x) = \alpha_0 x^m + \alpha_1 x^{m-1} + \cdots + \alpha_{m-1}x + \alpha_m$; by Remark 3 we may assume that $\alpha_0 \ne 0$. By 9.5.28 each element α of $\mathbf{K}$ is of the form $\alpha = p(\theta)$, where θ generates $\mathbf{K}$, of degree n, and $p(x) \in \mathbf{Z}[x]$ is a polynomial of degree $\le n - 1$. The conjugates of α are, by definition (see 9.5.25 and 9.5.28) $\alpha^{(j)} = p(\theta^{(j)})$, where $\theta^{(j)}(j = 1, 2, ..., n)$ are the conjugates of θ. In particular, let $\alpha_i = p_i(\theta)$ $(i = 0, 1, ..., m)$. In the polynomial $g(x) = \prod_{j=1}^{n}\{p_0(\theta^{(j)})x^m + \cdots + p_m(\theta^{(j)})\} = \sum_{j=0}^{N}c_j x^{N-j}(N = m \cdot n)$ the coefficients c_j are symmetric polynomials with integral rational coefficients of $\theta = \theta^{(1)}, \theta^{(2)}, ..., \theta^{(n)}$; hence, by 9.5.27, they are polynomials with rational, integral coefficients in the coefficients $A_1, A_2, ..., A_n$ of the irreducible equation satisfied by θ. These A_j being rational, so are the coefficients c_j. On the other hand, they are products of integers, as follows from the product representation of $g(x)$. Consequently, the c_j's are rational integers, and $g \in \mathbf{Z}[x]$. Also, $g(x) = f(x)h(x)$, so that $h(x) = g(x)/f(x)$ is a rational function with coefficients in $\mathbf{K}$. However, again from the product representation of $g(x)$ it is clear that $h(x)$ is a polynomial in x with integer coefficients; consequently, $h \in \mathbf{I}[x]$, say, $h(x) = \beta_0 x^k + \cdots + \beta_{k-1}x + \beta_k$, $(\beta_j \in \mathbf{I}, \beta_0 \ne 0)$. If we define $\mathfrak{b} = (\beta_0, \beta_1, ..., \beta_k)$ we claim that $\mathfrak{a} \cdot \mathfrak{b} = (c)$, where c is the content of $g(x)$.

Indeed, by its definition, $c = (c_0, c_1, ..., c_N)$. It is a consequence of Gauss' Lemma (see 9.5.19, also Appendix B, Section 4(c)) that $c \mid c_j$ (for all j) $\Rightarrow$ $c \mid \alpha_i \beta_j$ (all i, j) $\Rightarrow$ $(c) \supset (\alpha_0 \beta_0, \alpha_0 \beta_1, ..., \alpha_i \beta_j, ...) = \mathfrak{a} \cdot \mathfrak{b}$. Also $\{c_j/c\}$ is a set of rational integers whose g.c.d. is one. Therefore (recall, Problem 9 in Chapter 3), there exist integers $a_j \in \mathbf{Z}$ such that

$$a_0 \frac{c_0}{c} + a_1 \frac{c_1}{c} + \cdots + a_j \frac{c_j}{c} + \cdots + a_N \frac{c_N}{c} = 1,$$

or

$$a_0 c_0 + \cdots + a_j c_j + \cdots + a_N c_N = c.$$

Replacing the c_j's by their values $\sum_k \alpha_k \beta_{j-k}$,

$$c = \sum_{j=0}^{N} \sum_k \alpha_k \beta_{j \rightarrow k} \Rightarrow c \in \mathfrak{a} \cdot \mathfrak{b} \Rightarrow (c) \subset \mathfrak{a} \cdot \mathfrak{b}.$$

These two opposite inclusions prove that $\mathfrak{a}\mathfrak{b} = (c)$, as claimed.

Theorem 11.   *If (γ) is a principal ideal and $(\gamma)\mathfrak{a} = (\gamma)\mathfrak{b}$ then $\mathfrak{a} = \mathfrak{b}$.*

PROOF. By hypothesis, for every $\alpha \in \mathfrak{a}$, $\gamma\alpha$ equals an integer of the form $\gamma\beta$, $\beta \in \mathfrak{b}$; or, to each integer $\alpha \in \mathfrak{a}$ corresponds an integer $\beta \in \mathfrak{b}$ such that $\alpha = \beta$. This shows that $\mathfrak{a} \supset \mathfrak{b}$. By symmetry, $\mathfrak{b} \supset \mathfrak{a}$, whence $\mathfrak{a} = \mathfrak{b}$ follows immediately.

Theorem 12 (Cancellation Law).   *If $\mathfrak{a}, \mathfrak{b}, \mathfrak{c}$ are ideals of $\mathbf{K}$, then $\mathfrak{c}\mathfrak{a} = \mathfrak{c}\mathfrak{b} \Rightarrow \mathfrak{a} = \mathfrak{b}$.*

PROOF. By Theorem 10 we can find an ideal $\mathfrak{d} \ni \mathfrak{d}\mathfrak{c} = (c)$. Hence, $\mathfrak{c}\mathfrak{a} = \mathfrak{c}\mathfrak{b} \Rightarrow \mathfrak{d}\mathfrak{c}\mathfrak{a} = \mathfrak{d}\mathfrak{c}\mathfrak{b} \Rightarrow (c)\mathfrak{a} = (c)\mathfrak{b} \Rightarrow \mathfrak{a} = \mathfrak{b}$ by Theorem 11.

REMARK 6. One should remember that in the statement and proof of Theorem 12 (like in other statements and proofs) it is tacitly assumed that $\mathfrak{c} \neq \mathfrak{o}$.

Theorem 13. $\mathfrak{a} \supset \mathfrak{b} \Rightarrow \mathfrak{a} \mid \mathfrak{b}$.

REMARK 7. Theorem 13 is the converse of Theorem 6.

PROOF OF THEOREM 13. $\mathfrak{a} \supset \mathfrak{b} \Rightarrow \mathfrak{c}\mathfrak{a} \supset \mathfrak{c}\mathfrak{b}$ for any $\mathfrak{c}$. In particular, if $\mathfrak{c}$ has been chosen so that $\mathfrak{c}\mathfrak{a} = (d)$, then each element of $\mathfrak{c}\mathfrak{b}$ is a multiple of d and, therefore, $\mathfrak{c}\mathfrak{b}$ is of the form $(d)(\gamma_1, \gamma_2, ..., \gamma_r) = \mathfrak{c}\mathfrak{a}(\gamma_1, \gamma_2, ..., \gamma_r)$. By Theorem 12 cancellation is permitted and

$$\mathfrak{c}\mathfrak{b} = \mathfrak{c}\mathfrak{a}(\gamma_1, ..., \gamma_r) \Rightarrow \mathfrak{b} = \mathfrak{a}(\gamma_1, ..., \gamma_r) \Rightarrow \mathfrak{a} \mid \mathfrak{b}.$$

REMARK 8. In more general situations it is convenient to make a distinction between the concepts of maximal ideal, prime ideal and irreducible ideal;

but these objects coincide in the present setting. The three conceptually distinct properties which an ideal may have:

(i) to have no factors, except i and itself (irreducibility);

(ii) to divide at least one factor if it divides a product of two integers of **I** (primality); or

(iii) not to be contained properly in any other ideal except i (maximality),

go together for ideals in algebraic number fields. Either an ideal has all three, or none of them. This is the reason why we did not define formally irreducible, prime and maximal ideals, but only prime ideals (Definition 6), which we characterized by property (i). On account of Theorems 6 and 13 it is clear that properties (i) and (iii) are equivalent. One can easily prove directly also (iii) ⟺ (ii), but we shall not do it, because the implication (i) or (iii) ⟹ (ii) will come out anyway, as a corollary, and the implication (ii) ⟹ (i) or (iii) is left to the reader.

4. UNIQUENESS OF FACTORIZATION OF IDEALS INTO PRIME IDEALS

Theorem 14. *If* $a \mid b$, $a \neq b$, *then* a *has fewer factors than* b.

PROOF. $b = ac$, $c \neq i$; therefore, every factor of a is also a factor of b. However, b has at least one factor which is not a factor of a, namely, b itself.

Theorem 15. *Every ideal* a *can be factored into prime ideals.*

PROOF. If in every factorization $a = bc$ either $b = i$ or $c = i$ then a is a prime ideal and the Theorem holds. Otherwise, by Theorem 9, a contains only a finite number of factors; by Theorem 14, each of the ideals b and c contain fewer factors than a. Hence, repeating the reasoning on them, in a finite number of steps we reach ideals with at most one factor, that is, prime ideals.

Theorem 16. *If* p *and* q *are distinct rational primes and the prime ideal* $\mathfrak{p} \mid (p)$, *then* $\mathfrak{p} \nmid (q)$.

PROOF. By Corollary 3.6.3, $(p, q) = 1 \Rightarrow \exists\, m, n \ni mp + nq = 1$ or $(p, q) = (1)$. (This illustrates the double meaning of the symbol (p, q), which, however cannot lead to any ambiguity!) If $\mathfrak{p} \mid (p)$ and $\mathfrak{p} \mid (q)$, then every multiple of p and every multiple of q belongs to $\mathfrak{p}$. But $\mathfrak{p}$ is an ideal; hence, by Theorem 1, it contains in particular, $mp + nq = 1$ so that $\mathfrak{p} = (1)$, which is contrary to the definition of a prime ideal.

Corollary 16.1.   *In every field of algebraic numbers there exist infinitely many prime ideals.*

PROOF left to the reader.

Definition 8.   Let $\mathfrak{a}$ and $\mathfrak{b}$ be ideals in **K**. If there exists in **K** an ideal $\mathfrak{d}$ such that:

   (i) $\mathfrak{d} \mid \mathfrak{a}, \mathfrak{d} \mid \mathfrak{b}$; and

   (ii) $\mathfrak{c} \mid \mathfrak{a}, \mathfrak{c} \mid \mathfrak{b} \Rightarrow \mathfrak{c} \mid \mathfrak{d}$,

then $\mathfrak{d}$ is called the *greatest common divisor* (g.c.d.) of $\mathfrak{a}$ and $\mathfrak{b}$.

Theorem 17.   *Any two ideals $\mathfrak{a}$ and $\mathfrak{b}$ of **K** have a g.c.d. $\mathfrak{d}$, in symbols* $\mathfrak{d} = (\mathfrak{a}, \mathfrak{b})$.

PROOF. If $\mathfrak{a} = (\alpha_1, \alpha_2, \ldots, \alpha_r)$ and $\mathfrak{b} = (\beta_1, \beta_2, \ldots, \beta_s)$, then one verifies that $\mathfrak{d} = (\alpha_1, \ldots, \alpha_r, \beta_1, \ldots, \beta_s)$ has the required properties.

Corollary 17.1.   *The elements of $(\mathfrak{a}, \mathfrak{b})$ are of the form $\alpha + \beta$ with $\alpha \in \mathfrak{a}$, $\beta \in \mathfrak{b}$.*

PROOF. The proof follows from the fact that $\mathfrak{d} = (\alpha_1, \ldots, \alpha_r, \beta_1, \ldots, \beta_s)$ (see Proof of Theorem 17).

Definition 9.   If $(\mathfrak{a}, \mathfrak{b}) = \mathfrak{i}$, then $\mathfrak{a}$ and $\mathfrak{b}$ are called *coprime*.

Corollary 17.2. $(\mathfrak{a}, \mathfrak{b}) = \mathfrak{i} \Rightarrow \exists \alpha \in \mathfrak{a}, \beta \in \mathfrak{b} \ni \alpha + \beta = 1$.

PROOF. $1 \in \mathfrak{i}$; hence, the result follows from Corollary 17.1.

Theorem 18.   *If $\mathfrak{p}$ is a prime ideal, then $\mathfrak{p} \mid \mathfrak{ab}, \mathfrak{p} \nmid \mathfrak{a} \Rightarrow \mathfrak{p} \mid \mathfrak{b}$.*

PROOF. $\mathfrak{p} \nmid \mathfrak{a} \Rightarrow (\mathfrak{p}, \mathfrak{a}) = \mathfrak{i} \Rightarrow \exists \alpha \in \mathfrak{a}, \pi \in \mathfrak{p} \ni \alpha + \pi = 1$ (because of Corollary 17.1). Therefore, for every $\beta \in \mathfrak{b}$, $\beta\alpha + \beta\pi = \beta$. By assumption, $\mathfrak{p} \mid \mathfrak{ab}$ so that $\alpha\beta \in \mathfrak{p}$; also, $\beta\pi \in \mathfrak{p}$; consequently, for every $\beta \in \mathfrak{b}$, also $\beta \in \mathfrak{p}$ holds, so that $\mathfrak{b} \supset \mathfrak{p}$ or $\mathfrak{p} \mid \mathfrak{b}$, by Theorem 13.

Corollary 18.1. $\mathfrak{p} \mid (\alpha)(\beta), \mathfrak{p} \nmid (\alpha) \Rightarrow \mathfrak{p} \mid (\beta)$.

PROOF. Take $\mathfrak{a} = (\alpha)$ and $\mathfrak{b} = (\beta)$ in Theorem 18.

REMARK 9. This proves the implication (i) or (iii) $\Rightarrow$ (ii) alluded to in Remark 8.

Theorem 19.   *If $\mathfrak{p}$ is a prime ideal, and $\mathfrak{p} \mid \mathfrak{a}_1, \cdots \mathfrak{a}_r$, then $\mathfrak{p}$ divides at least one ideal $\mathfrak{a}_j (1 \leq j \leq r)$.*

PROOF. By induction on r, starting with $r = 2$, which is Theorem 18.

The reader will already have sensed a certain parallelism between the last few theorems and some results of Chapter 3 leading to the unique factorization in $\mathbf{Z}$. This is indeed the case and we are actually ready to draw the principal conclusion, namely,

Theorem 20. *The ideals of* $\mathbf{K}$ *factor into prime ideals and this factorization is unique except for order.*

PROOF. The same as that of Theorem 3.3, using Theorem 19 instead of Corollary 3.4.1.

5. IDEAL CLASSES AND THE CLASS-NUMBER

Definition 10. Two integers α and β of $\mathbf{I}$ are said to be *congruent modulo an ideal* $\mathfrak{a}$, in symbols $\alpha \equiv \beta \pmod{\mathfrak{a}}$, if $\mathfrak{a} \mid \alpha - \beta$ or, equivalently (because of Definition 5), if $\mathfrak{a} \mid (\alpha - \beta)$.

Theorem 21. *Congruence modulo an ideal is an equivalence relation.*

PROOF left to the reader.

Theorem 22. $\alpha \equiv \beta \pmod{\mathfrak{a}}$ *and* $\mathfrak{c} \mid \mathfrak{a} \Rightarrow \alpha \equiv \beta \pmod{\mathfrak{c}}$.

PROOF left to the reader.

Corollary 22.1. *Let* $\alpha, \beta, \gamma, \delta, \lambda \in \mathbf{I}$ *and let* $\mathfrak{a}$ *be an ideal in* $\mathbf{K}$; *then* $\alpha \equiv \beta \pmod{\mathfrak{a}}$, $\gamma \equiv \delta \pmod{\mathfrak{a}} \Rightarrow \alpha \pm \gamma \equiv \beta \pm \delta \pmod{\mathfrak{a}}$, $\alpha\gamma \equiv \beta\delta \pmod{\mathfrak{a}}$ *and* $\lambda\alpha \equiv \lambda\beta \pmod{\mathfrak{a}}$.

PROOF left to the reader.

Theorem 23. *The set of residue classes modulo an ideal is finite.*

PROOF OF THEOREM 23. Let $\mathfrak{a}$ be an ideal in $\mathbf{K}$. By Theorem 10 we can find an ideal $\mathfrak{b}$ so that $\mathfrak{a} \cdot \mathfrak{b} = (c)$, $c > 0$. Let $\omega_1, \omega_2, \ldots, \omega_n$ be an integral basis; then every $\alpha \in \mathbf{I}$ has a representation $\alpha = a_1\omega_1 + \cdots + a_n\omega_n (a_j \in \mathbf{Z})$. If we consider first the number of residue classes modulo c, it is clear that each coefficient a_j may belong to only c residue classes; consequently, α can belong to at most (actually, exactly!) c^n residue classes $\pmod{c}$. This is also the number of residue classes $\pmod{(c)}$. By Theorem 22 it now follows that there are at most c^n residue classes mod $\mathfrak{a}$.

Definition 11. The number of residue classes of integers of $\mathbf{I}$ modulo an ideal $\mathfrak{a}$ is called the *norm* of $\mathfrak{a}$, in symbols; $N(\mathfrak{a})$ or $N\mathfrak{a}$. In the case of principal ideals we write $N((\alpha))$ to avoid confusion with $N\alpha = N(\alpha)$.

The reader may wonder whether this terminology could not lead to confusion. Indeed, we already have a definition for the norm $N(\alpha)$ of an integer

$\alpha \in I$. Now, we give a new definition for the norm of the corresponding principal ideal, $N((\alpha))$. As a matter of fact, the two are closely related by

Theorem 24.   *If* $\alpha \in I$, *then,* $N((\alpha)) = |N(\alpha)|$.

The proof will not be given, and the Theorem, quoted mainly for completeness, will be used only once (in the proof of Lemma 3). Proofs may be found, for instance, in [4], p. 107 or [1], p. 119; see also Problem 17.

REMARK 10. $N\mathfrak{a} = 1 \Leftrightarrow \mathfrak{a} = \mathfrak{i}$, because $N\mathfrak{a} = 1$ means that all integers are congruent to each other, hence to $0 (\in \mathfrak{a})$ so that all belong to $\mathfrak{a}$.

Theorem 25.   *If* $\mathfrak{a}$ *is an ideal and* $\mathfrak{p}$ *a prime ideal of* $\mathbf{K}$ *then* $N\mathfrak{a} \cdot N\mathfrak{p} = N(\mathfrak{a}\mathfrak{p})$.

PROOF. $\mathfrak{p} \neq \mathfrak{i} \Rightarrow \mathfrak{a}\mathfrak{p} \neq \mathfrak{a}$; hence, $\exists \alpha \in I \ni \mathfrak{a} \mid \alpha$, $\mathfrak{a}\mathfrak{p} \nmid \alpha$ or, equivalently (see Definition 5), $\mathfrak{a} \mid (\alpha)$, $\mathfrak{a}\mathfrak{p} \nmid (\alpha)$. We also note that if $(\alpha) = \mathfrak{a} \cdot \mathfrak{b}$, then $\mathfrak{p} \nmid \mathfrak{b}$; otherwise $\mathfrak{a}\mathfrak{p} \mid \mathfrak{a}\mathfrak{b} \Rightarrow \mathfrak{a}\mathfrak{p} \mid (\alpha)$, which is false.

Consider now the $N\mathfrak{a}$ residue classes mod $\mathfrak{a}$ and let $\alpha_1, \alpha_2, ..., \alpha_{N\mathfrak{a}}$ be integers of I, incongruent mod $\mathfrak{a}$; select similarly $\pi_1, \pi_2, ..., \pi_{N\mathfrak{p}}$ as representatives of the $N\mathfrak{p}$ distinct residue classes mod $\mathfrak{p}$. We claim that the $N\mathfrak{a} \cdot N\mathfrak{p}$ integers $\alpha\pi_j + \alpha_k (1 \leq j \leq N\mathfrak{p}, 1 \leq k \leq N\mathfrak{a})$ have the following two properties:

    (i) no two of them are congruent mod $\mathfrak{a}\mathfrak{p}$; and

    (ii) every integer $\gamma \in I$ is congruent to one of them mod $\mathfrak{a}\mathfrak{p}$.

This will finish the proof that there exist exactly $N\mathfrak{a} \cdot N\mathfrak{p}$ residue classes mod $\mathfrak{a}\mathfrak{p}$, as asserted by the Theorem.

PROOF OF (i). Assume $\alpha\pi_{j_1} + \alpha_{k_1} \neq \alpha\pi_{j_2} + \alpha_{k_2}$, with $\alpha\pi_{j_1} + \alpha_{k_1} \equiv \alpha\pi_{j_2} + \alpha_{k_2} (\mathrm{mod}\ \mathfrak{a}\mathfrak{p})$; by Theorem 22, $\alpha\pi_{j_1} + \alpha_{k_1} \equiv \alpha\pi_{j_2} + \alpha_{k_2} (\ \mathrm{mod}\ \mathfrak{a})$ or (remember: $\mathfrak{a} \mid \alpha$) $\alpha_{k_1} \equiv \alpha_{k_2} (\mathrm{mod}\ \mathfrak{a})$, so that $k_1 = k_2$ and the original congruence reduces to $\alpha\pi_{j_1} \equiv \alpha\pi_{j_2} (\mathrm{mod}\ \mathfrak{a}\mathfrak{p})$, that is, $\mathfrak{a}\mathfrak{p} \mid \mathfrak{a}\mathfrak{b}(\pi_{j_1} - \pi_{j_2})$, or $\mathfrak{p} \mid \mathfrak{b}(\pi_{j_1} - \pi_{j_2})$. But $\mathfrak{p} \nmid \mathfrak{b}$; hence $\mathfrak{p} \mid (\pi_{j_1} - \pi_{j_2})$ which is possible only if $j_1 = j_2$ and the two integers were not distinct, contrary to our assumption.

PROOF OF (ii). If $\gamma \in I$, then it is congruent to some $\alpha_j (\mathrm{mod}\ \mathfrak{a})$, that is, $\gamma = \alpha' + \alpha_j$, $\alpha' \in \mathfrak{a}$. From $\mathfrak{p} \nmid \mathfrak{b}$ follows that $((\alpha), \mathfrak{p}\mathfrak{a}) = (\mathfrak{b}\mathfrak{a}, \mathfrak{p}\mathfrak{a}) = \mathfrak{a}$, so that, by Corollary 17.1, $\alpha' \in \mathfrak{a} \Rightarrow \alpha' = \lambda\alpha + \mu(\lambda \in I, \mu \in \mathfrak{p}\mathfrak{a})$. By the definition of the π_j's, $\exists k (1 \leq k \leq N\mathfrak{p}) \ni \lambda \equiv \pi_k (\mathrm{mod}\ \mathfrak{p})$, that is, $\lambda = \pi' + \pi_k$, $\pi' \in \mathfrak{p}$. Consequently,

$$\gamma = \lambda\alpha + \mu + \alpha_j = (\pi' + \pi_k)\alpha + \mu + \alpha_j = (\pi'\alpha + \mu) + \pi_k\alpha + \alpha_j.$$

However, $\pi'\alpha \in \mathfrak{p}\mathfrak{a}$, $\mu \in \mathfrak{p}\mathfrak{a}$ so that $\gamma \equiv \pi_k\alpha + \alpha_j (\mathrm{mod}\ \mathfrak{a}\mathfrak{p})$ as claimed and the proof is complete.

Theorem 26. *Let* $\mathfrak{a}$, $\mathfrak{b}$, $\mathfrak{c}$ *be ideals in* **K**; *then* $\mathfrak{a} \cdot \mathfrak{b} = \mathfrak{c} \Rightarrow N\mathfrak{a} \cdot N\mathfrak{b} = N\mathfrak{c}$.

PROOF. The proof is by induction on the number of factors of $\mathfrak{b}$. If $\mathfrak{b} = \mathfrak{p}$, $N\mathfrak{a} \cdot N\mathfrak{p} = N(\mathfrak{a}\mathfrak{p})$ by Theorem 25; if Theorem 25 is known to hold for $\mathfrak{b}$ containing $k - 1$ prime ideal factors, then it holds also for $\mathfrak{b} = \mathfrak{p}_1 \cdots \mathfrak{p}_{k-1}\mathfrak{p}$ as follows: Let $\mathfrak{b} = \mathfrak{b}_1\mathfrak{p}$; then $N(\mathfrak{a} \cdot \mathfrak{b}) = N(\mathfrak{a} \cdot \mathfrak{b}_1 \cdot \mathfrak{p}) = N(\mathfrak{a}\mathfrak{b}_1) \cdot N\mathfrak{p}$ by Theorem 25. Also, by the induction assumption, $N(\mathfrak{a}\mathfrak{b}_1) = N\mathfrak{a} \cdot N\mathfrak{b}_1$; hence, $N(\mathfrak{a} \cdot \mathfrak{b}) = N\mathfrak{a} \cdot N\mathfrak{b}_1 \cdot N\mathfrak{p} = N\mathfrak{a} \cdot N(\mathfrak{b}_1 \cdot \mathfrak{p})$ by Theorem 25. Replacing $\mathfrak{b}_1 \cdot \mathfrak{p}$ by $\mathfrak{b}$, the Theorem is proven.

Theorem 27. *If* $\mathfrak{a}$ *is an ideal of* **K**, *then* $\mathfrak{a} \mid N\mathfrak{a}$ (i.e. $\mathfrak{a} \mid (N\mathfrak{a})$).

PROOF. If $\alpha_1, \alpha_2, ..., \alpha_{N\mathfrak{a}}$ are a maximal set of integers incongruent mod $\mathfrak{a}$ (so that there is exactly one out of every residue class), then the same property belongs also to the set $\alpha_1 + 1, \alpha_2 + 2, ..., \alpha_{N\mathfrak{a}} + 1$; consequently $\alpha_1 + \alpha_2 + \cdots + \alpha_{N\mathfrak{a}} \equiv (\alpha_1 + 1) + \cdots + (\alpha_{N\mathfrak{a}} + 1) \,(\mathrm{mod}\,\mathfrak{a})$ or, simplifying, $0 \equiv 1 + 1 + \cdots + 1 = N\mathfrak{a}\,(\mathrm{mod}\,\mathfrak{a})$.

Theorem 28. *For every* $m \in \mathbf{Z}^+$, *there exist only finitely many ideals* $\mathfrak{a}$ *such that* $N\mathfrak{a} = m$.

PROOF. By Theorem 27, $\mathfrak{a} \mid m$; by Theorem 8 there exist only finitely many such ideals $\mathfrak{a}$, for any given $m \in \mathbf{Z}^+$.

Definition 12. Two ideals $\mathfrak{a}$ and $\mathfrak{b}$ of **K** are said to be *equivalent*, in symbols $\mathfrak{a} \sim \mathfrak{b}$, if there exist algebraic integers $\alpha, \beta \in \mathbf{I}$ such that $(\alpha)\mathfrak{a} = (\beta)\mathfrak{b}$.

Theorem 29. *The equivalence of ideals is an equivalence relation.*

PROOF.

(i) $\mathfrak{a} \sim \mathfrak{a}$ because $(1)\mathfrak{a} = (1)\mathfrak{a}$;

(ii) $\mathfrak{a} \sim \mathfrak{b}$ means $(\alpha)\mathfrak{a} = (\beta)\mathfrak{b}$ for some $\alpha, \beta \in \mathbf{I}$, so that $(\beta)\mathfrak{b} = (\alpha)\mathfrak{a}$ and $\mathfrak{b} \sim \mathfrak{a}$;

(iii) $\mathfrak{a} \sim \mathfrak{b}$, $\mathfrak{b} \sim \mathfrak{c} \Leftrightarrow (\alpha)\mathfrak{a} = (\beta_1)\mathfrak{b}$, $(\beta_2)\mathfrak{b}, = (\gamma)\mathfrak{c} \Leftrightarrow (\beta_2)(\alpha)\mathfrak{a} = (\beta_2)(\beta_1)\mathfrak{b}$ $= (\beta_1)(\gamma)\mathfrak{c} \Leftrightarrow (\beta_2\alpha)\mathfrak{a} = (\beta_1\gamma)\mathfrak{c}$ with $\alpha, \beta_1, \beta_2, \gamma \in \mathbf{I}$ and $\mathfrak{a} \sim \mathfrak{c}$.

Definition 13. The classes induced by the equivalence relation $\sim$ among ideals are called ideal classes.

REMARK 11. The principal ideals are equivalent to each other (and to $\mathfrak{i} = (1)$); hence, they form one of the classes, sometimes called the *principal class*.

We come now to one of the fundamental results of the theory of ideals, namely,

Theorem 30.   *In every field* **K** *of algebraic numbers, the number of ideal classes is finite.*

The proof of Theorem 30 requires several Lemmas.

Lemma 1.   *Let* $\mathfrak{a}$, $\mathfrak{b}$, $\mathfrak{c}$, $\mathfrak{d}$ *be ideals in* **K**; *then* $\mathfrak{a} \sim \mathfrak{b}$, $\mathfrak{c} \sim \mathfrak{d} \Rightarrow \mathfrak{ac} \sim \mathfrak{bd}$.

PROOF.   By   assumption $\exists \, \alpha, \beta, \gamma, \delta \in \mathbf{I} \ni (\alpha)\mathfrak{a} = (\beta)\mathfrak{b}, \, (\gamma)\mathfrak{c} = (\delta)\mathfrak{d}$;   consequently $(\alpha\gamma)\mathfrak{ac} = (\beta\delta)\mathfrak{bd}$, so that $\mathfrak{ac} \sim \mathfrak{bd}$.

Lemma 2.   *For every field* **K** *of algebraic numbers there exists a positive integer* $m = m(\mathbf{K})$ *with the property that in every ideal* $\mathfrak{a}$ *of* **K** *there exists an integer* $\alpha \in \mathfrak{a}$ *such that* $|N\alpha| \leq m \cdot N\mathfrak{a}$.

PROOF.   Let $\omega_1, \ldots, \omega_n$ be an integral basis for **K**. By 9.5.3 and 9.5.28 each ω_j is (uniquely) represented by a polynomial in the generator θ of **K**, $\omega_j = g_j(\theta)$. If $\theta = \theta^{(1)}, \theta^{(2)}, \ldots, \theta^{(n)}$ are the conjugates of θ, then the conjugates of ω_j are $\omega_j^{(k)} = g_j(\theta^{(k)})$. Let $M = \prod_{k=1}^{n} \{\sum_{j=1}^{n} |\omega_j^{(k)}|\}$; then M has the required property and we may take $m = [M] + 1$. Indeed, for every ideal $\mathfrak{a}$ we can determine an integer r such that $r^n \leq N\mathfrak{a} < (r + 1)^n$. Next, consider the set of integers of **I** represented by $a_1\omega_1 + a_2\omega_2 + \cdots + a_n\omega_n$ with $0 \leq a_j \leq r$. Each a_j may take $r + 1$ distinct values; hence, we obtain $(r + 1)^n$ different integers of **I**. But these cannot be all incongruent mod $\mathfrak{a}$, because there exist only $N\mathfrak{a} < (r + 1)^n$ residue classes mod $\mathfrak{a}$. Hence, among these integers,   there   are   at   least   two,   say $\alpha = a_1\omega_1 + \cdots + a_n\omega_n$ and $\beta = b_1\omega_1 + \cdots + b_n\omega_n$, such that $\alpha \neq \beta$, but $\alpha \equiv \beta \pmod{\mathfrak{a}}$, and with $0 \leq a_j \leq r$, $0 \leq b_j \leq r$. Then $0 \neq \gamma = \alpha - \beta \equiv 0 \pmod{\mathfrak{a}}$ so that $\gamma \in \mathfrak{a}$. Also $|N\gamma| = |\prod_{k=1}^{n} \gamma^{(k)}|$; however,

$$|\gamma^{(k)}| = |\sum_{j=1}^{n} (a_j - b_j)\omega_j^{(k)}| \leq \sum_{j=1}^{n} r|\omega_j^{(k)}| = r \sum_{j=1}^{n} |\omega_j^{(k)}|,$$

so that

$$|N\gamma| = \prod_{k=1}^{n} |\gamma^{(k)}| \leq r^n \prod_{k=1}^{n} \left\{ \sum_{j=1}^{n} |\omega_j^{(k)}| \right\} = r^n M \leq N\mathfrak{a} \cdot M,$$

and $\gamma \in \mathfrak{a}$ has $|N\gamma| \leq M \cdot N\mathfrak{a}$, as claimed.

REMARK 12.   The above string of inequalities is clearly very wasteful. One would surmise that a much stronger result ought to hold. This is indeed the case and one may take a much smaller value for m, but then the statement becomes harder to prove and we shall not need the stronger result.

Lemma 3.   *Let* $m = m(\mathbf{K})$ *be defined as in Lemma 2; then in each class of ideals there exists an ideal* $\mathfrak{a}$ *such that* $N\mathfrak{a} \leq m$.

PROOF. Let $\mathfrak{A}$ be any class of ideals in **K**; select in $\mathfrak{A}$ an arbitrary ideal $\mathfrak{b}$. By Theorem 10, there exists an ideal $\mathfrak{c}$ in **K** such that $\mathfrak{cb}$ is principal. By Lemma 2 we may select in $\mathfrak{c}$ an integer γ such that $|N\gamma| \leq m \cdot N\mathfrak{c}$. From $\gamma \in \mathfrak{c}$ follows $(\gamma) \subset \mathfrak{c}$, that is, $\mathfrak{c} \mid (\gamma)$; hence, $\mathfrak{ca} = (\gamma)$ for some ideal $\mathfrak{a}$ in **K**. Two remarks are now in order: First, by Lemma 1, from $\mathfrak{ca} \sim \mathfrak{cb}$ (indeed, both ideals are principal) follows that $\mathfrak{a} \sim \mathfrak{b}$: hence, $\mathfrak{a} \in \mathfrak{A}$. Secondly, by Theorem 26, Theorem 24 and Lemma 2 it follows that $\mathfrak{ca} = (\gamma) \Rightarrow N\mathfrak{c} \cdot N\mathfrak{a} = N((\gamma)) = |N\gamma| \leq m \cdot N\mathfrak{c}$, so that indeed $N\mathfrak{a} \leq m$ and the Lemma is proven.

PROOF OF THEOREM 30. The proof of Theorem 30 is now rather trivial. By Theorem 28, there exist only finitely many ideals of a given norm; hence, only finitely many, whose norm does not exceed any given bound. Suppose that there are t ideals of norm $\leq m$. By Lemma 3, in each class there exists at least one ideal of norm $\leq m$; therefore, there exist at most t classes of ideals.

Definition 14. The (finite) number of classes of ideals in **K** is called the class number of **K** and is denoted by $h = h(\mathbf{K})$.

Theorem 31. *If h is the class number of the algebraic number field* **K**, *then for every ideal $\mathfrak{a}$ of* **K**, $\mathfrak{a}^h$ *is a principal ideal.*

PROOF. Consider a set of h inequivalent ideals in **K**, $\mathfrak{a}_1, \mathfrak{a}_2, ..., \mathfrak{a}_h$. Their number being h, there is exactly one from each class in this set. If $\mathfrak{a}$ is any ideal of **K**, then $\mathfrak{aa}_1, \mathfrak{aa}_2, ..., \mathfrak{aa}_h$ is again a set of h inequivalent ideals (because, by Theorem 10 and Lemma 1 it follows that $\mathfrak{aa}_j \sim \mathfrak{aa}_k \Rightarrow \mathfrak{baa}_j \sim \mathfrak{baa}_k \Leftrightarrow (c)\mathfrak{a}_j \sim (c)\mathfrak{a}_k \Leftrightarrow \mathfrak{a}_j \sim \mathfrak{a}_k$). Consequently, in the set $\{\mathfrak{aa}_j \mid 1 \leq j \leq h\}$ there is again exactly one ideal from each of the h classes. It now follows from Lemma 1 that $\mathfrak{a}_1\mathfrak{a}_2 \cdots \mathfrak{a}_h \sim \mathfrak{aa}_1 \cdot \mathfrak{aa}_2 \cdots \mathfrak{aa}_h = \mathfrak{a}^h\mathfrak{a}_1 \cdots \mathfrak{a}_h$ and, using once more Theorem 10 and Lemma 1, $(1) \sim \mathfrak{a}^h$, as claimed.

In developing the theory of ideals we have reached approximately the point corresponding to the first six theorems in Chapter 3 for the rational integers. It seems plain that the theory will not stop here. Indeed, this chapter has only laid the foundations for the study of ideals in number fields. But we shall not pursue the matter further. On the one hand, it is likely that the reader will have gathered the general flavor of this theory. On the other hand, we now have at our disposal sufficient information, in order to be able to take up once more the Fermat Conjecture with some hope of new progress. The interested reader, however, is advised not to stop here, but to consult some of the excellent books either on algebraic numbers (such as [1], [4], or [5]), or on abstract ideal theory (see, e.g. [2] or [3]).

PROBLEMS

1. Prove Theorem 1.

2. Prove Theorem 3.

3. Justify Remark 5.

4. Prove Theorem 5.

5. Write out in detail the proof of Theorem 6.

6. Prove Corollary 6.1.

7. Let α be an integer of an algebraic number field $\mathbf{K}$ and let $\alpha^{(2)}, \alpha^{(3)}, \ldots,$ $\alpha^{(n)}$ be its conjugates.
   Prove that $\alpha^{(2)} \cdot \alpha^{(3)} \cdot \ldots \cdot \alpha^{(n)}$ is also an integer in $\mathbf{K}$.

8. Where does the proof of Theorem 12 break down if $\mathfrak{c} = 0$?

9. With reference to Remark 8, show that if an integer of an algebriac number field $\mathbf{K}$ has the property of "primality," then it has also that of "irreducibility," or "maximality."

10. Prove Corollary 16.1

11. Give a detailed proof of Theorem 17.

12. Give a detailed proof of Corollary 17.1.

13. Write out the proof of Theorem 20 in detail.

14. Write out the proof of Theorem 21 in detail.

15. Write out the proof of Theorem 22 in detail.

16. Write out the proof of Corollary 22.1 in detail.

17. (a) Prove that in a field of degree n, there are exactly $|a|^n$ residue classes mod a, if $a \in \mathbf{Z}$.

    (b) If $\mathfrak{a} = (a)$ is a principal ideal, $a \in \mathbf{Z}$, $a > 0$, prove that there are a^n residue classes mod $\mathfrak{a}$.

18. Prove the following generalization of Fermat's theorem to ideals:
    For every $\alpha \in \mathbf{I}$ and $\mathfrak{p}$, a prime ideal of $\mathbf{K} \ni \mathfrak{p} \nmid \alpha$, $\alpha^{N\mathfrak{p}-1} \equiv 1 \pmod{\mathfrak{p}}$.

BIBLIOGRAPHY

1. E. Landau, *Vorlesungen über Zahlentheorie*, Vol. 3. Leipzig: S. Hirzel, 1927.

2. N. H. McCoy, *Rings and Ideals* (Carus Monograph No. 8). La Salle, Illinois: Open Court Publishing Co., 1948.

3. D. G. Northcott, *Ideal Theory*. Cambridge: Cambridge University Press, 1953.

4. H. Pollard, *The Theory of Algebraic Numbers* (Carus Monograph No. 9). New York: J. Wiley & Sons, 1950.

5. E. Weiss, *Algebraic Number Theory*. New York: MacGraw-Hill Book Company, 1963.

CHAPTER 11

Proof of Fermat's Conjecture
for Regular Primes

1. INTRODUCTION

After this lengthy excursion into the theory of ideals, we shall return to equation (1') of Chapter 3. We shall keep previous notations, $\omega = e^{2\pi i/p}$, $\lambda = 1 - \omega$, denote by $\mathbf{K} = \mathbf{Q}(\omega)$ the cyclotomic field generated by the p-th root of unity ω and by $\mathbf{I}$ the ring of integers of $\mathbf{K}$.

In view of our experience with $p = 3$, we are tempted to try to prove a statement like the following: "Let p be an odd, rational prime; then the equation

$$\xi^p + \eta^p + \zeta^p = 0 \tag{1}$$

has no solutions in integers $\xi, \eta, \zeta \in \mathbf{I}$, satisfying $\xi\eta\zeta \neq 0$." This, however, would imply the truth of the FC and up to now this statement has neither been proven, nor disproven. Not even the easier Case I has been settled. However, Kummer succeeded to prove the FC for a certain class of primes, which he called *regular primes*.

Definition 1. Let p be a rational prime and denote by h the class number of the cyclotomic field $\mathbf{K} = \mathbf{Q}(\omega)$; then p is said to be a *regular prime*, if $p \nmid h$.

REMARK 1. The small primes are all regular (37 is the first irregular one) but among larger primes many are not regular. How large the class of regular

200

primes is, one does not know; one does not even know today whether there are infinitely many regular primes, or not.

In what follows we shall see a proof of the FC in both Case I and Case II. The proof of Case I seems to be the longer and more difficult one, but that is not really the case. Indeed, the proof of Case I is given essentially in full, while in Case II we shall make use of a Theorem of Kummer, which we shall not prove. Its statement is very simple, but the proof takes over 30 pages (in [8]).

2. PROOF OF THE FC FOR REGULAR PRIMES IN CASE I

Theorem 1. *Let p be a regular prime. Then* (1) *has no primitive solution in integers $\xi, \eta, \zeta \in \mathbf{I}$, none divisible by $\lambda = 1 - \omega$.*

REMARK 2. The conditions $\lambda \nmid \xi$, $\lambda \nmid \eta$, $\lambda \nmid \zeta$ are the natural generalization of the original condition $p \nmid x \cdot y \cdot z$ that characterizes Case I. For want of a better expression any solution satisfying all conditions of Theorem 1 will be called, an *admissible solution*.

The relevance of the condition that p be regular may be better appreciated in the light of

Theorem 2. *If p is a regular prime, then $\mathfrak{a}^p \sim \mathfrak{b}^p \Rightarrow \mathfrak{a} \sim \mathfrak{b}$ for all ideals of* **K**.

PROOF. By Lemma 10.1, $\mathfrak{a}^p \sim \mathfrak{b}^p \Rightarrow \mathfrak{a}^{kp} \sim \mathfrak{b}^{kp}$ for every $k \in \mathbf{Z}^+$. Also, $(h, p) = 1 \Rightarrow mh - kp = 1$ for some $m, k \in \mathbf{Z}^+$. Hence, using Theorem 10.31, $\mathfrak{a}^h \sim (1) \Rightarrow \mathfrak{a}^{kp} = \mathfrak{a}^{1+mh} \sim \mathfrak{a}$; similarly, $\mathfrak{b}^{kp} = \mathfrak{b}^{1+mh} \sim \mathfrak{b}$ and the result follows.

Corollary 2.1. *If p is a regular prime, and $\mathfrak{a}^p$ is a principal ideal of* **K**, *then so is $\mathfrak{a}$.*

PROOF. Take $\mathfrak{b} = (1)$ in Theorem 2.

Finally, the proof of Theorem 1 is made easier, if we introduce one more definition, namely,

Definition 2. An integer $\alpha \in \mathbf{I}$ is said to be *primary* if
  (i) $\lambda \nmid \alpha$; and
  (ii) $\alpha \equiv a \pmod{\lambda^2}$, $a \in \mathbf{Z}$.

REMARK 3. This is Landau's ([8], p. 227) terminology; modern authors would call integers with this property *semi-primary* (see [13]) and reserve the term *primary* for integers $\alpha \in \mathbf{I}$ satisfying the congruence $\alpha \equiv c^p$ (mod λ^p). However, we shall have no need for this stronger property; therefore, I prefer to use the simpler term of the property described in Definition 2.

The following theorem gives criteria by which one can identify primary integers.

Theorem 3. *If $\alpha \in \mathbf{I}$, $\lambda \nmid \alpha$, then*
   (i)   *α^p is always primary;*
   (ii) *$\exists\, k \in \mathbf{Z} \ni \omega^k\alpha$ is primary;*
   (iii) *$\alpha \in \mathbf{R} \Rightarrow \alpha$ primary.*

PROOF. By Lemma 9.9 $\exists\, a \in \mathbf{Z} \ni \alpha^p \equiv a$ (mod λ^p); for $p \geq 2$ this implies $\alpha^p \equiv a$ (mod λ^2), hence (i).

By Lemma 9.3 we know that there are exactly p residue classes mod λ; therefore, $\exists\, a \in \mathbf{Z} \ni \alpha \equiv a$ (mod λ), or $\alpha = a + \mu\lambda$, $\mu \in \mathbf{I}$. For the same reason, $\mu \equiv m$ (mod λ) or $\mu = m + \nu\lambda$, $\nu \in \mathbf{I}$, so that $\alpha = a + m\lambda + \nu\lambda^2$ or $\alpha \equiv a + m\lambda$ (mod λ^2). From $\lambda \nmid \alpha$ follows $\lambda \nmid a$ and, *a fortiori*, $p \nmid a$. Therefore, we can determine $k \in \mathbf{Z}^+ \ni ka \equiv m$ (mod p). Observing that

$$\omega^k = (1 - \lambda)^k = 1 - k\lambda + \binom{k}{2}\lambda^2 \cdots \equiv 1 - k\lambda \;(\text{mod } \lambda^2),$$

it follows that

$$\omega^k\alpha \equiv (1 - k\lambda)(a + m\lambda)\;(\text{mod } \lambda^2) \text{ or } \omega^k\alpha \equiv a + \lambda(m - ka) \equiv a\;(\text{mod } \lambda^2)$$

(the last congruence holds because $p \mid m - ka \Rightarrow \lambda \mid m - ka$) and (ii) is proven.

Finally, remembering that $\lambda = 1 - \omega$, from $\alpha \equiv a + m\lambda$ (mod λ^2) follows that $\alpha \equiv a + m - m\omega$ (mod λ^2). Also, taking complex conjugates α being real, and $\bar{\lambda}$ being associate to λ (indeed

$$\frac{\lambda}{\bar{\lambda}} = \frac{\omega(1 - \omega)}{\omega(1 - \omega^{-1})} = \frac{\omega - \omega^2}{\omega - 1} = -\omega,$$

a unit), $\bar{\alpha} = \alpha \equiv a + m - m\bar{\omega}$ (mod λ^2); therefore, subtracting,

$$m(\omega - \bar{\omega}) = m(\omega - \omega^{-1}) \equiv 0\;(\text{mod } \lambda^2),$$

or

$$\omega^{-1}m(\omega^2 - 1) = \omega^{-1}m(\omega + 1)(\omega - 1) = -\omega^{-1}(\omega + 1)m\lambda \equiv 0\;(\text{mod } \lambda^2).$$

-1, ω^{-1}, and $\omega + 1$ are units; hence, the last congruence becomes $m\lambda \equiv 0 \pmod{\lambda^2}$ and $\alpha = a + m\lambda \pmod{\lambda^2}$ reduces to $\alpha \equiv a \pmod{\lambda^2}$, proving (iii).

After this preparation we are now ready to start the

PROOF OF THEOREM 1. If (1) has any admissible solutions, then it also has solutions with ξ, η, ζ primary. Indeed, if, say, ξ is not primary, then, by Theorem 3, $\xi_1 = \xi\omega^k$ is primary for some $k \in \mathbf{Z}^+$; also $\xi_1^p = \xi^p\omega^{pk} = \xi^p$ and $\lambda \nmid \xi \Leftrightarrow \lambda \nmid \xi_1$. Hence, in (1) ξ may be replaced by ξ_1 and similarly, η and ζ may be replaced by η_1, ζ_1, both primary, with

$$\xi^p = \eta^p + \zeta^p = \xi_1^p + \eta_1^p + \zeta_1^p, \quad \lambda \nmid \xi_1, \quad \lambda \nmid \eta_1, \quad \lambda \nmid \zeta_1.$$

Therefore, without loss of generality, we may, and shall, assume that in any admissible solution of (1)

$$\xi \equiv a, \eta \equiv b, \zeta \equiv c \pmod{\lambda^2}, \qquad \text{with } a, b, c \in \mathbf{Z}.$$

Proceeding as in Chapter 9, (1) may be written as $-\xi^p = \eta^p + \zeta^p = \prod_{j=0}^{p-1} (\eta + \omega^j\zeta)$. In terms of ideals, this is equivalent to

$$(\xi)^p = \prod_{j=0}^{p-1} (\eta + \omega^j\zeta), \tag{2}$$

where $(\eta + \omega^j\zeta)$ now stands for the principal ideal of multiples of $\eta + \omega^j\zeta$; clearly, $\lambda \nmid \xi \Rightarrow (\lambda) \nmid (\eta + \omega^j\zeta)$ $(0 \leq j \leq p - 1)$. We can no more conclude that if the solution is primitive, then ξ, η, ζ have to be coprime in pairs, because the ideal (η, ζ), for instance, need not be a principal ideal. But if $(\eta, \zeta) = \mathfrak{d} \neq (1)$, then

(i) $\mathfrak{d}$ divides every factor $(\eta + \omega^j\zeta)$, which is rather obvious; and

(ii) $\mathfrak{d}$ is actually the g.c.d. of any two such factors, which may not be completely obvious. To convince ourselves, let $\mathfrak{f}$ be any common factor of $(\eta + \omega^j\zeta)$ and $(\eta + \omega^{j'}\zeta)$, $j < j'$. We have to prove that $\mathfrak{f} \mid \mathfrak{d}$. We observe that $\mathfrak{f}$ divides the difference $(\eta + \omega^j\zeta) - (\eta + \omega^{j'}\zeta)$ or $\mathfrak{f} \mid \omega^j (1 - \omega^{j'-j})\zeta$. Suppressing units it follows that $\mathfrak{f} \mid (1 - \omega)\zeta = \lambda\zeta$. I claim that actually $\mathfrak{f} \mid \zeta$. To conclude this it is sufficient to show that the prime ideal (λ) does not divide $\mathfrak{f}$. Indeed, $\mathfrak{f} \mid (\eta + \omega^j\zeta)$ and $(\eta + \omega^j\zeta) \mid (\xi)^p$; therefore, $\mathfrak{f} \mid (\xi)^p$. Hence, if $(\lambda) \mid \mathfrak{f}$, then $(\lambda) \mid (\xi)^p \Rightarrow \lambda \mid \xi$, contradicting one of our assumptions. We have, therefore, proven that $\mathfrak{f} \mid \zeta$. In exactly the same way one shows that $\mathfrak{f} \mid \eta$; hence $\mathfrak{f} \mid (\eta, \zeta) = \mathfrak{d}$, as claimed. We now set $\eta + \omega^i\zeta = \mathfrak{d}\mathfrak{c}_i$ and (1) becomes $(\xi)^p = \mathfrak{d}^p \prod_{j=0}^{p-1} \mathfrak{c}_j$.

By the analog of 9.5.40, each $\mathfrak{c}_j$ is the p-th power of an ideal in **K**, say $\mathfrak{c}_j = \mathfrak{e}_j^p$ and $(\eta + \omega^j\zeta) = \mathfrak{d}\mathfrak{e}_j^p$, $(\lambda) \nmid \mathfrak{e}_j$. One observes that all ideals $\mathfrak{d}\mathfrak{e}_j^p$ are principal, and, consequently, equivalent; by Lemma 10.1 and Theorem 10.10 it now easily follows that $\mathfrak{e}_j^p \sim \mathfrak{e}_i^p$ or, by Theorem 2 that $\mathfrak{e}_j \sim \mathfrak{e}_i$ for all $i, j, 0 \le j \le p - 1$. It should be emphasized that this crucial conclusion makes essential use of Theorem 2, which, in turn was proven only for regular primes.

From the definition of equivalence we know that there exist principal ideals (α_j) and (β_j) such that $(\alpha_j)\mathfrak{e}_j = (\beta_j)\mathfrak{e}_0$. Remembering that $(\lambda) \nmid \mathfrak{e}_j$, it is clear that if $\lambda^k \mid \alpha_j$, then $\lambda^k \mid \beta_j$. Dividing out, if necessary, this highest power of λ, we obtain an equality of the form $(\gamma_j)\mathfrak{e}_j = (\delta_j)\mathfrak{e}_0$, $\lambda \nmid \gamma_j$, $\lambda \nmid \delta_j$, whence $(\gamma_j^p)\mathfrak{e}_j^p = (\delta_j^p)\mathfrak{e}_0^p$ or $(\gamma_j^p)\mathfrak{e}_j^p\mathfrak{d} = (\delta_j^p)\mathfrak{e}_0^p\mathfrak{d}$, that is,

$$(\gamma_j^p)(\eta + \omega^j\zeta) = (\delta_j^p)(\eta + \zeta). \tag{3}$$

This equality (3) involves only principal ideals; therefore, on account of Theorem 10.2, we may just as well replace them by their respective generators, that is, by integers of **I**, provided we also introduce some, as yet not further determined unit of the ring **I**. As a mattter of fact, we have used the ideals so far, in order to be able to factor without ambiguity and to replace coprime factors, whose product was a p-th power, by the p-th power of some other factor. The ideals have done their duty but from here on we return to integers of **I**; in particular, equation (3) is equivalent to $\gamma_j^p(\eta + \omega^j\zeta) = \delta_j^p(\eta + \zeta)\varepsilon_j'$, with ε_j' a unit. We now invoke again Lemma 9.8, according to which $\varepsilon_j' = \omega^{k_j}\varepsilon_j$, with ε_j real and $k_j \in \mathbf{Z}$. Taking congruences mod λ^p we may (see Lemma 9.9) replace also γ_j^p and δ_j^p by rational integers, say, c_j and d_j and obtain

$$c_j(\eta + \omega^j\zeta) \equiv d_j(\eta + \zeta)\omega^{k_j}\varepsilon_j \, (\text{mod } \lambda^p), \qquad \lambda \nmid c_jd_j. \tag{4}$$

We now determine a rational integer g_j by the condition $g_jc_j \equiv d_j \, (\text{mod } p^2)$. Any such congruence will hold, *a fortiori*, mod λ^p. Multiplying (4) by g_j and simplifying, we obtain $\eta + \omega^j\zeta \equiv (\eta + \zeta)\omega^{k_j}g_j\varepsilon_j \, (\text{mod } \lambda^p)$, $\lambda \nmid g_j$. Denote $g_j\varepsilon_j$ by β_j; then β_j is real and $\lambda \nmid \beta_j$ so that (4) becomes

$$\eta + \omega^j\zeta \equiv \beta_j\omega^{k_j}(\eta + \zeta) \, (\text{mod } \lambda^p). \tag{5}$$

By Theorem 3, β_j is primary, because it is real, so that $\beta_j \equiv a_j \, (\text{mod } \lambda^2)$, $a_j \in \mathbf{Z}$. Actually, more is true, namely, $a_j = 1$ for all $j(0 \le j \le p - 1)$. In order to prove this assertion, we recall that η and ζ are themselves primary, so that $\eta \equiv b \, (\text{mod } \lambda^2)$, $\zeta \equiv c \, (\text{mod } \lambda^2)$, $b, c \in \mathbf{Z}$. Also, as already observed in the proof of Theorem 3, $\omega^k = (1 - \lambda)^k \equiv 1 - k\lambda \, (\text{mod } \lambda^2)$, so that $\eta + \omega^j\zeta \equiv b + (1 - j\lambda)c \, (\text{mod } \lambda^2)$, $\beta_j\omega^{k_j}(\eta + \zeta) \equiv \beta_j(1 - k_j\lambda)(b + c) \, (\text{mod } \lambda^2)$

and (5) becomes $b + (1 - j\lambda)c \equiv \beta_j(b + c)(1 - k_j\lambda) \pmod{\lambda^2}$. Simplifying and taking the congruences only mod λ, we obtain $b + c \equiv \beta_j(b + c) \pmod{\lambda}$; from $\lambda \nmid b + c$ (see Problem 6) now follows $\beta_j \equiv 1 \pmod{\lambda}$. On the other hand β_j being primary $\beta_j \equiv a_j \pmod{\lambda^2}$. Comparing the last two congruences it is clear that $\beta_j \equiv 1 \pmod{\lambda^2}$, as claimed. Using this result and taking congruences mod λ^2 rather than mod λ^p, (5) now becomes $b + (1 - j\lambda)c \equiv (b + c)(1 - k_j\lambda) \pmod{\lambda^2}$, which simplifies to $-j\lambda c \equiv -(b + c)k_j\lambda \pmod{\lambda^2}$, or $jc \equiv (b + c)k_j \pmod{\lambda}$. Here both sides are rational integers; hence, if they are congruent mod λ, then they are also congruent mod p (why?) (*Hint:* See the proof of Theorem 9.5; also Problem 8), so that

$$jc \equiv (b + c)k_j \pmod{p}. \tag{6}$$

We now determine $r \in \mathbf{Z} \ni r(b + c) \equiv c \pmod{p}$; this is always possible, because $p \nmid b + c$. Multiplying (6) by r we obtain

$$rjc \equiv r(b + c)k_j \equiv ck_j \pmod{p} \quad \text{or} \quad rj \equiv k_j \pmod{p}.$$

We can now replace the (so far unknown) k_j in (5) and obtain (remark that now β_j reappears: it is congruent to one only mod λ^2, but not necessarily mod λ^p, $p > 2$)

$$\eta + \omega^j\zeta \equiv \beta_j\omega^{rj}(\eta + \zeta) \pmod{\lambda^p}.$$

From here on we may proceed as in Chapter 9. First, taking complex conjugates, $\bar{\eta} + \omega^{-j}\bar{\zeta} \equiv \beta_j\omega^{-rj}(\bar{\eta} + \bar{\zeta}) \pmod{\bar{\lambda}^p}$, because β_j is real. However, $\lambda = 1 - \omega$ and $\bar{\lambda} = 1 - \bar{\omega} = 1 - \omega^{p-1}$ are associates (see p. 202); hence, the last congruence holds also mod λ^p. Next, we eliminate the unknown β_j between these two congruences. For that, we multiply the first by $(\bar{\eta} + \bar{\zeta})\omega^{-rj}$ and the second by $(\eta + \zeta)\omega^{rj}$; then both second members become $\beta_j(\eta + \zeta)(\bar{\eta} + \bar{\zeta})$ and the corresponding first members have to be congruent mod λ^p, that is,

$$(\bar{\eta} + \bar{\zeta})\omega^{-rj}(\eta + \omega^j\zeta) \equiv (\eta + \zeta)\omega^{rj}(\bar{\eta} + \omega^{-j}\bar{\zeta}) \pmod{\lambda^p}. \tag{7}$$

Before proceeding, let us observe that, again as in Chapter 9, both $r \equiv 0$, $\pmod{p}$ and $r \equiv 1 \pmod{p}$ have to be ruled out. Indeed, if $r \equiv 0 \pmod{p}$, then

$$r(b + c) \equiv c \pmod{p} \Rightarrow p \mid c,$$

which is false and if $r \equiv 1 \pmod{p}$ then

$$r(b + c) \equiv c \pmod{p} \Rightarrow p \mid b,$$

which is equally false.

Simplifying and rearranging the terms, (7) may be written as

$$(\bar{\eta} + \bar{\zeta})\eta + \omega^j(\bar{\eta} + \bar{\zeta})\zeta - \omega^{(2r-1)j}(\eta + \zeta)\bar{\zeta} - \omega^{2rj}(\eta + \zeta)\bar{\eta} \equiv 0 \,(\text{mod } \lambda^p), (8)$$

and this congruence has to hold for $j = 0, 1, 2, ..., p - 1$. It is conceivable that changing j into $p - j$ we obtain congruences that are not essentially distinct; but in any case, we seem to get $(p + 1)/2$ distinct congruences, by taking, for instance, $j = 0, 1, 2, ..., ((p - 1)/2)$. Case I has already been settled for $p = 3$ and $p = 5$; therefore, we may assume that $p \geq 7$, $(p + 1)/2 \geq 4$, so that η and ζ have to satisfy at least 4 congruences like (8). These are non-linear, which is rather unpleasant. However, if we take as "unknowns" the four expressions $\phi = (\bar{\eta} + \bar{\zeta})\eta$, $\psi = (\bar{\eta} + \bar{\zeta})\zeta$, $\bar{\phi} = (\eta + \zeta)\bar{\eta} = \chi$, and $\bar{\psi} = (\eta + \zeta)\bar{\zeta} = \theta$, then the congruences become linear and homogeneous in ϕ, ψ, χ, θ, namely,

$$\phi + \omega^j\psi - \omega^{(2r-1)j}\theta - \omega^{2rj}\chi \equiv 0 \,(\text{mod } \lambda^p). \tag{8'}$$

Exactly as in the case of linear equations, a system of m linear, homogeneous congruences, in t variables, say, $\phi_1, \phi_2, ..., \phi_t$, whose coefficients are integers in some number field **K** and with more congruences modulo an ideal $\mathfrak{a}$ of **K** than variables, has, in general, no solutions. Even if the number of congruences is the same as the number of variables, that is, $m = t$, there are, in general, no solutions, except the trivial ones; by this we understand solutions $\phi_1, \phi_2, ..., \phi_m$ such that $((\phi_j), \mathfrak{a}) \neq \mathfrak{i}$ for all $j(1 \leq j \leq m)$. The system has nontrivial solutions, that is, solutions where $((\phi_j,) \mathfrak{a}) = \mathfrak{i}$ holds at least for one $j(1 \leq j \leq m)$, only if the determinant formed with the coefficients is congruent to zero mod $\mathfrak{a}$. The proof follows step by step that of Cramer's rules for linear equations and is left as an exercise to the reader (see Problem 10).

In our present situation, $\lambda \nmid \eta$, $\lambda \nmid \zeta$; but also $\lambda \nmid \eta + \zeta$, because $\eta + \zeta$ is a factor of ξ^p, so that $\lambda \mid \eta + \zeta \Rightarrow \lambda \mid \xi$, contrary to our assumptions. It follows that the required solutions of (8') are nontrivial and, restricting ourselves only to the first 4 congruences of (8') (which always exist for $p \geq 7$) the determinant δ of the coefficients has to satisfy $\delta \equiv 0 \,(\text{mod } \lambda^p)$. One easily computes

$$\delta = \begin{vmatrix} 1 & 1 & 1 & 1 \\ 1 & \omega & \omega^{2r-1} & \omega^{2r} \\ 1 & \omega^2 & \omega^{4r-2} & \omega^{4r} \\ 1 & \omega^3 & \omega^{6r-3} & \omega^{6r} \end{vmatrix}$$

because this is a Vandermond determinant. We find

$$\delta = (1 - \omega)(1 - \omega^{2r-1})(1 - \omega^{2r})(\omega - \omega^{2r-1})(\omega - \omega^{2r})(\omega^{2r-1} - \omega^{2r}).$$

Remembering that $r \not\equiv 0, 1$, one sees that the factors $1 - \omega^{2r}$ and $\omega - \omega^{2r-1}$ cannot vanish; hence,

$$1 - \omega^{2r} = \lambda(1 + \omega + \cdots + \omega^{2r-1}) = \lambda\varepsilon_1,$$

$$\omega - \omega^{2r-1} = \omega(1 - \omega^{2r-2}) = \omega\lambda(1 + \omega + \cdots + \omega^{2r-3}) = \lambda\varepsilon_2,$$

with ε_1 and ε_2 units. Consequently, replacing also $1 - \omega$ by λ and $\omega^{2r-1} - \omega^{2r}$ by $\omega^{2r-1}\lambda$, $\delta = \lambda^4\varepsilon_0\varepsilon_1\varepsilon_2(1 - \omega^{2r-1})^2$, ε_0 unit. We now verify that $2r \equiv 1 \pmod{p}$; indeed, if $2r \not\equiv 1 \pmod{p}$, then $1 - \omega^{2r-1} = \lambda(1 + \omega + \cdots + \omega^{2r-2}) = \lambda\varepsilon_3$, $\delta = \lambda^6\varepsilon_0\varepsilon_1\varepsilon_2\varepsilon_3^2$ or, defining the unit ε by $\varepsilon\varepsilon_0\varepsilon_1\varepsilon_2\varepsilon_3^2 = 1$, $\varepsilon\delta = \lambda^6$. Consequently, $\delta \equiv 0 \pmod{\lambda^p}$ implies $\lambda^6 \equiv 0 \pmod{\lambda^p}$ or $\lambda^p \mid \lambda^6$, obviously impossible for $p \geq 7$. It follows that indeed $2r \equiv 1 \pmod{p}$. Now, r was defined by $c \equiv r(b + c) \pmod{p}$; hence, $2c \equiv 2r(b + c) \equiv b + c \pmod{p}$, or $b \equiv c \pmod{p}$ and, *a fortiori*, $b \equiv c \pmod{\lambda}$. Consequently, $\eta \equiv \zeta \pmod{\lambda}$. Proceeding in the same way, but writing (1) as $-\zeta^p = \xi^p + \eta^p$, we obtain $\xi \equiv \eta \pmod{\lambda}$. Consequently, $\xi \equiv \eta \equiv \zeta \pmod{\lambda}$, $\xi^p + \eta^p + \zeta^p \equiv 3\xi^p \pmod{\lambda}$. From $p > 3$ follows $\lambda \nmid 3$; hence, if (1) holds, then $\lambda \mid \xi$, contrary to our assumption. So far, we were able to avoid threatening contradictions, by proper choices of parameters. This is no longer possible. The assumption that (1) has solutions in **I** and that p is regular leads to $\lambda \mid \xi$ hence, there are no solutions in Case I. The reader may even have obtained the impression that we actually proved more. Indeed, from $\xi \equiv \eta \equiv \zeta \pmod{\lambda}$ and (1) follows $0 = \xi^p + \eta^p + \zeta^p \equiv 3\xi^p \equiv 3\eta^p \equiv 3\zeta^p \pmod{\lambda}$; hence, from $\lambda \nmid 3$ follows $\lambda \mid \xi$, $\lambda \mid \eta$, $\lambda \mid \zeta$ and the solution is not even primitive. This suggests the conclusion that (1) cannot have any admissible solutions (regardless of Case I or Case II), because it cannot have primitive solutions. This reasoning, however, is not warranted, because in the present proof we have repeatedly made use of the assumption $\lambda \nmid \xi$, $\lambda \nmid \eta$, $\lambda \nmid \zeta$; consequently the conclusion is valid only in Case I. In any case, Theorem 1 is proven as stated. The remaining Case II will be the object of the following section.

3. PROOF OF THE FC FOR REGULAR PRIMES IN CASE II

Let us take up once more equation (1), keeping the assumption that p is a regular prime and restricting, as always, our attention to primitive solutions (in the sense that ξ, η, ζ are not simultaneously divisible by any *integer*

$\alpha \in \mathbf{I}$, α not a unit, but not necessarily in the sense that $(\xi, \eta) = (\eta, \zeta) = (\zeta, \xi) = 1$) which is, clearly, sufficient. We want to drop, however, the restriction that $\lambda = 1 - \omega$ may not divide any of the integers ξ, η, ζ. In other words, our aim in the present section is to prove

Theorem 4.   *Let p be a regular prime; then* (1) *has no solutions in integers* $\xi, \eta, \zeta \in \mathbf{I}$, $\xi \cdot \eta \cdot \zeta \neq 0$.

This statement is already much more satisfactory than that of Theorem 9.6, although it still falls short of the goal, because of the restriction on p to be regular, coupled with our present knowledge of the fact that there are infinitely many primes that are not regular (see [7]).

As already mentioned in the introductory paragraphs, we shall use, without proof, the following result due to Kummer.

Theorem 5.   *If p is a regular prime and ε is a unit of $\mathbf{I}$ satisfying $\varepsilon \equiv a$ (mod λ^p) for some $a \in \mathbf{Z}$, then there exists in $\mathbf{I}$ a unit ε_1, such that $\varepsilon = \varepsilon_1^p$.*

Besides the already mentioned proof in [8], pp. 240–270, one may find some others, for instance, in [14] or [4], but all are rather long and cumbersome, and it seems preferable at a first study of the subject, to accept this result without proof, in order to get a clearer picture of the scheme of the proof of Theorem 4.

Some further preliminary remarks are in order: First, if ξ, η, $\zeta \in \mathbf{I}$, and are a primitive solution of (1), then λ now divides one, but not all of ξ, η, ζ. If it divides any two, then, by (1) it follows that it divides also the third, which is ruled out for primitive solutions. Consequently, it divides exactly one of the integers ξ, η, ζ. On account of the symmetry of (1) in ξ, η, ζ it does not matter which we select to be divisible by λ and, in order to maintain the notational analogy with the cases $p = 2$ and $p = 3$, let $\lambda \mid \xi$. If $\xi = \lambda^k \alpha$, $\lambda \nmid \alpha$, then (1) becomes $\lambda^{kp}\alpha^p + \eta^p + \zeta^p = 0$. Secondly, we remember that, while the FC has been proven directly for $p = 5$ in Case I (see Theorem 9.5), Case II for $p = 5$ has not been previously discussed; therefore, the present section ought (and shall) take care also of $p = 5$. Finally, just as in the case $p = 3$, it turns out that it is easier to prove a slightly stronger statement, namely,

Theorem 6.   *If p is a regular prime, then the equation*

$$\varepsilon \lambda^{kp}\alpha^p + \eta^p + \zeta^p = 0 \tag{9}$$

has no solutions in integers $\alpha, \eta, \zeta \in \mathbf{I}$, none divisible by λ, for any unit ε of $\mathbf{I}$ and any rational integer $k > 0$.

Theorem 6 contains, in particular (namely, for $\varepsilon = 1$) the statement that for p regular the equation $\xi^p + \eta^p + \zeta^p = 0$ has no solutions in integers

$\xi, \eta, \zeta \in \mathbf{I}$, $\lambda \mid \xi$, $\lambda \nmid \eta$, $\lambda \nmid \zeta$. Combining this result with Theorem 1, we obtain immediately Theorem 4. It only remains to prove Theorem 6. Any primitive solution of (9), satisfying all conditions of Theorem 6, will be called simply an *admissible solution*.

PROOF OF THEOREM 6. We shall proceed, as in the case $p = 3$, in two steps:

(i)   show that in (9), k has to satisfy $k \geq 2$; and

(ii) show that from every admissible solution α, η, ζ of (9), with some $k = k_0 \geq 2$, we can construct another admissible solution with $k \leq k_0 - 1$.

These two statements, being plainly contradictory, prove that there cannot exist an admissible solution of (9); hence, Theorem 6 holds.

As in the study of Case I, there is no loss of generality in assuming ξ, η, and ζ to be primary,

$$\xi \equiv a, \quad \eta \equiv b, \quad \zeta \equiv c \pmod{\lambda^2}. \tag{10}$$

THE PROOF OF (i) is almost as easy as in the particular case $p = 3$. Indeed, (9) may be written as

$$-\varepsilon \lambda^{kp} \alpha^p = \eta^p + \zeta^p = \prod_{j=0}^{p-1} (\eta + \omega^j \zeta),$$

or, passing from integers to ideals,

$$(\lambda)^{kp} (\alpha)^p = \prod_{j=0}^{p-1} \eta(+ \omega^j \zeta), \tag{11}$$

where now $(\eta + \omega^j \zeta)$ stands for the principal ideal generated by the integer $\beta_j = \eta + \omega^j \zeta$ of $\mathbf{I}$. Now, $\beta_0 - \beta_j = \zeta(1 - \omega^j) = \zeta(1 + \omega + \cdots + \omega^{j-1})(1 - \omega) = \zeta \varepsilon \lambda$, ($\varepsilon$ a unit, but this is irrelevant here). Consequently, $\beta_0 \equiv \beta_j \pmod{\lambda}$ for all $j (0 \leq j \leq p - 1)$ and either all, or none of the principal ideals (β_j) are divisible by (λ). Their product being divisible, all are divisible.

In particular, using (10), and $\lambda \mid \beta_0$, $\beta_0 = \eta + \zeta \equiv b + c \pmod{\lambda^2} \Rightarrow \lambda \mid b + c \Rightarrow p \mid b + c \Leftrightarrow \varepsilon \lambda^{p-1} \mid b + c \Rightarrow \lambda^{p-1} \mid b + c$; consequently, $0 \equiv b + c \equiv \eta + \zeta \pmod{\lambda^2}$. It follows that the product $\prod_{j=0}^{p-1} (\eta + \omega^j \zeta)$ contains the ideal factor (λ) at least $p + 1$ times; but $(\lambda) \nmid (\alpha)$, so that, on account of (11), $kp \geq p + 1$, or $k \geq 1 + \dfrac{1}{p} > 1$, that is, $k \geq 2$ because k is a rational integer.

This proves part (i); but again, as in the particular case $p = 3$, the real difficulty lies in

THE PROOF OF (ii). Let $(\eta, \zeta) = \mathfrak{d}$ (unfortunately, as already mentioned, from the fact that no integer of $\mathbf{I}$ is a common factor of η and ζ, one cannot infer that η and ζ are coprime; they may have as greatest common divisor a nonprincipal ideal $\mathfrak{d}$ of $\mathbf{K}$). From $\lambda \nmid \eta$ follows that $(\lambda) \nmid \mathfrak{d}$. Also, $\mathfrak{d} \mid \eta$, $\mathfrak{d} \mid \zeta \Rightarrow \mathfrak{d} \mid (\eta + \omega^j \zeta)$ for every $j(0 \leq j \leq p - 1)$. Hence, remembering also that $(\lambda) \mid (\beta_j)(0 \leq j \leq p - 1)$, it follows that $(\lambda)\mathfrak{d}$ is the greatest common ideal divisor of the β_j's, even taken in pairs. To prove this it is sufficient to show that every common ideal divisor $\mathfrak{c}$ of β_j and $\beta_m (m > j)$, also divides $(\lambda)\mathfrak{d}$.

From $\mathfrak{c} \mid \beta_j$, $\mathfrak{c} \mid \beta_m$ and $(\beta_j - \beta_m) = (\omega^j(1 - \omega^{m-j})\zeta) = (\lambda)(\zeta)$ follows $\mathfrak{c} \mid (\lambda)(\zeta)$; similarly (or directly, by considerations of symmetry), $\mathfrak{c} \mid (\lambda)(\eta)$ and $\mathfrak{c} \mid (\lambda)(\eta, \zeta)$, or $\mathfrak{c} \mid (\lambda)\mathfrak{d}$, as claimed.

In particular it follows also that (λ) cannot divide any (β_j), $j \neq 0$ to higher than the first power, because we saw that $(\lambda)^2 \mid (\beta_0)$, while $(\lambda) \nmid \mathfrak{d}$. We may, therefore, set $(\beta_j) = (\lambda)\mathfrak{d}b_j(j \neq 0)$, $(\beta_0) = (\lambda)^{kp-p+1}\mathfrak{d}b_0$, with pairwise coprime ideals b_j $(j = 0, 1, ..., p - 1)$; also, $(\lambda) \nmid b_j$. Equation (11) now becomes

$$(\lambda)^{kp}(\alpha)^p = \prod_{j=0}^{p-1}(\beta_j) = (\lambda)^{kp}\mathfrak{d}^p \prod_{j=0}^{p-1} b_j,$$

or, by Theorem 10.12, $(\alpha)^p = \mathfrak{d}^p \prod_{j=0}^{p-1} b_j$. From $\mathfrak{d}^p \mid (\alpha)^p$ it follows that $(\alpha) = \mathfrak{d}f$, so that $\prod_{j=0}^{p-1} b_j = f^p$ and, by a now already familiar reasoning (see 9.5.40), that each ideal b_j is the p-th power of some ideal q_j in $\mathbf{K}$, $b_j = q_j^p$, say. Clearly, $(\lambda) \nmid b_j \Rightarrow (\lambda) \nmid q_j$. Returning to the β_j's, $(\beta_0) = (\lambda)^{kp-p+1}\mathfrak{d}q_0^p$ and $(\beta_j) = (\lambda)\mathfrak{d}q_j{}^p(j \neq 0)$. From the fact that all (β_j) and (λ) are principal ideals it now follows that all $\mathfrak{d}q_j^p$ belong to the same class, (actually, all are principal ideals) say that of $\mathfrak{d}q_1^p$. By Lemma 10.1 and Theorem 10.10 it follows further that $q_j^p \sim q_1^p$.

So far we have made no use of our assumption that p is a regular prime; that is, the results obtained up to this point are valid for all primes p, regular or not. The next step, however, consists in inferring that all ideals q_j belong to the same class, and for that we have to invoke Theorem 2, which assumes the regularity of p. Therefore, reluctantly, we restrict ourselves from here on to the class of regular primes, use Theorem 2 and infer from $q_j^p \sim q_1^p$ that $q_j \sim q_1$. This means, by the definition of equivalence, that there exist integers $\mu_j, v_j \in \mathbf{I}$ such that $(\mu_j)q_j = (v_j)q_1$. Remembering that $(\lambda) \nmid q_j$, it is clearly possible to select the μ_j's and v_j's so that $\lambda \nmid \mu_j$, $\lambda \nmid v_j(0 \leq j \leq p - 1)$.

Of the $p - 1$ equalities just proven, we select two, say, for $j = 0$ and $j = 2$ and have a closer look at them. The first one, $(\mu_0)q_0 = (v_0)q_1$ is equivalent to

$$\mathfrak{d}(\lambda)^{(k-1)p+1}(\mu_0^p)q_0^p = \mathfrak{d}(\lambda)^{(k-1)p} \cdot (\lambda)(v_0^p)q_1^p,$$

that is, to $(\eta + \zeta)(\mu_0^p) = (\lambda)^{(k-1)p}(\eta + \omega\zeta)(v_0^p)$. Similarly, the second one, $(\mu_2)q_2 = (v_2)q_1$, leads to $(\eta + \omega^2\zeta)(\mu_2^p) = (\eta + \omega\zeta)(v_2^p)$.

Once more we have used the theory of ideals in order to be able to factor without ambiguity, but have managed to end up with products involving only principal ideals. We may, therefore, pass back to integers of **I**, by introducing appropriate units, and obtain:

$$(\eta + \zeta)\mu_0^p = \varepsilon_1\lambda^{(k-1)p}(\eta + \omega\zeta)v_0^p$$

and

$$(\eta + \omega^2\zeta)\mu_2^p = \varepsilon_2(\eta + \omega\zeta)v_2^p,$$

respectively. If we multiply the first equation by $\omega\mu_2^p$ and the second by μ_0^p and add, we obtain

$$\mu_0^p\mu_2^p\{\omega(\eta + \zeta) + \eta + \omega^2\zeta\} = \{\varepsilon_1\lambda^{(k-1)p}\omega v_0^p\mu_2^p + \varepsilon_2 v_2^p\mu_0^p\}(\eta + \omega\zeta).$$

In the first member,

$$\omega\eta + \omega\zeta + \eta + \omega^2\zeta = \eta(1 + \omega) + \omega\zeta(1 + \omega) = (\eta + \omega\zeta)(1 + \omega).$$

Replacing the bracket by this value and simplifying by $\eta + \omega\zeta (\neq 0)$, one obtains $\mu_0^p\mu_2^p(1 + \omega) = \varepsilon_1\lambda^{(k-1)p}\omega v_0^p\mu_2^p + \varepsilon_2 v_2^p\mu_0^p$, or, dividing by the unit $1 + \omega$ and setting $\alpha_1 = v_0\mu_2$, $\gamma_1 = v_2\mu_0$, $\zeta_1 = -\mu_0\mu_2$,

$$\varepsilon_3\lambda^{(k-1)p}\alpha_1^p + \varepsilon_4\gamma_1^p + \zeta_1^p = 0. \tag{12}$$

From $\lambda \nmid \mu_j$, $\lambda \nmid v_j$ follows, of course, that $\lambda \nmid \alpha_1$, $\lambda \nmid \gamma_1$, $\lambda \nmid \zeta_1$; hence, we have almost proven part (ii). Indeed, (12) resembles very much (9) and has the factor $\lambda^{(k-1)p}$ instead of λ^{kp}. However, in (12) we have the extra unit ε_4. In the particular case $p = 3$, when we reached this point, we could simply try out all six units in $\mathbf{Q}(e^{2\pi i/3})$ and check that all, except $\varepsilon_4 = \pm 1$ led to contradictions. In the present, general case, such a procedure is clearly not feasible. Yet actually, it is not even necessary to show that $\varepsilon_4 = \pm 1$; all one would need to know is that in **I** there exists a unit ε_5, such that $\varepsilon_4 = \varepsilon_5^p$. Then, indeed, $\varepsilon_4\gamma_1^p = \varepsilon_5^p\gamma_1^p = (\varepsilon_5\gamma_1)^p = \eta_1^p$ with $\eta_1 = \varepsilon_5\gamma_1 \in \mathbf{I}$, $\lambda \nmid \eta_1$ and (12) becomes $\varepsilon_3\lambda^{(k-1)p}\alpha_1^p + \eta_1^p + \zeta_1^p = 0$, $\lambda \nmid \alpha_1$, $\lambda \nmid \eta_1$, $\lambda \nmid \zeta_1$, which would finish the proof of part (ii), hence that of Theorem 6. The proof of the existence of ε_5 is actually the most difficult point in the whole proof of Theorem 4. Having, however, at our disposal Theorem 5, all we have to do, in order to obtain the desired result is to show that $\varepsilon_4 \equiv a \pmod{\lambda^p}$, for some $a \in \mathbf{Z}$. This we achieve as follows.

By Lemma 9.9, there exist $s, t \in \mathbf{Z} \ni \gamma_1^p \equiv s$, $\zeta_1^p \equiv t \pmod{\lambda^p}$. We now look at (12) modulo λ^p and observing that $k \geq 2$ we obtain $\varepsilon_4\gamma_1^p + \zeta_1^d \equiv \varepsilon_4 s + t \equiv 0 \pmod{\lambda^p}$. From $\lambda \nmid \gamma_1$ follows $\lambda \nmid s$ and, because $s \in \mathbf{Z}$, that

$p \nmid s$; consequently, one can solve the congruence $sx \equiv 1 \pmod{p^2}$. This congruence will hold, *a fortiori*, mod λ^p. From $\varepsilon_4 s + t \equiv 0 \pmod{\lambda^p}$ now follows $\varepsilon_4 sx + tx \equiv 0 \pmod{\lambda^p}$ or $\varepsilon_4 + tx \equiv 0 \pmod{\lambda^p}$; but $a = -tx \in \mathbf{Z}$, so that Theorem 5 is indeed applicable. This means that a unit ε_5 exists in $\mathbf{I}$ such that $\varepsilon_5^p = \varepsilon_4$ and, setting $\eta_1 = \varepsilon_5 \gamma_1$, (12) now becomes

$$\varepsilon_3 \lambda^{(k-1)p} \alpha_1^p + \eta_1^p + \zeta_1^p = 0, \quad \lambda \nmid \alpha_1, \quad \lambda \nmid \eta_1, \quad \lambda \nmid \zeta_1;$$

the proof of Theorem 6 is complete and with Theorem 6, also Theorem 4 is proven.

4. SOME FINAL REMARKS

The reader whose patience has let him reach this point, will have convinced himself that it is hardly profitable to try to penetrate deeper into the problem of the FC, without a solid study of algebraic number fields and of related topics. Therefore, the following completions are given for the information of the curious, rather than for the edification of the thorough student. For the latter, there is no shortcut. It is recommended that he study the theory of algebraic numbers (see, e.g. [6], [1], or [15]) and then continue with the more specialized work on the FC, for instance, by Dickson [2], Vandiver [13], Furtwängler [5], Landau [8], and others.

For the former, however, the following may be of some interest. First, as already mentioned in Section 9.2, Kummer found a criterion, which permits to decide whether a prime p is regular, or not, without the need to compute the class number $h = h(\mathbf{K})$ of $\mathbf{K} = \mathbf{Q}(e^{2\pi i/p})$. This criterion states that p is regular, if it does not divide the numerators of any of the first $(p-3)/2$ Bernoulli numbers of even index.

In 1909 Wieferich [16] showed that (1) has no solutions in Case I, unless $2^{p-1} \equiv 1 \pmod{p^2}$. It may be observed that $p = 1093$ is the first prime for which this congruence holds. Shortly afterwards (1910; see [10] and [11]) Mirimanoff showed that (1) can have no solutions in Case I, unless also $3^{p-1} \equiv 1 \pmod{p^2}$ holds. It seems likely that the existence of a solution of (1) in Case I actually would imply *all* congruences $q^{p-1} \equiv 1 \pmod{p^2}$ for q any prime different from p. This would essentially rule out solutions of (1) in Case I, but, apparently the best result known at present in this direction is due to Furtwängler (1912; see [5]) and states that if $x_1^p + x_2^p + x_3^p = 0$ with $x_1, x_2, x_3 \in \mathbf{Z}$ is a primitive solution, then $q^{p-1} \equiv 1 \pmod{p^2}$ holds for every q which is a factor of those among the integers $x_i \, (i = 1, 2, 3)$, which are not divisible by p (there are at least two of them); and the congruence also holds for the factors q of $x_i + x_j$ and $x_i - x_j$ provided i and j are such that $p \nmid x_i^2 - x_j^2$ (again, at least two such couples i, j exist, because the solution is primitive). This criterion is not sufficient to settle the problem, not even in the easier Case I. However, the many congruences of the type $q^{p-1} \equiv 1 \pmod{p^2}$, each hard to satisfy by itself, have permitted to reach the result quoted earlier (see [9]) that the FC in Case I holds at least for $p < 253,747,889$. In Case II much more delicate procedures are needed and only much more recently has it been possible to show that the FC holds unconditionally for all primes at least up to $p \leq 4,001$ (see [12]).

This discussion of the FC would be incomplete without the mention of two nonmathematical items. The first refers to the fact that in 1908, P. Wolfskehl left the Academy of Sciences of Göttingen (Gesellschaft der Wissenschaften zu Göttingen) a legacy of 100,000 Mark to be paid as a prize for the first complete proof of the FC. This enormous amount of money shrank to insignificance during the inflation following the first World War. But from 1908 to the early 1920's it represented a strong temptation—for nonmathematicians. It seems (see [3], p. 764) that between 1908 and 1912, over 1000 false proofs were published. Most of these contain such gross errors, that one can spot them at a glance and no serious journal printed them. But their authors could not be convinced (often they were unable to understand even how a factorization in **I** could be anything but unique) and went ahead anyhow with private printings. Incidentally, Wolfskehl himself, by all appearances a wealthy man, was a very competent mathematician. Presumably he himself had tried to prove the FC, but without success—at least he does not seem to have published anything on this subject. He did work, however, and successfully too, on the class number of certain fields (see [17]) and was fully equipped to appreciate the difficulty of the task.

This brings us to the last item; it had been mentioned already in Chapter 1 and we shall conclude the present Chapter with it. It is simply a reflection upon the fact, which no student of the last three chapters could have failed to notice, that the abundance of deep, fertile ideas generated by the attempt to find a proof for a conjecture made by the Judge Pierre de Fermat, who died just three hundred years ago (in 1665) far exceeds in value the relevance of the conjecture itself.

PROBLEMS

1. Let η, ζ, $\alpha \in \mathbf{I}$, and set $(\eta, \zeta) = \mathfrak{d}$; prove that $\mathfrak{d} \mid (\eta + \alpha\zeta)$.

2. Prove that if the ideal $\mathfrak{f}$ divides two principal ideals (α) and (β), then it divides the principal ideal of their difference, $\mathfrak{f} \mid (\alpha - \beta)$.

3. Let $\lambda, \xi \in \mathbf{I}$, with λ a prime (in the sense of being indecomposable in $\mathbf{I}$) and assume that $(\lambda) \mid (\xi)^p$; prove that $\lambda \mid \xi$.

4. Let $\mathfrak{a}_j (1 \le j \le k)$ and $\mathfrak{b}$ be ideals in $\mathbf{K}$, with $\mathfrak{a}_1 \mathfrak{a}_2 \cdots \mathfrak{a}_k = \mathfrak{b}^p$; if $(\mathfrak{a}_i, \mathfrak{a}_j)$ $= (1)$ for all $i \ne j$, then show that there exist ideals $\mathfrak{c}_j$ in $\mathbf{K}$ such that $\mathfrak{a}_j = \mathfrak{c}_j^p (1 \le j \le k)$.

5. (a) If $c, d \in \mathbf{Z}$ and $\lambda \nmid c$, why is it always possible to determine $g \in \mathbf{Z}$ such that $gc \equiv d \pmod{p^2}$?

   (b) If $gc \equiv d \pmod{p^2}$, why does also $gc \equiv d \pmod{\lambda^p}$ hold?

6. In the proof of Theorem 1 an auxiliary result was that $\beta_j \equiv 1 \pmod{\lambda^2}$. While proving it, use was made of the fact that $\lambda \nmid b + c$, where $\eta \equiv b, \zeta \equiv c \pmod{\lambda^2}$; justify this fact!

7. From $\beta \equiv 1 \pmod{\lambda}$ and the fact that there exists some $a \in \mathbf{Z}$ such that $\beta \equiv a \pmod{\lambda^2}$, prove that $\beta \equiv 1 \pmod{\lambda^2}$.

8. Prove: If $a \in \mathbf{Z}$, then $\lambda \mid a \Rightarrow p \mid a$.
   (*Hint:* $\lambda \mid a \Rightarrow a = \lambda\mu$; now take norms, remembering that $Na = a^n = a^{p-1}$ and $N\lambda = p$).

9. In (8) is the set of congruences with $j > p/2$ *linearly dependent* on the set with $j < p/2$ or not?

10. Let $\alpha_{kj} \in \mathbf{I}$ and let $\mathfrak{a}$ be an ideal in $\mathbf{K}$; prove that the system of linear, homogeneous congruences $\sum_{j=1}^m \alpha_{kj}\phi_j \equiv 0 \pmod{\mathfrak{a}} (1 \le k \le m)$ can have nontrivial solutions, that is solutions where at least one ϕ_j satisfies $((\phi_j), \mathfrak{a}) = \mathfrak{i})$, only if the determinant δ of the α_{kj} is divisible by $\mathfrak{a}$. (*Hint:* Let γ_{kj} be the cofactors of the α_{kj}; then

$$\sum_{k=1}^m \alpha_{kj}\gamma_{ki} = \begin{cases} \delta & \text{if } j = i, \\ 0 & \text{if } j \ne i. \end{cases}$$

Hence,

$$\sum_{k=1}^m \gamma_{ki} \sum_{j=1}^m \alpha_{kj}\phi_j = \sum_{j=1}^m \phi_j \sum_{k=1}^m \alpha_{kj}\gamma_{ki} = \delta\phi_i.$$

If the left-hand member is divisible by $\mathfrak{a}$, then so is the right-hand member, and if $\mathfrak{a} \nmid \delta$, then $((\phi_i), \mathfrak{a}) \ne (1)$ for each i).

11. Consider the following two meanings of "coprimality" for integers $\xi, \eta \in \mathbf{I}$:

   (a) $\alpha \mid \xi, \alpha \mid \eta \Rightarrow \alpha = \varepsilon$, a unit of $\mathbf{I}$; and

   (b) $((\xi), (\eta)) = \mathfrak{i}$.

Does (a) $\Rightarrow$ (b)? Does (b) $\Rightarrow$ (a)? Or is it true that (a) $\Leftrightarrow$ (b)? Which statement (if any) is stronger?

12. Justify the sequence of implications following (11): $\{\lambda \mid \beta_0$ and $\beta_0 = \eta + \zeta \equiv b + c \,(\text{mod } \lambda^2)\} \Rightarrow \lambda \mid b + c \Rightarrow p \mid b + c \Rightarrow \lambda^{p-1} \mid b + c$, used in the proof of Theorem 6.

13. Prove that $\mathfrak{c} \mid (\lambda)\,(\eta)$, $\mathfrak{c} \mid (\lambda)\,(\zeta) \Rightarrow \mathfrak{c} \mid (\lambda)\mathfrak{d}$, where $\mathfrak{d} = (\eta, \zeta)$.

14. Let $(\lambda) \nmid \mathfrak{d}$ and let $(\lambda)\mathfrak{d}$ be the g.c.d. of the ideals (β_0), (β_1), ..., (β_{p-1}) taken in pairs; show that $(\lambda)^2 \mid (\beta_0) \Rightarrow (\lambda)^2 \nmid (\beta_j)$ for $j \neq 0$.

BIBLIOGRAPHY

1. E. Artin, *Theory of Algebraic Numbers* (Lectures), translated by G. Striker. *Mathem. Instit. Göttingen*, 1959.

2. L. E. Dickson, *Quarterly Journal of Math.*, **40**, 1907, pp. 27–45.

3. L. E. Dickson, *History of the Theory of Numbers*, Vol. 2. Carnegie Institute of Washington, 1952.

4. R. Fueter, *Synthetische Zahlentheorie*. Berlin: DeGruyter, 1925.

5. P. Furtwängler, *Sitzungsberichte Akad. Wissenschaften Wien*, **121**, 1912, pp. 589–592.

6. E. Hecke, *Theorie der Algebraischen Zahlen*, Leipzig: Akademische Verlagsgesellschaft, 1923; New York: Chelsea, 1948.

7. K. L. Jensen, *Nyt Tidsskrift for Mathematik, Afdeling, B.* 1915, pp. 73–83.

8. E. Landau, *Vorlesungen über Zahlentheorie*, Vol. 3. Leipzig: S. Hirzel, 1927.

9. D. H. Lehmer and E. Lehmer, *Bull. American Mathem. Soc.*, **47**, 1941, pp. 139–142.

10. D. Mirimanoff, *Comptes Rendus de l'Academie des Sciences*, (Paris), **150**, 1910, pp. 204–206.

11. D. Mirimanoff, *Journal für die reine u. angew. Mathem.*, **139**, 1911, pp. 309–324.

12. J. L. Selfridge, H. S. Vandiver, C. A. Nicol, *Proceedings National Acad. Sciences* (U.S.A.), **41**, 1955, pp. 970–973.

13. H. S. Vandiver, *American Math. Monthly*, **53**, 1946, pp. 555–578.

14. H. Weber, *Lehrbuch der Algebra*, Vol. 2. Braunschweig: F. Vieweg & Sohn, 1899.

15. H. Weyl, *Algebraic Theory of Numbers*, Annals of Math. Studies, No. 1. Princeton, N.J.: Princeton University Press, 1940.

16. A. Wieferich, *Journal f. d. reine u. angew. Mathem.*, **136**, 1909, pp. 293–302.

17. P. Wolfskehl, *Journal f. d. reine u. angew. Mathem.*, **99**, 1886, pp. 173–178.

CHAPTER 12

The Theory of Partitions

1. INTRODUCTION

Since the 18th century, the theory of partitions has interested some of the best minds. While it seems to have only little, or no practical application, it has, in a certain sense, just the right degree of difficulty: the problems are far from trivial—but, at the same time, they are not so hard as to discourage any attempt of a solution. Besides, through the introduction by Euler (1707–1783) of generating functions, the highly developed apparatus of the theory of functions became available for the study of partitions. A further circumstance of great help in this study, is the fact that the generating functions which occur in the theory of partitions, and functions closely related to them belong to two important classes of functions, namely, the theta functions and the modular functions, both of which have received much attention and have been most thoroughly investigated since the time of Jacobi (1804–1851).

In the following pages it will be possible to consider only a few, mostly classical aspects of the theory of partitions. It is my hope that the reader's curiosity will not have been satisfied with (or dulled by) this limited selection of topics. In case his interest has been sufficiently stimulated, so that he may want to learn something about the many facets of the theory, which, unfortunately, had to be ignored here, then I would suggest as a starting point some of the survey papers, like [11] or [5], where also more extensive bibliographies may be found.

2. DEFINITIONS AND NOTATIONS

The following definitions will clarify the meaning of some of the technical terms used, or to be used; some others will be explained later. Throughout this chapter we shall often have to refer to the set Z_0 of non-negative integers $0, 1, 2, \ldots$; clearly, $Z_0 = \{0\} \cup Z^+$ and $Z_0 \subset Z$.

Definition 1. Let $f(n)$ be a function defined for $n \in Z_0$ and let $F(x) = \sum_{n=0}^{\infty} f(n)x^n$; then $F(x)$ is said to be the *generating function* of $f(n)$.

REMARK 1. The definition does not imply that the series converges anywhere if $x \neq 0$; but, as a matter of fact, the generating functions that we shall meet with, will all converge in some finite circle, usually the unit circle.

Although the reader already knows from our introductory remarks what is meant by the word "partition," this concept will be further clarified and be made more precise by the following definition.

Definition 2. Let $A = \{a_1, a_2, \ldots, a_r, \ldots\}$ be a finite, or infinite set of positive integers. If $a_{i_1} + a_{i_2} + \cdots + a_{i_r} = n$, with $a_{i_j} \in A(j = 1, 2, \ldots, r)$, then we say that the sum $a_{i_1} + a_{i_2} + \cdots + a_{i_r}$ is a *partition* of n into summands (or parts) belonging to the set A.

REMARK 2. If $n \in A$, then n itself has to be counted as a partition of itself (see the examples, with $n = 5$).

REMARK 3. According to the definition of partitions, the summands do not have to be distinct; an explicit restriction to have all summands distinct, may, however be added.

The order of the summands is irrelevant; two partitions of n, that differ only by the order of the summands, are not considered distinct†. Hence, rearranging if necessary the summands and grouping together summands that are equal, every partition can be written, uniquely, in the form $n = k_1a_1 + k_2a_2 + \cdots + k_ia_i + \cdots$, where $a_1, a_2, \cdots$ are the distinct elements of A in increasing order and where the k_i are non-negative integers, only finitely many of which are different from zero. Each coefficient k_i indicates how often a given summand $a_i \in A$ occurs in the partition under consideration and it is called the *frequency* of a_i in that partition of n. It should be clear that any given partition is completely determined by the set of its frequencies.

---

† If we prefer to distinguish between partitions with identical summands, taken in different order, then we call them *representations* rather than partitions.

Definition 3.   Let **A** be a finite, or infinite set of positive integers. The number of distinct partitions of a natural integer n, into summands (or parts) belonging to **A** is denoted by $p_A(n)$ and is called the *partition function* relative to the set **A**. If no further conditions are imposed, we also call $p_A(n)$ the number of *unrestricted partitions* of n into parts that belong to **A**. If **A** is the set Z^+ of all natural integers, the partition function is denoted simply by $p(n)$. If other conditions are imposed (such as to have all summands distinct, or no more than a fixed number m of summands, and so on) then the partitions are called partitions with restrictions, or *restricted partitions*.

Notations.   We shall use the following notations:

$p(n)$ stands for the number of partitions of n into natural integers, without any restrictions;

$p_A(n)$ stands for the number of partitions of n into parts belonging to **A**, without other restrictions;

$p_{A,m}(n)$ stands for the number of partitions of n into parts not exceeding m and belonging to **A**;

$p_A^{(m)}(n)$ stands for the number of partitions of n into at most m summands, all belonging to **A**;

$p_A^{(d)}(n)$ stands for the number of partitions of n into distinct summands, all belonging to **A**;

$p_{A,k}^{(d,m)}(n)$ stands for the number of partitions of n, into at most m distinct parts, not exceeding k, of the set **A**;

$p_A^{(o)}(n)$ stands for the number of partitions of n into an odd number of parts belonging to **A**;

$p_A^{(e)}$ stands for the number of partitions of n into an even number of parts, all belonging to **A**.

$p_A^{(o,d)}$ and $p_A^{(e,d)}$ stand for the number of partitions of n into an odd (respectively an even) number of distinct parts belonging to **A**. We denote the set of positive odd integers by **O** and the set of non-negative even integers by **E**; clearly, $O \cup E = Z_0$. Observe that $p_E(n)$, the number of partitions of n into *even summands* and $p^{(e)}(n)$, the number of partitions of n into an *even number of summands* is not the same thing (see examples below). Occasionally, a restriction that needs not to be specified, will be denoted by an *. Generating functions of partitions will be denoted by $F(x)$, with the same subscript or superscripts as the partitions they generate. So, for instance,

$$F_A^{(m)}(x) = \sum_{n=0}^{\infty} p_A^{(m)}(n)x^n, \text{ and so on.}$$

REMARK 4.   As already observed, each partition is completely determined by the set of its frequencies $k_1, k_2, ..., k_r, ...$; hence, the number $p_A(n)$ of partitions of n is precisely the number of distinct solutions of the diophantine equation $k_1 a_1 + k_2 a_2 + \cdots + k_i a_i + \cdots = n$, in positive integers k_i and elements $a_i \in \mathbf{A}$; in symbols

$$p_{\mathbf{A}}(n) = \sum_{\substack{\Sigma k_i a_i = n \\ a_i \in \mathbf{A}, k_i \in \mathbf{Z}^+}} 1.$$

EXAMPLES

For $n = 5$, we observe that $5 = 4 + 1 = 3 + 2 = 3 + 1 + 1 = 2 + 2 + 1 = 2 + 1 + 1 + 1 = 1 + 1 + 1 + 1 + 1$. Hence, $p_{\mathbf{Z}}^+ (5) = p(5) = 7; p_{\mathbf{E}}(5) = 0;\ p_{\mathbf{O}}(5) = 3;\ p_3(5) = 5,\ p^{(3)}(5) = 5;\ p_{\mathbf{O}}^{(d)}(5) = 1;\ p_3^{(d)} = 1;\ p_5(5) = 7; p_8(5) = 7; p^{(e)}(5) = 3(\neq p_{\mathbf{E}}(5) = 0)\ p^{(d, 2)}(5) = p^{(d, 3)}(5) = 3.$

In what precedes, we required the elements of $\mathbf{A}$ to be natural integers. Applying this condition strictly, it follows that zero has no partitions; that is, $p(0) = 0$. However usually (not always! see, e.g. the proof of Theorem 10) it is more convenient to define $p(0) = 1$ (and, similarly, $p_{\mathbf{A}, \bullet}^{(\bullet)}(0) = 1$); whenever this is the case, we shall not hesitate to do so.

3. SURVEY OF METHODS

Several methods have been used successfully in the theory of partitions. We already mentioned the method of *generating functions*, used brilliantly by Euler and his successors. Next are the purely *combinatorial methods*, whose usefulness is greatly enhanced by the use of *graphs*. Besides the use of generating function as a formal device, they may be used also in connection with algebraic methods, such as decomposition into *partial fractions* (see [1], [8], and [12]); or in connection with analytic methods, such as Cauchy's *theorem on residues, contour integration,* or *Tauberian theorems,* to quote only a few. In what follows we shall have occasion to examplify the use of several of these methods, but shall remain throughout on an elementary level, that is, we shall make no appeal to any deeper theorems of either algebra, or analysis.

4. GENERATING FUNCTIONS

Let $F_{\mathbf{A}}(x) = \sum_{n=0}^{\infty} p_{\mathbf{A}}(n) x^n$ and $F_{\mathbf{A}}^{(d)}(x) = \sum_{n=0}^{\infty} p_{\mathbf{A}}^{(d)}(n) x^n$ be the generating functions for $p_{\mathbf{A}}(n)$ and $p_{\mathbf{A}}^{(d)}(n)$, respectively; then the following theorem holds.

Theorem 1. $F_A(x) = \prod_{a \in A} (1 - x^a)^{-1}$ and $F_A^{(d)}(x) = \prod_{a \in A} (1 + x^a)$.

PROOF. Taking the product of $(1 - x^a)^{-1} = 1 + x^a + x^{2a} + \cdots + x^{ka} + \cdots$ over all $a \in A$, we obtain

$$\prod_{a \in A} (1 + x^2 + x^{2a} + \cdots + x^{ka} + \cdots) = \sum_{n=0}^{\infty} b_n x^n,$$

where b_n is the number of times we obtain n as a sum of terms of the form ka, all a's being distinct; that is, b_n is the number of solutions of the Diophantine equation $k_1 a_1 + k_2 a_2 + \cdots = n$, with $a_j \in A$, $a_i \neq a_j$ if $i \neq j$, and $k_j \in \mathbf{Z}_0$. Hence, by previous Remark 4, $b_n = p_A(n)$, proving the first statement. Similarly, $\prod_{a \in A} (1 + x^a) = \sum_{n=0}^{\infty} c_n x^n$, where c_n is the number of times we obtain n as a sum of distinct exponents $a \in A$, that is, $c_n = p_A^{(d)}(n)$.

REMARK 5. In both statements of Theorem 1, the coefficient of x^0 (that is, the constant term) is 1; hence, we are led to make the announced convention and set $p_A(0) = p_A^{(d)}(0) = 1$.

From Theorem 1 and Definitions 1, 2, and 3 we obtain almost immediately the following statements, which we list as

Corollary 1.1.

(1) $F(x) = \prod_{k=1}^{\infty} (1 - x^k)^{-1}$ is the generating function of $p(n)$.

(2) $F_E(x) = \prod_{k=1}^{\infty} (1 - x^{2k})^{-1}$ is the generating function of $p_E(n)$.

(3) $p_E(2n + 1) = 0$.

(4) $F_O(x) = \prod_{k=1}^{\infty} (1 - x^{2k-1})^{-1}$ is the generating function of $p_O(n)$.

(5) $F_m(x) = \prod_{k=1}^{m} (1 - x^k)^{-1}$ is the generating function of $p_m(n)$.

(6) $F^{(d)}(x) = \prod_{k=1}^{\infty} (1 + x^k)$ is the generating function of $p^{(d)}(n)$.

(7) $p_{A,m}^{(*)}(n) \leq p_A^{(*)}(n)$ for all $m \geq 1$.

(8) $p_{A,m}^{(*)}(n) = p_A^{(*)}(n)$ for $m \geq n$.

(9) $p^{(d)}(n) = p_O(n)$.

PROOFS. Statements (1), (2), (4), (5), and (6) are particular cases of Theorem 1.

Statement (3) simply restates that $F_E(x)$ has only even powers of x. Statement (7) follows from the remark, that adding restrictions (in this case, concerning the size of admissible summands) cannot increase the number of partitions. However, no parts in excess of n occur in any of its partitions; hence, if $m \geq n$, to restrict the parts not to exceed m is not to restrict them at all and statement (8) follows. It remains to prove statement (9). We do it, by showing that $p^{(d)}(n)$ and $p_0(n)$ have the same generating function, that is, that $\prod_{k=1}^{\infty} (1 + x^k) = \prod_{k=1}^{\infty} (1 - x^{2k-1})^{-1}$. We observe that $\prod_{k=1}^{\infty} (1 + x^k)$ $= \prod_{k=1}^{\infty} \dfrac{1 - x^{2k}}{1 - x^k}$. In the denominator occur all factors $1 - x^k$, both, with k even, and with k odd. In the numerator occur only, but all, factors $1 - x^{2k}$, with even exponent; these cancel the corresponding factors in the denominator, leaving 1 in the numerator and only (but all) factors $1 - x^{2k-1}$ in the denominator. The product has become precisely $\prod_{k=1}^{\infty} (1 - x^{2k-1})^{-1}$, as we wanted to prove.

The reader will have observed that we have not, so far, raised the question of convergence of the generating function, represented either as a series, or as a product. This is not by an oversight. Indeed, all that we are interested in at present are formal manipulations, that insure the identity of the coefficients of the formal power series expansions of the functions appearing on the right and on the left of the " $=$ " sign. So, for instance the formal series $\sum_{n=0}^{\infty} n! x^n$ is the generating function for the arithmetical function $f(n) = n!$; but, except for $x = 0$, the series does not converge. As a matter of fact, the series and products met in this chapter do converge, at least for $|x| < 1$; hence, they represent actually functions analytic at least inside the unit circle. Although this consideration, of great importance in some of the analytic methods, will hardly ever be used here (see however the proof of Theorem 8), we shall prove

Theorem 2. *The generating functions of the partition functions converge inside the unit circle.*

PROOF. The number of partitions of n, with, or without restrictions, is a non-negative integer; also, as already observed, the number of partitions can only decrease, if restrictions are added. Hence, the coefficients of the partition function are non-negative integers, nondecreasing when we remove restrictions so that, if z is a complex variable and

$$r = |z|, \ |F_A^{(\cdots)}...(z)| \leq F_A^{(\cdots)}...(r) \leq F(r)$$

$$= \prod_{k=1}^{\infty} (1 - r^k)^{-1} = \prod_{k=1}^{\infty} (1 + f_k(r)),$$

with

$$f_k(r) = r^k + r^{2k} + \cdots = \frac{r^k}{1 - r^k} (> 0) \quad \text{for} \quad 0 < r < 1.$$

The infinite product of factors $1 + f_k(r)$ (with $f_k(r) > 0$) converges (by 7.3.2), provided that the series $\sum_{k=1}^{\infty} f_k(r)$ converges and this is actually the case. Indeed, on account of $0 < r < 1$, $r_k \to 0$, as $k \to \infty$, and the series $\sum_{k=1}^{\infty} f_k(r)$ converges by comparison with the series $\sum_{k=1}^{\infty} r_k$.

REMARK 6. The convergence is uniform for $|z| \leq 1 - \varepsilon(\varepsilon > 0$, arbitrarily small).

REMARK 7. The series and products, representing the generating functions mentioned, do not converge outside the unit circle; this can be seen easily if we let $x \to 1^-$ in the product representation and observe that the functions cannot stay bounded.

Corollary 2.1. $\lim_{n \to \infty} \dfrac{p(n + 1)}{p(n)} = 1$.

PROOF. To each partition of n, counted by $p(n)$, we can make correspond a distinct partition of $p(n + 1)$, simply by increasing the largest (or one of the largest, if there are several equal summands larger than the others) summand occurring in a given partition of n, by one unity. In addition, $n + 1$ has the partition $1 + 1 + 1 + \cdots + 1$ ($n + 1$ parts each equal to unity), which has no "mate" among the partitions of n, under the correspondence we set up; hence, $p(n + 1) \geq p(n) + 1$. On the other hand, by Theorem 2, $F(x) = \sum_{n=0}^{\infty} p(n)x^n$ converges for any $0 \leq x < 1$; hence,

$$\lim_{n \to \infty} \left| \frac{p(n + 1)x^{n+1}}{p(n)x^n} \right| = \lim_{n \to \infty} \frac{p(n + 1)}{p(n)} |x| \leq 1.$$

Therefore,

$$\lim_{n \to \infty} \frac{p(n + 1)}{p(n)} \leq \frac{1}{|x|} \quad \text{for any } |x| < 1.$$

It follows that $\lim_{n \to \infty} p(n + 1)/p(n) \leq 1$. However, $p(n + 1) > p(n)$ implies $\lim_{n \to \infty} p(n + 1)/p(n) \geq 1$; hence, $\lim_{n \to \infty} p(n + 1)/p(n) = 1$, as asserted.

It is often easier to work with partitions where the size of the largest summand is limited, than with unrestricted partitions. It is for this reason that statements (7) and (8) of Corollary 1.1 are often useful. One reason why $p_m(n)$ is often easy to handle is the following theorem, which permits us to reduce $p_m(n)$ to $p_{m-1}(n)$.

Theorem 3.

$$p_m(n) = p_{m-1}(n) + p_m(n - m) \quad for \quad n \geq m, m \geq 1; \tag{1}$$

more generally,

$$p_m(n) = p_{m-1}(n) + p_{m-1}(n - m) + p_{m-1}(n - 2m) + \cdots$$

$$+ p_{m-1}(n - km) + p_m(n - (k + 1)m)$$

$$= p_{m-1}(n) + p_{m-1}(n - m) + \cdots + p_{m-1}(n - rm), \quad r = \left[\frac{n}{m}\right].$$

PROOF. Either a given partition of n does not contain the summand m, and then it is counted (exactly once) by $p_{m-1}(n)$; or else, it does contain m, and then it is of the form $n = a_1 + a_2 + \cdots + a_r + m(1 \leq a_j \leq m, j = 1, 2, ..., r)$. Here $a_1 + \cdots + a_r$ is a partition of $n - m$ and to each of the $p_m(n - m)$ such partitions of $n - m$ into summands not in excess of m corresponds exactly one partition of n, effectively containing m, which is precisely $a_1 + a_2 + \cdots + a_r + m$. This proves the first equality and the other two follow by induction on k and the remark that for $v > 0$, $p_m(-v) = 0$.

Among the easiest to handle and most important generating function is, of course,

$$F(x) = \sum_{n=0}^{\infty} p(n)x^n = \prod_{k=1}^{\infty} (1 - x^k)^{-1}.$$

Still simpler is the reciprocal, $F(x)^{-1}$, which we shall denote by $\Phi(x)$. This function $\Phi(x) = \prod_{n=1}^{\infty} (1 - x^n)$, introduced by Euler, seems to be the first appearance in the literature, of a *theta function*. The functions of this class have two important properties: (i) they may be represented by a product (which we know, in this instance); and (ii) they may be represented by a power series such that the exponents of the independent variable are polynomials of second degree in the summation index. In the particular case of the function $\Phi(x)$, these properties form the content of the following famous theorem of Euler, generally known as the "pentagonal numbers" theorem.

Theorem 4.

$$\Phi(x) = \prod_{k=1}^{\infty} (1 - x^k) = \sum_{n=-\infty}^{\infty} (-1)^n x^{n(3n+1)/2}$$

$$= 1 + \sum_{n=1}^{\infty} (-1)^n x^{n(3n+1)/2} + \sum_{n=1}^{\infty} (-1)^n x^{n(3n-1)/2}.$$

Before we prove this theorem, let us make a few applications, which will illustrate the power of the method of generating functions, introduced by Euler.

The obvious identity $F(x)\Phi(x) = 1$ leads to the following interesting *recurrence formula*, that permits the computation of $p(n)$, if $p(k)$ is already known for $k < n$.

Theorem 5. $p(n) = p(n - 1) + p(n - 2) - p(n - 5) - p(n - 7) + \cdots + (-1)^{j+1}p(n - n_j) + \cdots$ *where* $n_j = \frac{1}{2}j(3j \pm 1)$ *are the so-called "pentagonal numbers."*

REMARK 8. If we border a regular pentagon, marked by 5 dots, so as to obtain successively, pentagons with $3, 4, \ldots, j, \ldots$ dots on each side, then the total number of dots is $\frac{1}{2}j(3j - 1)$ (see Fig. 1).

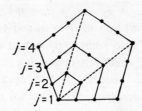

$j=4$
$j=3$
$j=2$
$j=1$

Figure 1.   Pentagonal Numbers

PROOF OF THEOREM 5.

$$1 = F(x)\Phi(x) = \sum_{k=0}^{\infty} p(k)x^k \sum_{m=-\infty}^{\infty} (-1)^m x^{m(3m+1)/2}$$

$$= \sum_{n=0}^{\infty} x^n \sum_{k+\frac{m(3m+1)}{2}=n} (-1)^m p(k)$$

$$= \sum_{n=0}^{\infty} x^n \sum_{\frac{m(3m+1)}{2} \le n} (-1)^m p\left(n - \frac{m(1m + 3)}{2}\right)$$

Identifying coefficients, it is clear that, except for $n = 0$ (which implies $m = 0$ in the inner sum), all coefficients of x^n have to vanish. Hence, making successively

$$m = 0, +1, -1, +2, -2, \ldots,$$

we obtain

$$0 = \sum_m (-1)^m p\left(n - \frac{m(3m + 1)}{2}\right) = p(n) - p(n - 1) - p(n - 2)$$

$$+ p(n - 5) + p(n - 7) - \cdots$$

The series breaks off, when $m(3m + 1)/2 > n$, and Theorem 5 is proven. Only slightly more complicated is the proof of

Theorem 6.

$$np(n) = p(0)\sigma(n) + p(1)\sigma(n - 1) + \cdots + p(r)\sigma(n - r) + \cdots$$

$$+ p(n - 1)\sigma(1).$$

PROOF. From $F(x) = 1/\Phi(x)$, we obtain, by differentiation,

$$F'(x) = -\frac{\Phi'(x)}{\Phi^2(x)} = -\frac{\Phi'(x)}{\Phi(x)}\frac{1}{\Phi(x)} = -\frac{\Phi'(x)}{\Phi(x)}F(x).$$

We now proceed to replace each function by its power series expansion: From $\Phi(x) = \prod_{k=1}^{\infty} (1 - x^k)$ follows

$$\log \Phi(x) = \sum_{k=1}^{\infty} \log(1 - x^k) \quad \text{and} \quad \frac{\Phi'(x)}{\Phi(x)} = -\sum_{k=1}^{\infty} \frac{kx^{k-1}}{1 - x^k}.$$

Hence,

$$F'(x) = \sum_{n=1}^{\infty} np(n)x^{n-1} = -F(x)\frac{\Phi'(x)}{\Phi(x)} = -\sum_{m=0}^{\infty} p(m)x^m \left(-\sum_{k=1}^{\infty} \frac{kx^{k-1}}{1 - x^k}\right),$$

or, successively,

$$\sum_{n=1}^{\infty} np(n)x^n = \sum_{m=0}^{\infty} p(m)x^m \sum_{k=1}^{\infty} k(x^k + x^{2k} + \cdots + x^{rk} + \cdots) = \sum_{n=1}^{\infty} x^n \sum_{m+rk=n} kp(m)$$

$$= \sum_{n=1}^{\infty} x^n \sum_{m=0}^{n} p(m) \sum_{k|n-m} k = \sum_{n=1}^{\infty} x^n \sum_{m=0}^{n} p(m)\sigma(n - m)$$

and we obtain the theorem, if we identify the coefficients of the first and last member.

ALTERNATIVE PROOF (see [2]). Let us write out explicitly all partitions of n, say, $n = a_1 + a_2 + \cdots + a_r$. Adding them all up, we obtain on the left $np(n)$. On the right, we regroup the summands according to their size. We have to determine how often a specific summand, say m, occurs. As we already had an opportunity to observe, if m appears in a given partition of n, the other summands form one of the partitions of $n - m$; hence, so far, m occurred $p(n - m)$ times. However, m may occur also in some of these partitions of $n - m$ (because it could occur more than once in a given partition of n). Reasoning as before we find that if m actually occurs in a partition of $n - m$, then the other summands form a partition of $n - 2m$, of which there are exactly $p(n - 2m)$, and so forth. All together, if we add up all summands m that occur we obtain $\sum_{k=1}^{[n/m]} mp(n - km)$. And if we add up *all* summands, we obtain $\sum_{m=1}^{n} \sum_{k=1}^{n/m} mp(n - km)$. We formulate the result obtained as

Theorem 7.

$$np(n) = \sum_{m=1}^{n} \sum_{k=1}^{n/m} mp(n - km).$$

From Theorem 7 we can immediately obtain again Theorem 6, namely, if we set $km = r$,

$$np(n) = \sum_{m=1}^{n} \sum_{k=1}^{n/m} mp(n - km) = \sum_{r=1}^{n} p(n - r) \sum_{m|r} m = \sum_{r=1}^{n} p(n - r)\sigma(r).$$

We still owe the reader a proof of Theorem 4. There are several proofs of this important theorem. The simplest, conceptually, is Euler's own. This consists in a systematic multiplication of the product $(1 - x)(1 - x^2)(1 - x^3)\cdots$, with a skillful arrangement of the cancellations and an easy induction.

Another, very elegant proof, is due to Professor N. Fine [3]; it consists in formal work with power series, involving additional parameters. It has, however, several rather subtle points. Actually, Theorem 4 follows as a simple Corollary from an important identity due to Jacobi ([7], Section 64), which we shall discuss next. For the reader, who does not want to get involved with Jacobi's identity, a direct combinatorial proof of Theorem 4, using graphs, will also be presented.

Theorem 8. (Jacobi). *For $z \neq 0$, and $|x| < 1$,*

$$\prod_{n=1}^{\infty} \{(1 - x^{2n})(1 + x^{2n-1}z)(1 + x^{2n-1}z^{-1})\} = \sum_{n=-\infty}^{\infty} x^{n^2}z^n. \qquad (2)$$

Assuming for a moment the validity of Theorem 8, let us prove Theorem 4. In (2) we replace x by $u^{3/2}$ and z by $-u^{1/2}$; then the first member becomes

$$\prod_{n=1}^{\infty} \{(1 - u^{3n})(1 - u^{3n-\frac{3}{2}+\frac{1}{2}})(1 - u^{3n-\frac{3}{2}-\frac{1}{2}})\}$$

$$= \prod_{n=1}^{\infty} \{(1 - u^{3n-2})(1 - u^{3n-1})(1 - u^{3n})\} = \prod_{m=1}^{\infty} (1 - u^m) = \Phi(u).$$

The second member becomes

$$\sum_{n=-\infty}^{\infty} u^{\frac{3}{2}n^2}(-u^{1/2})^n = \sum_{n=-\infty}^{\infty} (-1)^n u^{n(3n+1)/2}.$$

and Theorem 4 is proven.

Besides Theorem 4, some other, important corollaries of Theorem 8 are the following:

Corollary 8.1. $\displaystyle\prod_{n=0}^{\infty} \{(1 - x^{2n+2})(1 + x^n)\} = \sum_{n=-\infty}^{\infty} x^{n(n+1)/2}.$

REMARK 9. $t_n = n(n + 1)/2$ is called the n-th triangular number.

PROOF. In (2), set $x = z = u^{1/2}$, obtaining in the first member

$$\prod_{n=1}^{\infty} \{(1 - u^n)(1 + u^{n-\frac{1}{2}+\frac{1}{2}})(1 + u^{n-\frac{1}{2}-\frac{1}{2}})\}$$

$$= \prod_{n=1}^{\infty} (1 - u^{2n})(1 + u^{n-1}) = \prod_{n=0}^{\infty} (1 - u^{2n+2})(1 + u^n);$$

and in the second member

$$\sum_{n=-\infty}^{\infty} u^{n^2/2 + n/2} = \sum_{n=-\infty}^{\infty} u^{n(n+1)/2},$$

proving the corollary.

Furthermore, by (9) of Corollary 10.1 (see its proof),

$$\prod_{n=1}^{\infty} (1 + x^n) = \prod_{n=1}^{\infty} \frac{1}{1 - x^{2n-1}} ;$$

hence,

$$\prod_{n=0}^{\infty} (1 + x^n) = 2 \prod_{n=1}^{\infty} (1 + x^n) = 2 \prod_{n=1}^{\infty} \frac{1}{1 - x^{2n-1}}$$

$$= 2 \frac{1}{(1 - x)(1 - x^3)(1 - x^5) \cdots}$$

and the first member in Corollary 8.1 may be written as

$$2 \frac{(1 - x^2)(1 - x^4)(1 - x^6)}{(1 - x)(1 - x^3)(1 - x^5)} \cdots.$$

We record this result as

Corollary 8.2. $\displaystyle\prod_{n=1}^{\infty} \frac{1 - x^{2n}}{1 - x^{2n-1}} = \sum_{n=0}^{\infty} x^{n(n+1)/2}.$

Corollary 8.3. $\displaystyle\Phi^3(x) = \prod_{n=1}^{\infty}(1 - x^n)^3 = \sum_{n=1}^{\infty}(2n + 1)x^{n(n+1)/2}.$

PROOF. We set $z = -xy$ in (2) and obtain the first member $\prod_{n=1}^{\infty}(1 - x^{2n})$. $(1 - yx^{2n})(1 - y^{-1}x^{2n-2})$. If we write the last factor as $1 - y^{-1}x^{2n}$, then, as n runs from 1 to ∞, the product is the same, except that we lose the factor $1 - y^{-1}$, corresponding to $n = 1$ in the original form of the product. Hence, the first member becomes

$$(1 - y^{-1})\prod_{n=1}^{\infty}(1 - x^{2n})(1 - yx^{2n})(1 - y^{-1}x^{2n}).$$

The second member of (2) becomes

$$\sum_{n=-\infty}^{\infty}(-1)^n x^{n^2+n}y^n$$

and we obtain by (2), after division by $(1 - y^{-1})$, that

$$\prod_{n=1}^{\infty}(1 - x^{2n})(1 - yx^{2n})(1 - y^{-1}x^{2n}) = \frac{1}{1 - y^{-1}}\sum_{n=-\infty}^{\infty}(-1)^n x^{n^2+n}y^n.$$

The second member may also be written

$$\sum_{n=0}^{\infty}(-1)^n \frac{x^{n(n+1)}(y^n - y^{-n-1})}{1 - y^{-1}}$$

$$= \sum_{n=0}^{\infty}(-1)^n x^{n(n+1)}(y^n + y^{n-1} + y^{n-2} + \cdots + 1 + y^{-1} + \cdots + y^{-n}).$$

If we write the equality of the first and second member for $y = 1$, we obtain

$$\prod_{n=1}^{\infty}(1 - x^{2n})^3 = \sum_{n=0}^{\infty}(-1)^n(2n + 1)x^{n(n+1)}$$

as asserted.

Theorem 8, and its corollaries, including Theorem 4, present examples of theta functions and state the identity, between their representations as infinite products and as power series.

*Proof of Theorem 8. Let[†]

$$\Phi_M(x, z) = \prod_{m=1}^{M} (1 + zx^{2m-1})(1 + z^{-1}x^{2m-1}).$$

Then

$$\Phi_M(x, x^2z) = \prod_{m=1}^{M} (1 + zx^{2m+1})(1 + z^{-1}x^{2m-3})$$

$$= \Phi_M(x, z) \frac{(1 + zx^{2M+1})(1 + z^{-1}x^{-1})}{(1 + zx)(1 + z^{-1}x^{2M-1})} = \Phi_M(x, z) \frac{1 + zx^{2M+1}}{xz + x^{2M}},$$

or

$$(xz + x^{2M})\Phi_M(x, x^2z) = (1 + zx^{2M+1})\Phi_M(x, z). \tag{3}$$

If we expand the (finite) product defining $\Phi_M(x, z)$, the coefficient of z^m will be a certain polynomial $P_m(x)$. The product Φ_M does not change, if we replace z by z^{-1}; hence, the coefficient of z^{-m} is the same polynomial, or $P_m(x) = P_{-m}(x)$. The highest power of x that occurs is, clearly, z^M and its coefficient is

$$P_M(x) = x^{1+3+\cdots+(2M-1)} = x^{M^2}.$$

Hence, $\Phi_M(x, z) = \sum_{m=-M}^{M} P_m(x)z^m$ with

$$P_M(x) = P_{-M}(x) = x^{M^2} \quad \text{and} \quad P_m(x) = P_{-m}(x).$$

Substituting this expansion in the recurrence relation (3), we obtain

$$(xz + x^{2M}) \sum_{m=-M}^{M} P_m(x)x^{2m}z^m = (1 + zx^{2M+1}) \sum_{m=-M}^{M} P_m(x)z^m. \tag{4}$$

Equating the coefficient of z^m on both sides,

$$x^{2m-1}P_{m-1} + x^{2(M+m)} P_m = P_m + x^{2M+1}P_{m-1},$$

$$\text{for} \quad -M \leq m - 1 < m \leq M. \tag{5}$$

We observe that in (4) also z^{-M} and z^{M+1} occur, to which the recurrence does not apply; but we also easily check that the corresponding equalities of coefficients still hold, and are, as a matter of fact the trivial $P_M(x) = P_M(x)$ and $P_{-M}(x) = P_{-M}(x)$; actually, we already know their common value x^{M^2}. From (5) we obtain

$$P_m(x) = x^{2m-1} \frac{1 - x^{2(M-m+1)}}{1 - x^{2(M+m)}} P_{m-1}(x) \tag{6}$$

† Exceptionally a rational integer is denoted here by *capital M*.

or

$$P_{m-1}(x) = P_m(x) \cdot x^{-2m+1} \frac{1 - x^{2(M+m)}}{1 - x^{2(M-m+1)}}.$$

In particular, for $m = M$:

$$P_{M-1}(x) = P_M(x) \cdot x^{-2M+1} \frac{1 - x^{4M}}{1 - x^2} = x^{(M-1)^2} \frac{1 - x^{4M}}{1 - x^2};$$

similarly, by (6),

$$P_{M-2}(x) = P_{M-1}(x) \cdot x^{-2M+3} \frac{1 - x^{4M-2}}{1 - x^4}$$

$$= x^{(M-1)^2 - 2(M-1)+1} \cdot \frac{1 - x^{4M}}{1 - x^2} \frac{1 - x^{4M-2}}{1 - x^4}$$

$$= x^{(M-2)^2} \cdot \frac{(1 - x^{4M})(1 - x^{4M-2})}{(1 - x^2)(1 - x^4)}$$

and, by induction,

$$P_{M-k}(x) = x^{(M-k)^2} \frac{(1 - x^{4M})(1 - x^{4M-2}) \cdots (1 - x^{4M-2k+2})}{(1 - x^2)(1 - x^4) \cdots (1 - x^{2k})}.$$

In particular,

$$P_0(x) = \frac{(1 - x^{4M})(1 - x^{4M-2}) \cdots (1 - x^{2M+2})}{(1 - x^2)(1 - x^4) \cdots (1 - x^{2M})}.$$

The careful reader will have observed the strong analogy between these rational expressions and the binomial coefficients. As a matter of fact, if the factors $1 - x$ $1 - x^k$ are replaced by the exponents k, we obtain ordinary binomial coefficients. Just as the ordinary binomial coefficients are actually integers, although they are written as fractions, so also our "Gaussian binomial coefficients" $P_m(x)$ are really polynomials, in spite of their appearance. Having obtained the polynomials $P_m(x)$, we can now, using (6), write

$$\Phi_M(x, z) = P_0(x)\Bigg\{1 + x \frac{1 - x^{2M}}{1 - x^{2M+2}} (z + z^{-1})$$

$$+ x^4 \frac{(1 - x^{2M})(1 - x^{2M-2})}{(1 - x^{2M+2})(1 - x^{2M+4})} (z^2 + z^{-2}) + \cdots$$

$$+ x^{M^2} \frac{(1 - x^{2M}) \cdots (1 - x^2)}{(1 - x^{2M+2}) \cdots (1 - x^{4M})} (z^M + z^{-M})\Bigg\}.$$

If we multiply both sides by $\prod_{m=1}^{M} (1 - x^{2m})$, this cancels the denominator of $P_0(x)$ and we obtain

$$\prod_{m=1}^{M} (1 - x^{2m})(1 + zx^{2m-1})(1 + z^{-1}x^{2m-1})$$

$$= (1 - x^{2M+2})(1 - x^{2M+4}) \cdots (1 - x^{4M})$$

$$\times \left\{ 1 + x\frac{1 - x^{2M}}{1 - x^{2M+2}}(z + z^{-1}) + \cdots \right.$$

$$\left. + x^{M^2}\frac{(1 - x^{2M}) \cdots (1 - x^2)}{(1 - x^{2M+2}) \cdots (1 - x^{4M})}(z^M + z^{-M}) \right\}.$$

We observe that in the denominator occur only factors $(1 - x^k)$ with $k \geq 2M + 2$; hence, in the expansion of

$$\frac{1}{1 - x^k} = 1 + x^k + x^{2k} + \cdots,$$

also only powers of x with exponent larger than $2M$ will occur. Furthermore, if we look only at the coefficients of $(z^n + z^{-n})$ with $n < M/2$, then the numerators have factors $(1 - x^{2M})(1 - x^{2M-2}) \cdots (1 - x^{2M-2n})$ and the lowest power of x that occurs has an exponent $2M - 2n > M$. Therefore

$$\prod_{m=1}^{M} (1 - x^{2m})(1 + zx^{2m-1})(1 + z^{-1}x^{2m-1})$$

$$= 1 + x(z + z^{-1})(1 + x^{k_1} + \cdots) + x^{2^2}(z^2 + z^{-2})(1 + x^{k_2} + \cdots) + \cdots$$

$$+ x^{n^2}(z^n + z^{-n})(1 + x^{k_n} + \cdots) + \cdots \qquad \text{with } k_j > M.$$

As $M \to \infty$, so do the exponents k_j and $x^{k_j} \to 0$, because $|x| < 1$. Therefore, the limit for $M \to \infty$, of the n-th summand (n fixed) is $x^{n^2}(z^n + z^{-n})$ and we have proved that

$$\prod_{m=1}^{\infty} (1 - x^{2m})(1 + zx^{2m-1})(1 + z^{-1}x^{2m-1})$$

$$= \lim_{M \to \infty} \prod_{m=1}^{M} (1 - x^{2m})(1 + zx^{2m-1})(1 + z^{-1}x^{2m-1})$$

$$= 1 + \sum_{n=1}^{\infty} x^{n^2}(z^n + z^{-n}) = \sum_{n=-\infty}^{\infty} z^n x^{n^2},$$

that is, Theorem 8.

As we saw, Theorem 8 (Jacobi's identity) yields a large number of results. However, if our aim is only to prove Theorem 4, we can obtain it with far less complicated machinery. For that reason, and also in order to introduce a new approach, we shall present another, extremely simple proof of Theorem 4. Our main tool will be the consideration of graphs.

5. GRAPHS

Graphs are pictorial representations of partitions. Each summand is represented as a number of dots, arranged, say, horizontally. The partition $3 + 2$ of five has the graph: ° ° °. The same graph may be interpreted, however, so that dots of the same vertical line correspond to a summand. Looked upon that way, the graph stands for the partition $2 + 2 + 1$. Two partitions related like $3 + 2$ and $2 + 2 + 1$, i.e. that are representable by the same graph, are called *conjugate partitions*. This concept of "conjugacy" establishes a pairing off, or correspondence between partitions; under this correspondence some partitions, like ° ° ° correspond to themselves; these are called *self-conjugate* partitions. If m is the largest summand in the graph of a partition, then the conjugate partition contains exactly m summands, and conversely. Hence, we infer that the number of partitions of n, having the largest summand m, is equal to the number of partitions of n into exactly m summands. It now follows, considering all partitions with largest summand not in excess of m, that this equals the number of partitions into no more than m summands and we have proven

Theorem 9.   *The number of partitions into parts not in excess of m, equals the number of partitions into at most m summands, or, in symbols*

$$p_m(n) = p^{(m)}(n).$$

The method of graphs will permit us to prove Theorem 4 by very elementary considerations. First, however, we shall transform the problem slightly. If we multiply out the product $(1 - x)(1 - x^2)(1 - x^3) \cdots$ it turns out that most powers of x have coefficient zero. This means that the products

$$(-x^{a_1})(-x^{a_2}) \cdots (-x^{a_r}) \qquad \text{with } a_1 + a_2 + \cdots + a_r = n$$

and an even number of factors, each with a different exponent, which lead to $+x^n$ occur, in general, exactly the same number of times as the products $(-x^{b_1}) \cdots (-x^{b_s})$ with $b_1 + b_2 + \cdots + b_s = n$, distinct b's and an odd number of terms, leading to $-x^n$. An exception occurs, according to Theorem 4, if, and only if $n = j(3j \pm 1)/2$, when the number of partitions of n into an odd number of distinct parts exceeds the number of partitions into an even number of distinct parts by exactly one, if j is odd and the number of n into an even number of distinct parts exceeds the number of partitions into an odd number of distinct parts (again by exactly one), if j is even. It is in this equivalent formulation,

$$p^{(e,d)}(n) - p^{(o,d)}(n) = \begin{cases} (-1)^j & \text{if } n = j(3j \pm 1)/2 \\ 0 & \text{otherwise,} \end{cases}$$

that we are going to prove Theorem 4.

This remarkable proof is due to Franklin, one of the first American mathematicians [4]. In order to prove the theorem, we shall try to construct a one-to-one correspondence between the partitions of n into an even, and an odd number of distinct summands; we shall find that the correspondence will break down, and that one, or the other kind of partitions will exceed the other kind by exactly one, precisely when n is of the form $j(3j \pm 1)/2$. In order to be certain that each partition is considered exactly once, we shall insist that all summands should be arranged in decreasing order. There will be no ambiguity, because all summands involved are distinct. Consider then such a partition of n, with summands all unequal and arranged in decreasing order and, for simplicity, let us place the dots at equal distance from each other, so that they lie on the vertices of little squares:

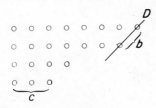

Figure 2

Denote the size of the smallest summand by c; consider also a line D from the upper right-hand corner, going down at 45°. We denote by b the number of dots of the graph on this line. If $b < c$ (as in Figure 2) we may remove the b dots of the line D, and add them at the bottom of the graph. In this way the number of summands has been increased by one; hence, its parity has been changed. If $c < b$, or even if $c = b$, the previous operation does not work, because the summand added at the bottom would be either larger than the preceding one, thus violating the rule of decreasing summands; or equal to it, while we insist on having distinct summands (see Fig. 3).

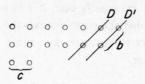

Figure 3

But in this case we can, in general, change the parity by the operation of distributing the last summand, consisting of c dots, among the c largest summands; this requires to add a line D', consisting of $c \leq b$ dots, parallel to D. Again, we obtain a legitimate partition, with one summand less; hence the parity of the number of summands has been changed. Clearly, either $b < c$; or else $c \leq b$; hence, only one of the operations is possible. It is clear that, whenever one, or the other of these operations can be performed, we can make correspond to each partition with an even number of summands, one with an odd number of summands; hence each kind of partition occurs the same number of times and $p^{(o,d)}(n) = p^{(e,d)}(n)$. However, there are exactly two cases, when *both* above operations become impossible.

   (i)   Let $b = c$ with D passing through the last dot of the smallest summand (see Fig. 4). If we try to remove the last summand, there are only $b - 1 = c - 1$ summands left, and we cannot distribute the c dots among

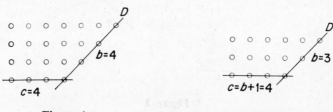

Figure 4   **Figure 5**

them, one to each ; and if we try to remove the $b = c$ dots of D and form a new summand, we leave only $c - 1$ dots in the last summand and are not allowed to add underneath a new summand of $b = c > c - 1$ dots.

   (ii)   A similar situation exists if $c = b + 1$ and D contains again the last dot of the smallest summand. The reasoning being similar to the preceding one, we leave it up to the reader to convince himself, using a graph like Fig. 5.

In case (i),

$$n = c + (c + 1) + (c + 2) + \cdots + (c + (b - 1)) = b(2c + b - 1)/2,$$

or, having $b = c$, $n = b(3b - 1)/2$. The excess partition (that without a match) has $b = c$ summands. Hence, if b, the number of summands, is even, there is an excess of one partition with an even number of summands over the number of partitions with an odd number of summands; if b is odd, then the lone extra partition has an odd number of summands. Similarly, in case (ii), with $c = b + 1$ as in Fig. 5, $n = b(2c + b - 1)/2 = b(3b + 1)/2$, with the same result. In either case, $p^{(e)}(n) - p^{(o)}(n) = (-1)^b$ and that finishes the proof of the theorem.

6. THE SIZE OF $p(n)$

Euler, Jacobi, and their immediate successors were mainly interested in pretty relations of the kind seen. They do not seem to have tried to estimate the size of $p_A(n)$. Clearly, Theorem 5 permits us to compute recursively every $p(n)$ exactly, by simple additions; this may have seemed sufficient in the 18th and early 19th century. But the numerical values of $p(n)$ increase so fantastically fast, that one cannot go really far in this way and must look for other methods of computing, or at least estimating $p(n)$. Now, methods for at least a rough appraisal of $p(n)$ were definitely accessible to Euler; therefore, the fact that no theorems in this direction are known earlier than the middle of the 19th century, suggests that before that time mathematicians were simply not interested in knowing how large $p(n)$ gets. They studied, instead, the theta function aspect of $F(x)^{-1} = \Phi(x)$ and obtained from it a whole host of identities, involving the partition function, some of which we saw. Then, around 1880, Sylvester [12] took up the study of $p(n)$ from a somewhat different point of view. His procedures are rather complicated, but are based on a simple idea, which goes back to Laguerre [8]. Let us consider $p_m(x)$, which, by (5) of Corollary 1.1, has the generating function

$$F_m(x) = \frac{1}{(1 - x)(1 - x^2)(1 - x^3) \cdots (1 - x^m)}.$$

Then, $F_m(x)$ may be decomposed into "partial fractions" of the form $C/(x - \alpha)^r$, with α a root of unity (that is $\alpha^h = 1$ for some integer h). The coefficients in the power series expansion of such simple "partial fractions" are easily written down and, equating their sum, for a given n, with $p_m(n)$ we obtain relations of a new type. The roots of unity can be expressed by trigonometric functions and these formulas then show that, in addition to a principal term, which increases monotonically with n, $p_m(n)$ has also a periodic, or oscillating part, that somehow reflects the arithmetic character of the problem. From $p_m(n)$ we are able to draw conclusions concerning $p(n)$ itself, with the help of relations of which (7) and (8) in Corollary 1.1 are examples. From the consideration of the principal, increasing term, we are able to estimate rather closely, how large $p(n)$ can be, for a given n. Actually, we can now formulate the problem of determining such a " principal term" precisely: Having learned that $p(n)$, as a function of n, is rather complicated, we want to split it into two parts, so that

$$p(n) = P(n) + r(n),\tag{7}$$

where $P(n)$ should be a function as simple as possible, and, at the same time, should represent well $p(n)$. By this we usually mean, that $r(n)$ stays small with respect to $P(n)$, or $p(n)$, i.e. that $\lim_{n \to \infty} r(n)/P(n) = 0$. It is clear that in this case, $\lim_{n \to \infty} p(n)/P(n) = 1$. As pointed out in Chapter 6†, whenever we succeed in finding a relation like (7), we say that $p(n)$ is " asymptotically equal" to $P(n)$; and, unless there is some special reason to focus our attention on $r(n)$, we neglect it completely and write (7) as $p(n) \sim P(n)$. This, as well as (7), may clearly also be written as $p(n) = P(n)(1 + o(1))$. It was mainly during the early part of the 20th century that real progress was made in the determination of good asymptotic formulas for $p(n)$, and most of the credit is due to Hardy and Ramanujan [6]. First, by elementary reasonings, they showed that

$$\log p(n) = \pi\sqrt{\frac{2}{3}}\sqrt{n} + o(\sqrt{n});\tag{8}$$

next, by the use of a Tauberian argument, they could show that

$$p(n) = \frac{1}{4\sqrt{3}n} e^{\pi\sqrt{2/3}\sqrt{n}}(1 + o(1)).\tag{9}$$

Finally, they showed that $F(x)$, the generating function of $p(n)$ is essentially a *modular form*. By that is meant the following: If we make the change of variable $x = e^{2\pi i \tau}$, then the denominator of $F(x)$ differs only by a simple factor from

$$\eta(\tau) = e^{\pi i \tau/12} \prod_{m=1}^{\infty} (1 - e^{2\pi i m \tau}).$$

† See p. 100; see also p. 9.

If $|x| < 1$, then the imaginary part of τ is positive. Now it turns out that if we replace τ by $\tau' = (a\tau + b)/(c\tau + d)$, where a, b, c, d, are integers with $ad - bc = 1$, then $\eta(\tau') = \omega(-i(c\tau + d))^{1/2}\eta(\tau)$, with ω rather complicated, but $|\omega| = 1$. In general, if a function $f(\tau)$ has the property that $f\left(\dfrac{a\tau + b}{c\tau + d}\right) = \omega(c\tau + d)^r f(\tau)$, with $|\omega| = 1$, we say that $f(\tau)$ is a modular form of dimension $-r$. Exploiting the modular character of $F(x)$, Hardy and Ramanujan were able to apply to $F(x)$ the general theory of Cauchy (residues!), concerning the determination of the coefficients in the power series expansion of a known function; in this way they found a representation of $p(n)$ by a series. At that time (1918) it was not known, whether the series does, or does not converge (it turned out that the series does *not* converge), but Hardy and Ramanujan could show that, if one stopped at some small term, the sum obtained differed from the true value of $p(n)$ by less than $\frac{1}{2}$; hence, $p(n)$ being an integer was the nearest integer to the partial sum of said series. Later (1937), Rademacher (see [10]) modified the Hardy-Ramanujan method and obtained an explicit representation of $p(n)$, by a convergent series. This fascinating work is, unfortunately, beyond the scope of these notes. Somewhat later, Erdös (1942; see [2]) proved by entirely elementary considerations that a formula of the type $p(n) = An^{-1}e^{\pi\sqrt{2/3}\sqrt{n}}(1 + o(1))$ holds and soon afterwards (1951), D. J. Newman [9] showed, also by elementary reasonings, that Erdös' constant A was in fact $1/4\sqrt{3}$. Actually, Erdös' "elementary" paper is not really easy and we shall not attempt to give here a proof of (9). We shall, however, still following Erdös, give a proof of the following theorem which, while weaker than (9), is stronger than, and implies (8):

Theorem 10.   *For every $\varepsilon > 0$*

$$e^{(\pi\sqrt{2/3}-\varepsilon)\sqrt{n}} < p(n) < e^{\pi\sqrt{2/3}\,\sqrt{n}} \tag{10}$$

holds, provided that n is sufficiently large.

7. SOME LEMMAS

In the proof of Theorem 10, we shall make use of some simple Lemmas, which we state and prove here.

Lemma 1.   (1) *For*

$$\alpha \le n, \quad \sqrt{n - \alpha} < \sqrt{n}\left(1 - \frac{\alpha}{2n}\right).$$

(2) *Given*

$$0 < \varepsilon_1 < 1, \quad for \quad n > \frac{\alpha}{\varepsilon_1},$$

$$\sqrt{n - \alpha} > \sqrt{n}\left(1 - \frac{\alpha}{2n}(1 + \varepsilon_1)\right).$$

PROOFS. (1) $\sqrt{n - \alpha} = \sqrt{n}\left(1 - \frac{\alpha}{n}\right)^{1/2} < \sqrt{n}\left(1 - \frac{\alpha}{2n}\right),$

because,

$$1 - \frac{\alpha}{n} < \left(1 - \frac{\alpha}{2n}\right)^2 = 1 - \frac{\alpha}{n} + \frac{\alpha^2}{4n^2}$$

(2) $\sqrt{n - \alpha} = \sqrt{n}\left(1 - \frac{\alpha}{n}\right)^{1/2} \geq \sqrt{n}\left(1 - \frac{\alpha}{2n}(1 + \varepsilon_1)\right),$

provided that

$$1 - \frac{\alpha}{n} \geq \left(1 - \frac{\alpha}{2n}(1 + \varepsilon_1)\right)^2,$$

which, solved for *n* gives

$$n \geq \frac{\alpha}{\varepsilon_1}\left(\frac{1 + \varepsilon_1}{2}\right)^2.$$

The result follows observing that $(1 + \varepsilon_1)/2 \leq 1$.

Lemma 2. $\displaystyle\sum_{v=1}^{\infty} vx^{-v} = \frac{x^{-1}}{(1 - x^{-1})^2} = \frac{x}{(x - 1)^2}.$

PROOF.

$$(x - 1)^{-2} = x^{-2}(1 - x^{-1})^{-2}$$

$$= x^{-2}\left(1 + \frac{2}{1}x^{-1} + \frac{2 \cdot 3}{1 \cdot 2}x^{-2} + \frac{2 \cdot 3 \cdot 4}{1 \cdot 2 \cdot 3}x^{-3} + \cdots\right)$$

$$= x^{-2}\sum_{v=1}^{\infty} vx^{-v+1} = \sum_{v=1}^{\infty} vx^{-v-1}$$

and, multiplying by *x*, we obtain the Lemma.

Lemma 3. (1) *For* $x > 0$, $\dfrac{e^{-x}}{(1 - e^{-x})^2} < \dfrac{1}{x^2}$;

(2) *for* $0 < x < \sqrt{6 \cdot \varepsilon_2} \leq 6$, $\dfrac{e^{-x}}{(1 - e^{-x})^2} > \dfrac{1}{x^2}(1 - \varepsilon_2).$

PROOFS. (1) We show that $(x^2 e^{-x})/(1 - e^{-x})^2 < 1$. Indeed,

$$\frac{x^2 e^{-x}}{(1 - e^{-x})^2} = \frac{x^2}{(e^{x/2} - e^{-x/2})^2} = \frac{(x/2)^2}{\left(\dfrac{e^{x/2} - e^{-x/2}}{2}\right)^2} = \frac{(x/2)^2}{\left(\dfrac{x}{2} + \dfrac{1}{3!}\left(\dfrac{x}{2}\right)^3 + \cdots\right)^2}$$

$$= \frac{1}{\left(1 + \dfrac{1}{3!}\left(\dfrac{x}{2}\right)^2 + \dfrac{1}{!5}\left(\dfrac{x}{2}\right)^4 + \cdots\right)^2} < 1.$$

(2) As before, we show that

$$\frac{x^2 e^{-x}}{(1 - e^{-x})^2} = \frac{1}{\left(1 + \dfrac{1}{3!}\left(\dfrac{x}{2}\right)^2 + \dfrac{1}{5!}\left(\dfrac{x}{2}\right)^4 + \cdots\right)}.$$

This exceeds $1 - \varepsilon_2$, provided that

$$\tfrac{1}{2}\varepsilon_2\left(1 + \frac{1}{3!}\left(\frac{x}{2}\right)^2 + \frac{1}{5!}\left(\frac{x}{2}\right)^4 + \cdots\right) > \frac{1}{3!}\left(\frac{x}{2}\right)^2 + \frac{1}{5!}\left(\frac{x}{2}\right)^4 + \cdots,$$

and, *a fortiori*, if

$$\tfrac{1}{2}\varepsilon_2 > \frac{1}{3!}\left(\frac{x}{2}\right)^2 + \frac{1}{5!}\left(\frac{x}{2}\right)^4 + \cdots;$$

but,

$$\frac{1}{3!}\left(\frac{x}{2}\right)^2 + \frac{1}{5!}\left(\frac{x}{2}\right)^4 + \cdots < \frac{\dfrac{1}{3!}\left(\dfrac{x}{2}\right)^2}{1 - \dfrac{x^2}{80}} < \frac{\dfrac{1}{3!}\left(\dfrac{x}{2}\right)^2}{1/2} \qquad \text{(for } x^2 < 40\text{)},$$

so that we only need

$$\varepsilon_2 > \frac{2}{3}\left(\frac{x}{2}\right)^2 \quad \text{or} \quad x < \sqrt{6 \cdot \varepsilon_2}.$$

8. PROOF OF THE THEOREM.

Let us denote the constant $\sqrt{2/3}\,\pi$ simply by α. We prove separately the two inequalities of (10) and start with

$$p(n) < e^{\alpha\sqrt{n}}. \tag{10'}$$

Exceptionally we find it convenient to define here $p(0) = p(-m) = 0$. We prove (10′) by induction on n. For $n = 1$, (10′) holds, because it reduces to $p(1) = 1 < e^{\alpha}$, which is true. Assuming now that (10′) holds for $p(k)$ with $k = 1, 2, \cdots, n - 1$, we shall prove that (10′) also holds for $p(n)$. For that we make use of Theorem 7; $np(n) = \sum_{k=1}^{n} \sum_{m=1}^{n/k} mp(n - km)$. By the induction assumption, all partition functions on the right satisfy (10′), so that $np(n) < \sum_{k=1}^{n} \sum_{n=1}^{n/k} me^{\alpha\sqrt{n-km}}$, or, by Lemma 1(1),

$$np(n) < \sum_{k=1}^{n} \sum_{m=1}^{n/k} me^{\alpha\sqrt{n}(1 - km/2n)} = \sum_{k=1}^{n} \sum_{m=1}^{n/k} me^{\alpha\sqrt{n}}e^{-\alpha(km/2\sqrt{n})}$$

$$< e^{\alpha\sqrt{n}} \sum_{k=1}^{\infty} \sum_{m=1}^{\infty} me^{-(\alpha k/2\sqrt{n}) \cdot m}.$$

By Lemma 2, the inner sum equals $\dfrac{e^{-(\alpha k/2\sqrt{n})}}{(1 - e^{-(\alpha k/2\sqrt{n})})^2}$; this, in turn, by Lemma 3, is less than $(2\sqrt{n}/\alpha k)^2$. Hence,

$$np(n) < e^{\alpha\sqrt{n}} \sum_{k=1}^{\infty} \frac{4n}{\alpha^2 k^2} = \frac{4n}{\alpha^2} e^{\alpha\sqrt{n}} \sum_{k=1}^{\infty} \frac{1}{k^2},$$

or, replacing α^2 by its value $2\pi^2/3$ and $\sum_{k=1}^{\infty} 1/k^2 = \zeta(2)$ by its value $\pi^2/6$ (see 7.3.31), we obtain $np(n) < (4n/(2\pi^2/3)) (\pi^2/6) e^{\alpha\sqrt{n}} = ne^{\alpha\sqrt{n}}$, or $p(n) < e^{\alpha\sqrt{n}}$, what we wanted to prove.

The opposite inequality,

$$p(n) > e^{(\alpha - \varepsilon)n}, \tag{10″}$$

for sufficiently large n, is somewhat harder to prove. Let us assume that we can prove first, that $p(n) > Ae^{(\alpha - \varepsilon/2)\sqrt{n}}$ holds for given $\varepsilon > 0$ and *all* n, provided that we have selected A small enough (A may actually depend on ε). Then we observe that if we keep ε and A fixed, and let n increase, for sufficiently large n we have that $p(n) > Ae^{(\alpha - \varepsilon/2)\sqrt{n}} = Ae^{\varepsilon\sqrt{n}/2}e^{(\alpha - \varepsilon)\sqrt{n}}$ and, for sufficiently large n, this is larger than $e^{(\alpha - \varepsilon)\sqrt{n}}$. Hence, the Theorem will be completely proven, if we can show that, for a given $\varepsilon > 0$, we can find a constant A such that

$$p(n) > Ae^{(\alpha - \varepsilon)\sqrt{n}} \tag{10‴}$$

holds for all n. The proof is, as before, by induction. Besides $\varepsilon > 0$, which occurs in (10‴), let also $\varepsilon_1, \varepsilon_2, \varepsilon_3$ be given, arbitrarily small positive quantities, chosen so as to satisfy

$$\varepsilon_1 + \varepsilon_2 + \frac{6}{\pi^2} \varepsilon_3 < \frac{\varepsilon}{\alpha} . \tag{11}$$

Furthermore, in order to avoid trivial complications, we shall assume from the start that $0 < \varepsilon, \varepsilon_1, \varepsilon_2, \varepsilon_3 < (1/50)$. For reasons that will become clear later, we start by determining $n_i (i = 1, 2, 3, 4)$ as the smallest integers satisfying the inequalities

$$n_1^\varepsilon \geq \frac{1}{\varepsilon_1}, \quad n_2 \geq \left(\frac{\alpha^2}{6 \cdot \varepsilon_2}\right)^3, \quad n_3 \geq \left(\frac{2}{\varepsilon_3}\right)^3, \quad n_4 \geq \left(\frac{2500\alpha}{\varepsilon}\right)^{3/2} \tag{12}$$

and then define†

$$N = \max((\max_{1 \leq i \leq 4} n_i), 2^7). \tag{13}$$

Next, for all $n \leq N$, consider the ratios $p(n)/e^{(\alpha-\varepsilon)\sqrt{n}} = A_n$ and select $A = \min_{1 \leq n \leq N} A_n$. Then, by the selection of A, (10‴) holds for all $n \leq N$. We now claim that (10‴) holds also for $n > N$. The proof is by induction and uses the (already established) fact that (10‴) holds for all integers up to and including $n - 1$. This will finish the proof by induction of (10‴), hence, that of the Theorem.

REMARK 10. One observes that here the induction starts not, as usually, with $n = 1$, but with $n = N + 1$.

By Theorem 7, $np(n) = \sum_{k=1}^{n} \sum_{m=1}^{n/k} mp(n - mk)$; by the choice of A and the induction assumption, $np(n) > A \sum_{k=1}^{n} \sum_{m=1}^{n/k} me^{(\alpha-\varepsilon)\sqrt{n-km}}$. We further reduce the second member, by summing only for $k \leq n^{1/3}$ and $m \leq n^{2/3-\varepsilon}$. Then, setting $c = km$ we have $c \leq n^{1-\varepsilon}$; hence, $(c/n) \leq n^{-\varepsilon} < \varepsilon_1$, because $n > N \geq n_1$. By Lemma 1(2), $\sqrt{n - c} > \sqrt{n}(1 - c(1 + \varepsilon_1)/2n)$; therefore,

$$(\alpha - \varepsilon)\sqrt{n - mk} > (\alpha - \varepsilon)\sqrt{n}\left(1 - \frac{km}{2n}(1 + \varepsilon_1)\right),$$

so that

$$np(n) > A \sum_{k=1}^{n^{1/3}} \sum_{m=1}^{n^{2/3-\varepsilon}} me^{(\alpha-\varepsilon)\sqrt{n}} \cdot \exp\left\{-\frac{(\alpha - \varepsilon)k(1 + \varepsilon_1)}{2\sqrt{n}} m\right\}$$

$$= Ae^{(\alpha-\varepsilon)\sqrt{n}} \sum_{k=1}^{n^{1/3}} \sum_{m=1}^{n^{2/3-\varepsilon}} m \exp\left\{-\frac{(\alpha - \varepsilon)(1 + \varepsilon_1)k}{2\sqrt{n}} \cdot m\right\}.$$

† For convenience, once more a rational integer is denoted by a capital letter, N.

We set $(\alpha - \varepsilon)(1 + \varepsilon_1) = \beta$ and observe, using $\alpha = \sqrt{2/3\pi}$ and $0 < \varepsilon, \varepsilon_1 < 1/50$, that $2.4 < \beta < 2.5$. The inner sum may be written as

$$\sum_{m=1}^{\infty} m e^{-\beta(k/2\sqrt{n})m} - \sum_{m > n^{2/3 - \varepsilon}} m e^{-\beta(k/2\sqrt{n})m}$$

As before, the first sum equals $e^{-\beta(k/2\sqrt{n})}/(1 - e^{-\beta(k/2\sqrt{n})})^2$ by Lemma 2. The second sum is actually bounded and may be estimated ("integral test" for series) as follows: Clearly, $m e^{-(\beta k/2\sqrt{n})m} \le m e^{-(\beta/2\sqrt{n})m}$, and the function $x e^{-(\beta/2\sqrt{n})x}$ is monotonically decreasing for $x > 2\sqrt{n}/\beta$; hence, if

$$x > n^{(2/3)-\varepsilon}\left(= n^{1/2} \cdot n^{(1/6)-\varepsilon} > n^{1/2} \frac{2}{2\cdot4} n^{(1/6)-\varepsilon} > n^{1/2}\frac{2}{\beta}\right), \text{ then}$$

$$m e^{-(\beta/2\sqrt{n})m} < \int_{m-1}^{m} x e^{-(\beta/2\sqrt{n})x}\, dx.$$

Setting $m_0 = [n^{(2/3)-\varepsilon}] + 1$, the desired sum satisfies:

$$\sum_{m \ge m_0} m e^{-\beta(k/2\sqrt{n})m} \le \sum_{m \ge m_0} m e^{-(\beta/2\sqrt{n})m} \le m_0 e^{-(\beta/2\sqrt{n})m_0}$$

$$+ \sum_{m=m_0+1}^{\infty} \int_{m-1}^{m} x e^{-(\beta/2\sqrt{n})x}\, dx = m_0 e^{-(\beta/2\sqrt{n})m_0} + \int_{m_0}^{\infty} x e^{-(\beta/2\sqrt{n})x}\, dx.$$

The integral can be computed explicitly (integration by parts), the result is further increased if we replace m_0 by $n^{(2/3)-\varepsilon}$, and, using also $\varepsilon < 1/50$, we obtain

$$n^{(2/3)-\varepsilon}e^{-(\beta/2)n^{(1/6)-\varepsilon}} + \left(\frac{2}{\beta} n^{(7/6)-\varepsilon} + \frac{4}{\beta^2} n\right)e^{-(\beta/2)n^{(1/6)-\varepsilon}}$$

$$= \frac{2}{\beta} n^{(7/6)-\varepsilon}e^{-(\beta/2)n^{(1/6)-\varepsilon}}\left(1 + \frac{2}{\beta} n^{-(1/6)+\varepsilon} + \frac{\beta}{2} n^{-1/2}\right)$$

$$< 1\cdot3 n^{(7/6)-\varepsilon}e^{-(\beta/2)n^{(1/6)-\varepsilon}} \quad \text{for } n > 2^7.$$

We increase this value still further, by replacing the exponent $(1/6) - \varepsilon$ by $1/7$ and by dropping ε in the exponent of n. Hence, the second sum is less than $1\cdot3 n^{7/6}e^{-(\beta/2)n^{1/7}}$. The function $x^{7/6}e^{-(\beta/2)x^{1/7}}$ increases from zero to a maximum $(49/3\beta e)^{49/6}$ (attained for $x = (49/3\beta)^7$) and then decreases monotonically to zero, as $x \to \infty$. Hence,

$$1 \cdot 3 n^{7/6} e^{-(\beta/2)n^{1/7}} \le 1 \cdot 3 \left(\frac{49}{3\beta e}\right)^{49/6} < 1 \cdot 3 \left(\frac{49}{3(2 \cdot 4)e}\right)^{49/6} < 2500,$$

so that

$$np(n) > A e^{(\alpha - \varepsilon)\sqrt{n}} \sum_{k=1}^{n^{1/3}} \left\{ \frac{e^{-(\beta k/2\sqrt{n})}}{(1 - e^{-(\beta k/2\sqrt{n})})^2} - 2500 \right\}. \tag{14}$$

Now, for $k < n^{1/3}$, $k/\sqrt{n} < n^{-1/6}$ so that the exponent

$$\frac{\beta k}{2\sqrt{n}} < \frac{\alpha}{2}\left(1 - \frac{\varepsilon}{\alpha}\right)(1 + \varepsilon_1)n^{-1/6} < \alpha n^{-1/6}.$$

However, by (12) and (13)

$$\alpha n^{-1/6} \le \alpha N^{-1/6} \le \alpha n_2^{-1/6} \le \sqrt{6 \cdot \varepsilon_2},$$

so that, by Lemma 3(2),

$$\frac{e^{-(\beta/2\sqrt{n})k}}{(1 - e^{-(\beta/2\sqrt{n})k})^2} > \frac{1 - \varepsilon_2}{(\beta k/2\sqrt{n})^2}.$$

Substituting this in (14), we obtain

$$np(n) > A e^{(\alpha - \varepsilon)\sqrt{n}}(1 - \varepsilon_2)\frac{4n}{\beta^2} \sum_{k=1}^{n^{1/3}} \frac{1}{k^2} - 2500 A e^{(\alpha - \varepsilon)\sqrt{n}} n^{1/3}$$

The sum

$$\sum_{k=1}^{n^{1/3}} \frac{1}{k^2} = \sum_{k=1}^{\infty} \frac{1}{k^2} - \sum_{k > n^{1/3}} \frac{1}{k^2} = \frac{\pi^2}{6} - \delta.$$

Here

$$\delta = \sum_{k > n^{1/3}} \frac{1}{k^2} \le \sum_{k > N^{1/3}} \frac{1}{k^2} < \frac{1}{N^{2/3}} + \int_{N^{1/3}}^{\infty} \frac{dx}{x^2} = \frac{1}{N^{2/3}} + \frac{1}{N^{1/3}} < \frac{2}{N^{1/3}} \le \varepsilon_3,$$

because $N \ge n_3 \ge \left(\frac{2}{\varepsilon_3}\right)^3$. Hence,

$$np(n) > A e^{(\alpha - \varepsilon)\sqrt{n}}(1 - \varepsilon_2)\frac{4n}{\frac{2}{3}\pi^2\left(1 - \frac{\varepsilon}{\alpha}\right)^2(1 + \varepsilon_1)^2}\left(\frac{\pi^2}{6} - \varepsilon_3\right)$$

$$- 2500 A e^{(\alpha - \varepsilon)\sqrt{n}} n^{1/3},$$

and

$$p(n) > Ae^{(\alpha-\varepsilon)\sqrt{n}} \frac{\left(1 - \dfrac{6}{\pi^2}\cdot\varepsilon_3\right)(1-\varepsilon_2)}{\left(1-\dfrac{\varepsilon}{\alpha}\right)^2(1+\varepsilon_1)^2} - \frac{2500}{n^{2/3}}\,Ae^{(\alpha-\varepsilon)\sqrt{n}}$$

$$= Ae^{(\alpha-\varepsilon)\sqrt{n}}\left(\frac{\left(1 - \dfrac{6}{\pi^2}\varepsilon_3\right)(1-\varepsilon_2)}{\left(1-\dfrac{\varepsilon}{\alpha}\right)^2(1+\varepsilon_1)} - \frac{2500}{n^{2/3}}\right)$$

$$> Ae^{(\alpha-\varepsilon)\sqrt{n}}\left(1 - \frac{6}{\pi^2}\varepsilon_3 - \varepsilon_2 + \frac{2\varepsilon}{\alpha} - \varepsilon_1 - \frac{2500}{n^{2/3}}\right).$$

By (11), $\varepsilon_1 + \varepsilon_2 + (6/\pi^2)\varepsilon_3 < (\varepsilon/\alpha)$; by (12) and (13)

$$\frac{1}{n^{2/3}} \le \frac{1}{N^{2/3}} \le \frac{1}{n_4^{2/3}} \le \frac{\varepsilon}{2500\alpha}.$$

Hence, the last bracket exceeds 1 and $p(n) > Ae^{(\alpha-\varepsilon)\sqrt{n}}$ holds for $n > N$, assuming that (10''') held for all integers up to $n - 1$. This finishes the proof that (10''') holds for all integers n; hence, that (10'') holds for all sufficiently large integers n. This, together with (10') finishes the proof of Theorem 10.

The Theory of Partitions does not end here, of course. The study of partition functions $p_{A,\ast,\cdots}^{(\ast,\ast,\cdots)}(n)$ with all kinds of restrictions and relative to many types of sets, has continued and led to most interesting results. Among the sets A considered we may mention "congruence sets," that is sets of the form

$$A = \{n \mid n \equiv a_i \,(\mathrm{mod}\; k), i = 1,2,...,r\}, \qquad \text{where } a_1, ..., a_r$$

are r distinct residues modulo k. Also $A = \{n \mid n = p^m\}$, that is, A is the set of all m-th powers of primes (m fixed, or arbitrary) has been considered. Some of the most fascinating results have to do with the ratios $\dfrac{p_A(n)}{p_B(n)}$, where A and B are "related sets," for instance the sets of quadratic residues, and of nonresidues modulo some fixed prime p, respectively. But these involve concepts like class-number and fundamental unit of algebraic number fields and properly belong to the theory of algebraic numbers. Therefore, I stop here, in the hope that the reader has become sufficiently interested *not* to stop here, but to go on . . .

PROBLEMS

1. (a) Find $p(n)$ for $n = 1, 2, 3, 4,$ and 5, by explicitly listing all partitions.
   (b) Verify the results of part (a) by Theorem 5.
   (c) Use the results of parts (a) and (b) with Theorem 5 in order to compute $p(n)$ for $6 \leq n \leq 10$.

2. Verify the results of Problem 1 with the help of Theorem 6.

3. Let **P** be the set of prime numbers; find $p_{\mathbf{P}}(5)$, $p_{\mathbf{P},3}(5)$, $p_{\mathbf{P}}^{(3)}(5)$, $p_{\mathbf{P}}^{(o)}(5)$, and $p_{\mathbf{P}}^{(e)}(5)$.

4. Let $\mathbf{R}(5)$ and $\mathbf{N}(5)$ stand for the set of quadratic residues modulo 5 and the set of quadratic nonresidues modulo 5, respectively; find the product representation of the generating functions for $p_{\mathbf{R}(5)}(n)$ and $p_{\mathbf{N}(5)}(n)$, respectively.

5. Complete all details in the proof of Corollary 8.2.

6. Complete all details in the proof of Corollary 8.3.

7. (a) Show that for every $n \in \mathbf{Z}^+$, $p_1(n) = 1$.
   (b) Show by a direct argument (that is, by enumeration of the partitions) that $p_2(n) = \frac{1}{2}n + 1$ if n is even and $p_2(n) = \frac{1}{2}(n + 1)$ if n is odd.
   (c) Obtain the result of part (b), by using Theorem 3.

8. Consider

$$F_2(x) = \frac{1}{(1 - x)(1 - x^2)} = \sum_{n=0}^{\infty} p_2(n)x^n.$$

Set up the decomposition into partial fractions

$$F_2(x) = \frac{1}{4}\left\{\frac{2}{(1 - x)^2} + \frac{1}{1 - x} + \frac{1}{1 + x}\right\},$$

replace each simple fraction by its Taylor series, then combine similar powers of x in order to obtain

$$F_2(x) = 1 + x + 2x + \cdots + (\tfrac{1}{2}(n+1) + \tfrac{1}{4}(1 + (-1)^n))x^n + \cdots.$$

Compare the value of $p_2(n)$ you find by this method with the result of Problem 7.

*9. (a) Treat $F_3(x) = \{(1 - x)(1 - x^2)(1 - x^3)\}^{-1}$ the way $F_2(x)$ was treated in Problem 8; hence, obtain a formula for $p_3(n)$.

(b)   Verify the result of part (a) by Theorem 5. (*Answer:*   for $n \equiv 1$ or $n \equiv 5 \pmod 6$, $p_3(n) = \frac{1}{12}(n + 1)(n + 5)$; otherwise it is the smallest integer larger than $\frac{1}{12}(n + 1)(n + 5)$).

**10.   Use the method of Problems 8 and 9 to show that, in general, for fixed m and $n \to \infty$,

$$p_m(n) = \frac{n^{m-1}}{m!(m-1)!}\left(1 + O\left(\frac{1}{n}\right)\right).$$

(*Hints:*   Observe that

$$F_m(x) = \prod_{k=1}^{m}(1 - x^k)^{-1} = \sum_{k=1}^{m} A_k(1 - x)^{-k} + \cdots$$

with $A_m = 1/m!$. Also

$$(1 - x)^{-k} = \sum_{n=0}^{\infty} \frac{(n + 1)\cdots(n + k - 1)}{(k - 1)!}x^n$$

$$= \sum_{n=0}^{\infty} c_{k,n}x^k \quad \text{with } c_{k,n} = \frac{n^{k-1}}{(k - 1)!}\left(1 + O\left(\frac{1}{n}\right)\right).$$

Summing over k, one finds that the summands $\sum_{k=1}^{m} A_k(1 - x)^{-k}$ of $F_m(x)$ contribute

$$\sum_{k=1}^{m} A_k c_{k,n} = \frac{n^{m-1}}{m!(m-1)!}\left(1 + O\left(\frac{1}{n}\right)\right)$$

to the coefficient of x^n and it only remains to show that the contribution of the neglected fractions of $F_m(x)$ is at most $O(n^{m-2})$.)

11.   Consider the rational fraction

$$\begin{bmatrix} n \\ m \end{bmatrix} = \frac{(1 - x^n)(1 - x^{n-1})\cdots(1 - x^{n-m+1})}{(1 - x)(1 - x^2)\cdots(1 - x^m)};$$

prove that $\begin{bmatrix} n \\ m \end{bmatrix}$ is actually a polynomial.

12.   Prove:

$$\prod_{n=0}^{\infty}\{(1 - x^{2kn + k - m})(1 - x^{2kn + k + m})(1 - x^{2kn + 2k})\}$$

$$= \sum_{n=-\infty}^{\infty}(-1)^n x^{kn^2 + nm}$$

(*Hint:*   Use Theorem 8)

13. Prove:

$$\prod_{\substack{m \in \mathbf{Z}^+ \\ m \notin \mathbf{N}(5)}} (1 - x^m) = \sum_{n=-\infty}^{\infty} (-1)^n x^{n(5n+1)/2}$$

(*Hint:* Choose appropriate numerical values for k and m in Problem 12).

14. Find a series expansion for $\prod_{\substack{m \in \mathbf{Z}^+ \\ m \in N(5)}} (1 - x^m)$ analogous to that occurring in Problem 13.

15. As an illustration of Sylvester's point of view, identify for $m = 2$ (if possible also for $m = 3$), the terms of $p_m(n)$ that increase monotonically with n and the periodic part of $p_m(n)$, which reflects the arithmetic nature of n; in particular show that the monotonic terms are a polynomial of degree $m - 1$ in n.

16. Give a proof of Lemma 2, by differentiating the identity $\sum_{v=0}^{\infty} z^v = (1 - z)^{-1}$ and replacing z by x^{-1}.

17. Write out in full detail the proof of (10‴).

18. Modify the proof of Theorem 10, so as to obtain the stronger result: Given $C > 0$, arbitrarily large and $\varepsilon > 0$, arbitrarily small, there exists an integer N such that for $n \geq N$ one has $Ce^{(\sqrt{2/3}\pi - \varepsilon)\sqrt{n}} < p(n) < e^{\sqrt{2/3}\pi\sqrt{n}}$.

BIBLIOGRAPHY

1. P. T. Bateman and P. Erdös, *Mathematika*, **3**, 1956, pp. 1–14.
2. P. Erdös, *Annals of Mathematics* (2), **43**, 1942, pp. 437–450.
3. N. Fine, *Hypergeometric Series*, (to be published by U. of Pa. Press).
4. F. Franklin, *Comptes Rendus de l'Acad. des Sciences* (Paris), **92**, 1881, pp. 448–450.
5. E. Grosswald, *Revista de la Union Mat. Argentina*, **20**, 1962, pp. 48–57.
6. G. H. Hardy and S. Ramanujan, *Proceedings, London Math. Soc.* (2), **17**, 1918, pp. 75–115.
7. G. J. Jacobi, *Fundementa Nova Theoriae Functionum Ellipticarum, Collected Works*, Vol. 1. Berlin: G. Reimer, 1881, pp. 49–239.
8. E. Laguerre, *Bull. Soc. Math. France*, **5**, 1877, pp. 76–78.
9. D. J. Newman, *Amer. Journal of Math.*, **73**, 1951, pp. 599–601.

10. H. Rademacher, *Proceedings, London Math. Soc.* (2), **43**, 1937, pp. 241–254.

11. H. Rademacher, Survey article in the *Bull. Amer. Math. Soc.*, **46**, 1940, pp. 59–73.

12. J. J. Sylvester, *Amer. Journal of Math.*, **5**, 1882, pp. 119–136. *Collected Papers*, Vol. 3. Camb. Univ. Press, 1904 (edited by H. F. Baker), pp. 605–622 and pp. 658–660.

Appendices

Selected Topics From Advanced
Calculus and General Analysis

1. COMPLEX NUMBERS AND COMPLEX VARIABLES

Let $z = x + iy$ be a complex variable. We recall the notations $r = |z| = \sqrt{x^2 + y^2}$, the *modulus* of z and $\theta = \arg z = \text{arc tg } y/x$, the *argument* of z. Also, $z_1 = x_1 + iy_1$ is equal to $z_2 = x_2 + iy_2$ if and only if $x_1 = x_2$ *and* $y_1 = y_2$.

Addition and multiplication are defined by

$$z_1 + z_2 = (x_1 + iy_1) + (x_2 + iy_2) = (x_1 + x_2) + i(y_1 + y_2) \qquad (1)$$

and

$$z_1 \cdot z_2 = (x_1 + iy_1)(x_2 + iy_2)$$

$$= x_1 x_2 + i(x_1 y_2 + x_2 y_1) + i^2 y_1 y_2$$

$$= x_1 x_2 - y_1 y_2 + i(x_1 y_2 + x_2 y_1),$$

respectively, where use has been made of $i^2 = -1$.

Consistent with the Taylor series for real variables,

$$e^x = 1 + \frac{x}{1!} + \cdots + \frac{x^n}{n!} + \cdots,$$

$$\cos x = 1 - \frac{x^2}{2!} + \cdots + (-1)^n \frac{x^{2n}}{(2n)!} + \cdots,$$

$$\sin x = \frac{x}{1!} - \frac{x^3}{3!} + \cdots + (-1)^n \frac{x^{2n+1}}{(2n+1)!} + \cdots$$

one defines

$$e^{iy} = 1 + \frac{iy}{1!} + \frac{(iy)^2}{2!} + \cdots + \frac{(iy)^n}{n!} + \cdots$$

$$= 1 - \frac{y^2}{2!} + \frac{y^4}{4!} - \cdots + i\left(\frac{y}{1!} - \frac{y^3}{3!} + \frac{y^5}{5!} - \cdots\right),$$

that is,

$$e^{iy} = \cos y + i \sin y. \tag{2}$$

This definition is consistent with both, the rules of exponentiation of reals $(e^{\alpha+\beta} = e^{\alpha} \cdot e^{\beta})$ and also with the trigonometric addition formulas. Indeed, the first requires that $e^{iy_1} \cdot e^{iy_2} = e^{i(y_1+y_2)}$; and actually, we find by (1) that

$$(\cos y_1 + i \sin y_1)(\cos y_2 + i \sin y_2)$$

$$= \cos y_1 \cos y_2 - \sin y_1 \sin y_2 + i(\sin y_1 \cos y_2 + \sin y_2 \cos y_1).$$

By the addition formulas of trigonometry, this equals $\cos(y_1 + y_2) + i \sin(y_1 + y_2)$, which, by (2), is precisely $e^{i(y_1+y_2)}$.

Two consequences of (2) will be mentioned:

(a) Setting $y = \pi/2$ in (2), we obtain

$$e^{i\pi/2} = \cos\frac{\pi}{2} + i \sin\frac{\pi}{2} = i;$$

and

(b) for $y_1 = y_2 = y$, $(\cos y + i \sin y)^2 = e^{2iy} = \cos 2y + i \sin 2y$ and, by iteration, $(\cos y + i \sin y)^n = e^{niy} = \cos ny + i \sin ny$, de Moivre's formula.

In order to remain once more consistent with the rules of exponentiation we also set $e^z = e^{x+iy} = e^x e^{iy} = e^x(\cos y + i \sin y)$. Consequently, $|e^z| = e^x$, $\arg e^z = y$. Furthermore, for $\alpha > 0$ one defines

$$\alpha^z = e^{(\log \alpha)z} = e^{(x+iy)\log \alpha} = e^{x \log \alpha} \cdot e^{iy \log \alpha}$$

$$= \alpha^x(\cos(y \log \alpha) + i \sin (y \log \alpha)),$$

where $\log \alpha$ stands for the real determination of the logarithm of α; in particular, $|\alpha^z| = \alpha^x$. Also if $|z| = r$, $\arg z = \theta$, then

$$z = r \cos \theta + ir \sin \theta = r(\cos \theta + i \sin \theta) = re^{i\theta}.$$

2. ANALYTIC FUNCTIONS

Let $f(z) = f(x + iy) = u(x, y) + iv(x, y)$, with $u(x, y)$, $v(x, y)$ real. If

$$\lim_{\Delta z \to 0} \frac{f(z + \Delta z) - f(z)}{\Delta z}$$

exists, regardless of arg $\Delta z(= \arg(\Delta x + i\Delta y))$, then, in particular, this limit must be the same, if, first, $\Delta z = \Delta x$ and, next, $\Delta z = i\Delta y$. In the first case,

$$\lim_{\Delta x \to 0} \frac{u(x + \Delta x, y) + iv(x + \Delta x, y) - (u(x, y) + iv(x, y))}{\Delta x} = \frac{\partial u}{\partial x} + i\frac{\partial v}{\partial x};$$

in the second case,

$$\lim_{\Delta y \to 0} \frac{u(x, y + \Delta y) + iv(x, y + \Delta y) - (u(x, y) + iv(x, y))}{i\Delta y} = \frac{1}{i}\frac{\partial u}{\partial y} + \frac{\partial v}{\partial y}.$$

By Section 1, these two expressions are equal if and only if

$$\frac{\partial u}{\partial x} = \frac{\partial v}{\partial y} \quad \text{and} \quad i\frac{\partial v}{\partial x} = \frac{1}{i}\frac{\partial u}{\partial y},$$

that is

$$\frac{\partial u}{\partial y} = -\frac{\partial v}{\partial x}.$$

These are precisely the Riemann-Cauchy equations. Conversely, let us assume that the Riemann-Cauchy equations hold. Furthermore, assume that

$$u(x + \Delta x, y + \Delta y) = u(x, y) + \Delta x\frac{\partial u}{\partial x} + \Delta y\frac{\partial u}{\partial y} + r_1, \quad \text{where } \frac{\partial u}{\partial x} \text{ and } \frac{\partial u}{\partial y}$$

are computed at x, y and where $r_1 = r_1(x, y, \Delta x, \Delta y)$ is such that $\lim_{\Delta z \to 0} r_1/\Delta z = 0$, with a corresponding formula for $v(x, y)$. Then

$$\frac{\Delta f}{\Delta z} = \frac{f(z + \Delta z) - f(z)}{\Delta z} = \frac{\Delta x\dfrac{\partial u}{\partial x} + \Delta y\dfrac{\partial u}{\partial y} + r_1 + i\left(\Delta x\dfrac{\partial v}{\partial x} + \Delta y\dfrac{\partial v}{\partial y} + r_2\right)}{\Delta x + i\Delta y}$$

$$= \frac{\Delta x\left(\dfrac{\partial u}{\partial x} + i\dfrac{\partial v}{\partial x}\right) + \Delta y\left(\dfrac{\partial u}{\partial y} + i\dfrac{\partial v}{\partial y}\right) + r_1 + r_2}{\Delta x + i\Delta y}.$$

Using the Riemann-Cauchy equations,

$$\frac{\partial u}{\partial y} + i\,\frac{\partial v}{\partial y} = i\left(\frac{\partial v}{\partial y} - i\,\frac{\partial u}{\partial y}\right) = i\left(\frac{\partial u}{\partial x} + i\,\frac{\partial v}{\partial x}\right),$$

so that

$$\frac{\Delta f}{\Delta z} = \frac{(\Delta x + i\Delta y)\left(\dfrac{\partial u}{\partial x} + i\,\dfrac{\partial v}{\partial x}\right) + r_1 + r_2}{\Delta x + i\Delta y} = \frac{\partial u}{\partial x} + i\,\frac{\partial v}{\partial x} + \frac{r_1 + r_2}{\Delta z}.$$

Taking the limit for $\Delta z \to 0$, $((r_1 + r_2)/\Delta z) \to 0$ and we obtain

$$\lim_{z \to 0} \frac{\Delta f}{\Delta z} = \frac{\partial u}{\partial x} + i\,\frac{\partial v}{\partial x}.$$

Hence, the Riemann-Cauchy equations (plus a weak regularity condition on u and v) are also sufficient to insure the existence of $\lim\limits_{\Delta z \to 0} (\Delta f/\Delta z)$. This limit is called the derivative of $f(z)$ and is denoted by $f'(z)$. If $f(z)$ is single valued in a neighborhood of $z = z_0$ and has a derivative at $z = z_0$, $f(z)$ is said to be analytic and regular, or simply analytic at z_0; if $f(z)$ is analytic at all points of a domain $\mathscr{D}$, it is said to be analytic in $\mathscr{D}$.

3. CAUCHY'S THEOREM

Let $f(z)$ be analytic in $\mathscr{D}$ and assume (only in order to make the proof easy; the condition is not really necessary) that its derivative $f'(z)$ is continuous there. Also, let $\mathscr{C}$ be a simply closed curve in $\mathscr{D}$. Then, by definition,

$$\int_{\mathscr{C}} f(z)\,dz = \int_{\mathscr{C}} (u + iv)(dx + i\,dy) = \int_{\mathscr{C}} (u\,dx - v\,dy) + i\int_{\mathscr{C}} (u\,dy + v\,dx).$$

Also, $f'(z)$ being continuous, the partial derivatives of u and v are continuous; hence, Green's Theorem (see [2], pp. 283–292) is applicable so that

$$\int_{\mathscr{C}} (u\,dx - v\,dy) = -\iint_{\mathscr{D}} \left(\frac{\partial v}{\partial x} + \frac{\partial u}{\partial y}\right) dx\,dy$$

and

$$\int_{\mathscr{C}} (u\,dy + v\,dx) = \iint_{\mathscr{D}} \left(\frac{\partial v}{\partial y} - \frac{\partial u}{\partial x}\right) dx\,dy.$$

However, the Riemann-Cauchy equations hold because $f(z)$ is analytic, so that both integrands vanish everywhere in $\mathscr{D}$; consequently, $\int_{\mathscr{C}} f(z)\, dz = 0$. This result holds for every closed rectifiable curve $\mathscr{C} \subset \mathscr{D}$, because such a curve can be decomposed into simply closed curves.

4. CONTOUR INTEGRALS

Let $f(z)$ be analytic in $\mathscr{D}$, except, perhaps, for a single point z_0, and let $\mathscr{C}_1$, $\mathscr{C}_2$ be two simply closed curves in $\mathscr{D}$, enclosing z_0. Then $\int_{\mathscr{C}_1} f(z)\, dz = \int_{\mathscr{C}_2} f(z)\, dz$.

For a proof, consider first the case where $\mathscr{C}_1$ and $\mathscr{C}_2$ do not intersect. Construct a contour $\mathscr{C} = ABCDA$ with BC arbitrarily close to AD. (See Fig. 1). The whole simply closed contour $\mathscr{C}$ is inside a domain $\mathscr{D}'$, where $f(z)$

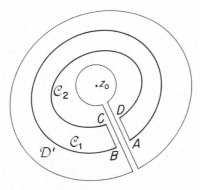

Figure 1

is analytic; hence, $\int_{AB} + \int_{BC} + \int_{CD} + \int_{DA} = 0$ by Section 3. However $\int_{BC} f(z)\, dz + \int_{DA} f(z)\, dz$ cancel each other in the limit (when $B \to A$ and $C \to D$) (this follows from Section 3, but also directly, because the function) $f(z)$ is integrated along the same path in opposite directions); consequently, $\int_{\mathscr{C}_1} f(z)\, dz + \int_{\mathscr{C}_2} f(z)\, dz = 0$ or,

$$\oint_{\mathscr{C}_1} f(z)dz = -\oint_{\mathscr{C}_2} f(z)dz = \oint_{\mathscr{C}_2} f(z)dz$$

as claimed.

If $\mathscr{C}_1$ and $\mathscr{C}_2$ intersect, construct $\mathscr{C}_3$ so close to z_0, that it does not intersect either $\mathscr{C}_1$ or $\mathscr{C}_2$; then

$$\int_{\mathscr{C}_1} f(z)dz = \int_{\mathscr{C}_3} f(z)dz = \int_{\mathscr{C}_2} f(z)dz$$

(see Fig. 2).

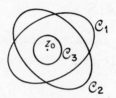

Figure 2

Another generalization is the following: Let $f(z)$ be analytic in $\mathscr{D}$, except, perhaps, at the finitely many points $z_1, z_2, \ldots, z_n$ and let $\mathscr{C}$ be a simply closed curve in $\mathscr{D}$, with $z_1, z_2, \ldots, z_k$ inside it. Let $\mathscr{C}_1, \mathscr{C}_2, \ldots, \mathscr{C}_k$ be simply closed curves, completely inside $\mathscr{C}$, and containing each exactly one of the points $z_j (1 \le j \le k)$. Then $\int_{\mathscr{C}} f(z)\,dz = \sum_{j=1}^{k} \int_{\mathscr{C}_j} f(z)\,dz$. The proof is entirely similar to that in previous case $n = 1$ as can be seen from Fig. 3, which illustrates the case $n = 4$, $k = 3$.

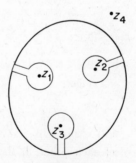

Figure 3

5. INTEGRALS OF POWERS

Let $k \in \mathbf{Z}$; then

$$\int_{|z|=r} z^k\, dz = 0 \text{ for } k \ge 0,$$

because of Section 3;

$$\int_{|z|=r} \frac{dz}{z} = \int_0^{2\pi} \frac{re^{i\theta}i\,d\theta}{re^{i\theta}} = 2\pi i;$$

finally, for $k \neq 1, k > 0$,

$$\int_{|z|=r} z^{-k}\,dz = \int_0^{2\pi} r^{-k}e^{-ki\theta} \cdot re^{i\theta}i\,d\theta = 0.$$

By Section 4, it is permitted to replace the circle $|z| = r$ by any simply closed curve $\mathscr{C}$ around $z = 0$; consequently, replacing also z by $z - z_0$,

$$\int_{\mathscr{C}} (z - z_0)^k\,dz = \begin{cases} 2\pi i & \text{if } k = -1, \\ 0 & \text{otherwise,} \end{cases}$$

where $\mathscr{C}$ is any simply closed curve around z_0.

6. TAYLOR AND LAURENT SERIES; RESIDUES

Let the series $\alpha_0 + \alpha_1(z - z_0) + \cdots + \alpha_n(z - z_0)^n + \cdots$ converge for $|z - z_0| < r$ and let $\varepsilon > 0$ be arbitrarily small, but fixed. Then the series converges uniformly for $|z - z_0| \leq r - \varepsilon$ and represents there a function of z, say, $f(z)$. Differentiating termwise, the series $\sum_{n=1}^{\infty} n\alpha_n(z - z_0)^{n-1}$ also converges in $|z - z_0| < r$, and uniformly for $|z - z_0| \leq r - \varepsilon$ (why?); consequently (see 7.3.1), this series is precisely the derivative $f'(z)$ of $f(z)$. This proves that inside its circle of convergence a power series represents an analytic function. On account of the uniform convergence of $\sum_{n=0}^{\infty}\alpha_n(z - z_0)^n$, one may also integrate termwise and, if $\mathscr{C}$ is a simply closed curve inside $|z - z_0| < r$, then

$$\int_{\mathscr{C}} f(z)\,dz = \sum_{n=0}^{\infty} \alpha_n \int_{\mathscr{C}} (z - z_0)^n\,dz = 0,$$

by Section 5. This is precisely what one had to expect according to Section 3.

Conversely, if $f(z)$ is analytic at $z = z_0$, then its Taylor series

$$\sum_{n=0}^{\infty} \frac{f^{(n)}(z_0)}{n!}(z - z_0)^n$$

converges inside some circle $|z - z_0| < r$. Neither the fact that the existence of all derivatives follows from the existence of the first, nor the bound on the growth of these derivatives, which insures the convergence of the Taylor series will be proven here (see, [1], p. 96–98).

If $f(z)$ is analytic in $\mathscr{D}$, except for a pole at z_0, then (see 7.3.19) there exists a $k \in \mathbf{Z}^+$ such that $g(z) = (z - z_0)^k f(z)$ is analytic in $\mathscr{D}$. Hence, there exist (in general complex) constants $\alpha_0, \alpha_1, ..., \alpha_n, ...,$ such that

$$(z - z_0)^k f(z) = g(z) = \alpha_0 + \alpha_1(z - z_0) + \cdots + \alpha_n(z - z_0)^n + \cdots,$$

or

$$f(z) = \frac{\alpha_0}{(z - z_0)^k} + \frac{\alpha_1}{(z - z_0)^{k-1}} + \cdots + \frac{\alpha_{k-1}}{z - z_0}$$

$$+ \alpha_k + \alpha_{k+1}(z - z_0) + \cdots + \alpha_{k+n}(z - z_0)^n + \cdots. \qquad (3)$$

The second member of (3) is called the *Laurent series* of $f(z)$ with center at z_0. The coefficient α_{k-1} is called the *residue* of $f(z)$ at $z = z_0$. Let $\mathscr{C}$ be a simply closed curve around z_0 inside the circle of convergence of (3); then, integrating termwise,

$$\int_{\mathscr{C}} f(z)\, dz = \sum_{n=-k}^{\infty} \alpha_{k+n} \int_{\mathscr{C}} (z - z_0)^n\, dz = 2\pi i \alpha_{k-1}.$$

Let $f(z)$ be analytic in $\mathscr{D}$, except at a finite number of points and let $\mathscr{C}$ be a simply closed curve in $\mathscr{D}$, such that $f(z)$ is analytic everywhere on $\mathscr{C}$ and fails to be analytic only at the points $z_1, z_2, ..., z_n$ inside $\mathscr{C}$ where it has poles. Then, by Section 4,

$$\int_{\mathscr{C}} f(z)\, dz = \sum_{m=1}^{n} \int_{\mathscr{C}_m} f(z)\, dz, \qquad \text{where } \mathscr{C}_m$$

are simply closed curves (say, circles) around $z_m (1 \le m \le n)$, such that each contains inside only the one pole z_m and is inside the circle of convergence of the Laurent series representing $f(z)$ in the neighborhood of z_m. If $\alpha^{(1)}$, $\alpha^{(2)}, ..., \alpha^{(n)}$ are the residues corresponding to $z_1, z_2, ..., z_n$, respectively, then, as just seen, $\int_{\mathscr{C}_m} f(z)\, dz = 2\pi i \alpha^{(m)}$; hence,

$$\int_{\mathscr{C}} f(z) = 2\pi i \sum_{m=1}^{n} \alpha^{(m)}, \qquad (4)$$

which is the statement of Cauchy's famous theorem on residues.

7. AN APPLICATION

Consider (see Fig. 4) the contour $\mathscr{C}: ABCDEFGA$ formed by a rectangle of which one cuts out a semicircle of radius η, and let $f(z) = e^{iz}/z$. Then

$f(z)$ is analytic inside and on $\mathscr{C}$ so that, by Section 3, $\int_{\mathscr{C}} f(z)\, dz = 0$. We start by showing that the integrals along BC, CD, and DE can be made arbitrarily small, if we take R and Y large enough. Indeed,

$$\left| \int_B^C f(z)\, dz \right| = \left| \int_0^Y \frac{e^{i(x+iy)}}{R + iy} i\, dy \right| \leq \frac{1}{R} \int_0^Y e^{-y}\, dy \leq \frac{1}{R} \int_0^\infty e^{-y}\, dy = \frac{1}{R},$$

and similarly, $\left| \int_D^E f(z)\, dz \right| \leq 1/R$; hence, selecting $R > 3/\varepsilon$,

$$\left| \int_B^C f(z)\, dz + \int_D^E f(z)\, dz \right| \leq \left| \int_B^C f(z)\, dz \right| + \left| \int_D^E f(z)\, dz \right| \leq \frac{2}{R} \leq \frac{2\varepsilon}{3}.$$

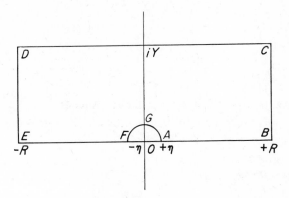

Figure 4

Having selected R, we estimate the integral $\int_C^D f(z)\, dz$. Clearly,

$$\left| \int_C^D f(z)\, dz \right| \leq \int_{-R}^R \frac{e^{-Y}}{Y}\, dx = \frac{2Re^{-Y}}{Y}.$$

It is now easy to select Y so large that $2Re^{-Y}/Y < \varepsilon/3$ (it is sufficient to take $Y = \max(1, \log(6R/\varepsilon))$). From $\int_{\mathscr{C}} f(z)\, dz = 0$ and $\left| \int_{BCDE} f(z)\, dz \right| < \varepsilon$ now follows that

$$\left| \int_E^F f(z)\, dz + \int_{FGA} f(z)\, dz + \int_A^B f(z)\, dz \right| < \varepsilon,$$

or, letting $R \to \infty$,

$$\lim_{R \to \infty} \left| \int_{-R}^{-\eta} f(z)\, dz + \int_{FGA} f(z)\, dz + \int_\eta^R f(z)\, dz \right| = 0.$$

The second integral can be estimated directly as

$$\int_\pi^0 \frac{e^{i\eta e^{i\theta}}}{\eta e^{i\theta}} \cdot \eta i e^{i\theta} \, d\theta = -i \int_0^\pi e^{i\eta e^{i\theta}} \, d\theta$$

and, if $\eta \to 0$ the integral approaches $-i \int_0^\pi d\theta = -\pi i$. Consequently,

$$\lim_{\substack{R \to \infty \\ \eta \to 0}} \left\{ \int_{-R}^{-\eta} f(z) \, dz + \int_\eta^R f(z) \, dz \right\} = \pi i.$$

Changing z into $-z$ in the first integral, it becomes

$$-\int_\eta^R \frac{e^{-iz}}{z} \, dz;$$

hence,

$$\lim_{\substack{R \to \infty \\ \eta \to 0}} \int_\eta^R \frac{e^{iz} - e^{-iz}}{z} \, dz = \pi i \quad \text{or} \quad \int_0^\infty \frac{e^{iz} - e^{-iz}}{2i} \frac{dz}{z} = \frac{\pi}{2}.$$

Observing that $(e^{iz} - e^{-iz})/2i = \sin z$, the result reads

$$\int_0^\infty \frac{\sin z}{z} \, dz = \frac{\pi}{2}.$$

8. THE GAMMA FUNCTION

Let

$$f(z; R; \eta) = \int_\eta^R t^{z-1} e^{-t} \, dt,$$

where $z = x + iy$. By Section 1, $|t^{z-1}| = t^{x-1}$, so that $|t^{z-1} e^{-t}| = t^{x-1} e^{-t} < e^{-t/2}$, say, for $t \to \infty$. Hence, $f(z; \eta) = \lim_{R \to \infty} f(z; R; \eta)$ always exists. For $t \to 0^+$, the integrand is less than t^{x-1} and the integral converges for $\eta \to 0$, provided that $\lim_{\eta \to 0} \int_\eta^R t^{x-1} \, dt$ exists, that is, for $x > 0$. Consequently, if $x > 0$, $\lim_{\substack{R \to \infty \\ \eta \to 0}} f(z; R; \eta)$ exists; this function is denoted by $\Gamma(z)$. Integrating by parts,

$$\Gamma(z) = \int_0^\infty t^{z-1} e^{-t} \, dt = -t^{z-1} e^{-t} \Big|_0^\infty + (z-1) \int_0^\infty t^{z-2} e^{-t} \, dt.$$

If $x > 1$, the integrated term vanishes, the last integral is, by definition $\Gamma(z - 1)$, so that $\Gamma(z) = (z - 1)\Gamma(z - 1)$, valid for Re $z > 1$, or $\Gamma(z + 1) = z\Gamma(z)$, valid for Re $z > 0$. In particular, if $z = n \in \mathbf{Z}^+$, we obtain by iteration:

$$\Gamma(n) = (n - 1)\Gamma(n - 1) = (n - 1)(n - 2)\Gamma(n - 2)$$

$$= \cdots = (n - 1)! \int_0^\infty e^{-t}\, dt = (n - 1)!$$

Having defined $\Gamma(z)$ by the integral for Re $z > 0$, we may use the functional equation $\Gamma(z) = (z - 1)(z - 2) \cdots (z - n)\Gamma(z - n)$ or, equivalently (writing $z + n$ for z),

$$\Gamma(z) = \frac{\Gamma(z + n)}{(z + n - 1)(z + n - 2) \cdots (z + 1)z},$$

in order to define $\Gamma(z)$ also if Re $z < 0$, provided only that z is not a negative integer or zero.

9. A DEFINITE INTEGRAL

Let $s = \sigma + it$ be a complex number and consider the integral $\int_{\mathscr{C}} f(z, s)\, dz$ with $f(z, s) = z^{s-1}e^{-z}$, taken along the square $\mathscr{C} = OABC$ (see Fig. 5)

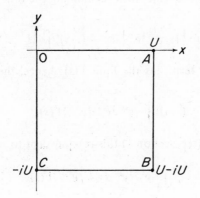

Figure 5

with vertices at $z = 0$, $z = U$, $z = U - iU$, and $z = -iU$. In general, if we set $z = x + iy$, then it is clear that on OA, $z = x(0 \le x \le U)$, while $z = U + iy(0 \ge y \ge -U)$ on AB, $z = x - iU(U \ge x \ge 0)$ on BC and $z = iy(-U \le y \le 0)$ on CO. Consequently,

$$\int_{\mathscr{C}} f(z, s)dz = \int_0^U x^{s-1}e^{-x}\, dx + \int_0^{-U} (U + iy)^{s-1}e^{-U-iy}\, d(iy)$$

$$+ \int_U^0 (x - iU)^{s-1}e^{-x+iU}\, dx + \int_{-U}^0 (iy)^{s-1}e^{-iy}\, d(iy)$$

or, changing y into $-y$ in the second and fourth integral,

$$\int_{\mathscr{C}} f(z, s)dz = \int_0^U x^{s-1}e^{-x}\, dx - i\int_0^U (U - iy)^{s-1}e^{-U+iy}\, dy$$

$$- \int_0^U (x - iU)^{s-1}e^{-x+iU}\, dx - \int_0^U (-iy)^{s-1}e^{iy}\, d(-iy).$$

We make the following remarks:

(i) $\int_{\mathscr{C}} f(z, s)\, dz = 0$, because $f(z, s)$ is analytic inside and on $\mathscr{C}$;

(ii)   if $\sigma > 0$, then, by Section 8, $\lim_{U \to \infty} \int_0^U x^{s-1}e^{-x}\, dx = \Gamma(s)$;

(iii) $\lim_{U \to \infty} \int_0^U (U - iy)^{s-1}e^{-U+iy}\, dy = 0$; and

(iv)   if $\sigma < 1$, then also $\lim_{U \to \infty} \int_0^U (x - iU)^{s-1}e^{-x+iU}\, dx = 0$.

Remarks (iii) and (iv) are not obvious and will have to be justified, but let us accept them for a moment; then, combining the four remarks, we obtain that

$$0 = \lim_{U \to \infty} \left\{ \int_0^U x^{s-1}e^{-x}\, dx - (-i)^s \int_0^U y^{s-1}e^{iy}\, dy \right\}.$$

For $\sigma > 0$, the first term has the limit $\Gamma(s)$; hence, the second also has a limit and

$$(-i)^s \int_0^{\infty} y^{s-1}e^{iy}\, dy = \Gamma(s).$$

With $-i = e^{-(\pi/2)i}$ (see Section 1) this is equivalent to

$$\int_0^{\infty} y^{s-1}e^{iy}\, dy = e^{\pi si/2}\Gamma(s).$$

If s is real (which means, in view of our previous conditions $0 < \sigma < 1$, for $0 < s < 1$) then, by equating the real and purely imaginary parts of the two members (see Section 1), one obtains

$$\int_0^{\infty} y^{s-1} \cos y\, dy = \Gamma(s) \cos \frac{\pi s}{2} \quad \text{and} \quad \int_0^{\infty} y^{s-1} \sin y\, dy = \Gamma(s) \sin \frac{\pi s}{2}. \tag{5}$$

The two equalities in (5) are established (still only tentatively, by assuming the so far unproven remarks (iii) and (iv)) only for $0 < s < 1$. However, in each equality of (5), both members are analytic functions of s, which coincide for $0 < s < 1$; this implies that they have identical Taylor expansions (see also 7.3.23). Hence, (5) remain valid also for complex s, as long as the respective terms are analytic, and regular, that is, at least for $0 < \sigma < 1$.

It only remains to justify remarks (iii) and (iv). If we write $U - iy = re^{i\theta}$, then

$$|(U - iy)^{s-1}| = |r^{\sigma - 1 + it}e^{i\theta(\sigma - 1 + it)}| = r^{\sigma - 1}e^{-\theta t}.$$

On AB, $U \le r \le 2U$, $|-\theta| = |\arg(U - iy)| \le \pi/4$, so that

$$|(U - iy)^{s-1}| \le C_1 U^{\sigma - 1} \qquad (C_1 = 2^{\sigma - 1}e^{(\pi/4)|t|})$$

and

$$\left|\int_0^U (U - iy)^{s-1}e^{-U+iy}\,dy\right| \le \int_0^U C_1 U^{\sigma - 1}e^{-U}\,dy$$

$$= C_1 U^\sigma e^{-U} \to 0 \quad \text{for} \quad U \to \infty;$$

remark (iii) is justified. Similarly,

$$\left|\int_0^U (x - iU)^{s-1}e^{-x+iU}\,dx\right| \le \int_0^U (2U)^{\sigma - 1}e^{-t\theta} \cdot e^{-x}\,dx \le C_2 U^{\sigma - 1}$$

$$\int_0^U e^{-x}\,dx = C_2 U^{\sigma - 1}(1 - e^{-U}) < C_2 U^{\sigma - 1}(C_2 = 2^{\sigma - 1}e^{(\pi/2)|t|}).$$

If $\sigma < 1$, then $\lim_{U \to \infty} U^{\sigma - 1} = 0$, so that also remark (iv) is justified and the proof of (5) is complete.

10. FOURIER SERIES

Let $f(t)$ be a periodic function, of period T and piecewise smooth. If we assume that $f(t)$ has a representation by the Fourier series

$$f(t) = \frac{\alpha_0}{2} + \sum_{n=1}^{\infty} \left\{\alpha_n \cos\frac{2\pi nt}{T} + \beta_n \sin\frac{2\pi nt}{T}\right\}, \tag{6}$$

and *assume* also the *uniform convergence* of this series, then it follows that the only possible values for α_n and β_n are given by

$$\alpha_n = \frac{2}{T}\int_\gamma^{\gamma + T} f(t)\cos\frac{2\pi nt}{T}\,dt, \qquad \beta_n = \frac{2}{T}\int_\gamma^{\gamma + T} f(t)\sin\frac{2\pi nt}{T}\,dt; \tag{7}$$

here γ is arbitrary because both integrands are periodic, of period T, so that a shift of the initial point does not affect the values of the integrals.

Indeed, if we multiply (6) by $\sin(2\pi mt/T)$ and integrate from γ to $T + \gamma$, one may integrate termwise on the right (because the convergence is uniform); but all integrals vanish, except one,

$$\int_{\gamma}^{\gamma+T} \beta_m \sin^2 \frac{2\pi mt}{T} \, dt = \frac{T}{2\pi m} \beta_m \int_0^{2\pi m} \sin^2 u \, du = \beta_m \frac{T}{2\pi} \int_0^{2\pi} \sin^2 u \, du$$

$$= \beta_m \frac{T}{2\pi} \int_0^{2\pi} \frac{1 - \cos 2u}{2} \, du = \frac{T}{2} \beta_m .$$

Consequently,

$$\beta_m = \frac{2}{T} \int_{\gamma}^{\gamma+T} f(t) \sin \frac{2\pi mt}{T} \, dt,$$

as claimed by (7); the formula for α_m is proven similarly.

Conversely, consider the finite sum

$$S_N(t) = \frac{\alpha_0}{2} + \sum_{n=1}^{N} \left(\alpha_n \cos \frac{2\pi nt}{T} + \beta_n \sin \frac{2\pi nt}{T} \right) \qquad \text{where } \alpha_n \text{ and } \beta_n$$

are given by (7). Substituting, one observes that

$$\alpha_n \cos \frac{2\pi nt}{T} + \beta_n \sin \frac{2\pi nt}{T}$$

$$= \frac{2}{T} \int_{\gamma}^{\gamma+T} f(\tau) \left(\cos \frac{2\pi nt}{T} \cos \frac{2\pi n\tau}{T} + \sin \frac{2\pi nt}{T} \sin \frac{2\pi n\tau}{T} \right) d\tau$$

$$= \frac{2}{T} \int_{\gamma}^{\gamma+T} f(\tau) \cos \frac{2\pi n(t - \tau)}{T} \, d\tau.$$

Remembering that

$$2 \sin \frac{u}{2} (\tfrac{1}{2} + \cos u + \cos 2u + \cdots + \cos Nu)$$

$$= \sin \frac{u}{2} + 2 \sin \frac{u}{2} \cos u + \cdots + 2 \sin \frac{u}{2} \cos ku + \cdots + 2 \sin \frac{u}{2} \cos Nu$$

$$= \sin \frac{u}{2} + \left(\sin \frac{3u}{2} - \sin \frac{u}{2} \right) + \cdots + \left(\sin(2k + 1)\frac{u}{2} - \sin(2k - 1)\frac{u}{2} \right)$$

$$+ \cdots + \left(\sin(2N + 1)\frac{u}{2} - \sin(2N - 1)\frac{u}{2} \right)$$

$$= \sin(2N + 1)\frac{u}{2},$$

so that

$$\tfrac{1}{2} + \sum_{n=1}^{N} \cos nu = \frac{\{\sin(2N + 1)u/2\}}{2 \sin u/2},$$

it now follows that

$$S_N(t) = \frac{1}{2} \cdot \frac{2}{T} \int_{\gamma}^{\gamma+T} f(\tau) \, d\tau + \frac{2}{T} \sum_{n=1}^{N} \int_{\gamma}^{\gamma+T} f(\tau) \cos \frac{2\pi n(\tau - t)}{T} \, d\tau$$

$$= \frac{2}{T} \int_{\gamma}^{\gamma+T} f(\tau) \frac{\sin\{(2N + 1)\pi(\tau - t)/T\}}{2 \sin\{\pi(\tau - t)/T\}} \, d\tau.$$

Here we may replace τ by $\tau + t$, by changing the limits to $\gamma - t$ and $\gamma - t + T$, respectively; yet, as already observed, we may shift the interval of integration at will, without changing the value of the integral. Consequently, we may write, for instance

$$S_N(t) = \frac{2}{T} \int_{-T/2}^{T/2} f(\tau + t) \frac{\sin\{2\pi(N + \tfrac{1}{2})\tau/T\}}{2 \sin(\pi\tau/T)} \, d\tau. \tag{8}$$

In particular, if $f(t) = 1$ for all t, then also $S_N(t) = 1$, so that

$$1 = \frac{2}{T} \int_{-T/2}^{T/2} \frac{\sin\{2\pi(N + \tfrac{1}{2})\tau/T\}}{2 \sin(\pi\tau/T)} \, d\tau$$

and

$$f(t) = \frac{2}{T} \int_{-T/2}^{T/2} f(t) \frac{\sin\{2\pi(N + \tfrac{1}{2})\tau/T\}}{2 \sin(\pi\tau/T)} \, d\tau.$$

Subtracting this from (8), we obtain

$$S_N(t) - f(t) = \frac{2}{T} \int_{-T/2}^{T/2} (f(t + \tau) - f(t)) \frac{\sin\{2\pi(N + \tfrac{1}{2})\tau/T\}}{2 \sin(\pi\tau/T)} \, d\tau. \tag{9}$$

The integrand may be written as $F(t, \tau)\sin\{(N + \tfrac{1}{2})(2\pi\tau/T)\}$, with

$$F(t, \tau) = \frac{T}{2\pi} \frac{f(t + \tau) - f(t)}{\tau} \frac{\pi\tau/T}{\sin(\pi\tau/T)}.$$

Any condition on $f(t)$ which insures that

$$\lim_{N \to \infty} \int_{-T/2}^{T/2} F(t, \tau)\sin\left\{(N + \tfrac{1}{2})\frac{2\pi\tau}{T}\right\} \, d\tau = 0,$$

automatically implies that $\lim_{N \to \infty} S_N(t) = f(t)$, that is,

(i) that the Fourier series converges; and

(ii) that the Fourier series converges actually to the value of the function $f(t)$. One such sufficient condition is that $f(t) \in C'$ i.e. that $f(t)$ has a continuous derivative on the closed interval $(-T/2, +T/2)$, (hence, everywhere); then $F(t, \tau)$ is continuous for $|\tau| \leq (T/2)$, and this implies uniform boundedness.

The statement is obvious for $\tau \neq 0$, because $f(t) \in C'$, and for $\tau \to 0$, $\lim\limits_{\tau \to 0} F(t, \tau) = (T/2\pi)f'(t)$ also exists and is bounded. Consequently,

$$\int_{-T/2}^{T/2} F(t, \tau)\sin(N + \tfrac{1}{2})\frac{2\pi\tau}{T}\, d\tau = -\frac{\cos(N + \tfrac{1}{2})\dfrac{2\pi\tau}{T}}{N + \tfrac{1}{2}} \cdot \frac{T}{2\pi} F(t, \tau)\Big|_{-T/2}^{T/2}$$

$$+ \frac{T}{2\pi}\frac{1}{N + \tfrac{1}{2}} \int_{-T/2}^{T/2} \frac{\partial F}{\partial \tau} \cos\left\{(N + \tfrac{1}{2})\frac{2\pi\tau}{T}\right\}\, d\tau.$$

The integrated part vanishes, the last integral is less in absolute value than

$$\int_{-T/2}^{T/2} \left|\frac{\partial F}{\partial \tau}\right|\, d\tau = A,$$

some finite constant; hence, $S_N(t) - f(t) = O(1/N)$, and this result is somewhat stronger and implies the assertions (i) and (ii) to be proven.

Two remarks are here in order. First, the same reasoning holds if we replace $\sin\{(N + \tfrac{1}{2})(\pi\tau/T)\}$ by $\sin(N\pi\tau/T)$ or by $\cos(N\pi\tau/T)$; then the integral

$$\frac{2}{T} \int_{-T/2}^{T/2} F(\tau) \frac{\sin}{\cos}\left(\frac{N\pi\tau}{T}\right)\, d\tau$$

stands for the Fourier coefficients of the function $F(\tau)$ and we have proven incidentally a version of the Riemann-Lebesgue theorem, namely,

If $F(t)$ is periodic, of period T, is differentiable and $\partial F/\partial \tau$ is bounded on $[-T/2, T/2]$, then the Nth Fourier coefficient of $F(t)$ is $O(1/N)$.

With somewhat weaker assumptions one proves the following (weaker) result.

Theorem. (Riemann-Lebesgue). *Let $-\infty \leq a < b \leq +\infty$; if $\int_a^b |F(t)|\, dt$ exists (and is finite) then $\lim\limits_{n \to \infty} \int_a^b F(t) \sin nt\, dt = \lim\limits_{n \to \infty} \int_a^b F(t) \cos nt\, dt = 0$.*

A proof for a, b finite may be found in [3], pp. 403–404 and for $a = -\infty$, $b = +\infty$ in [4], pp. 11–12; both proofs are very simple and short. See also Lemma 8.1 for a different version.

The second remark is that in (9) the integral $\int_{-T/2}^{T/2}$ can be split, if necessary, into a sum of abutting integrals; hence, in all preceding statements the condition $f(t) \in C'$ may be replaced by the weaker one, that $f(t)$ be piecewise smooth in $[-T/2, T/2]$ (see 7.3.28).

In that case, however, it may happen that t is a point of discontinuity for $f(t)$. One then may write

$$S_N(t) = \frac{2}{T}\left\{\int_{-T/2}^{0} + \int_{0}^{T/2} f(t+\tau)\, \frac{\sin\{(N+\frac{1}{2})2\pi\tau/T\}}{2\sin(\tau\pi/T)}\, d\tau\right\};$$

also,

$$f(t+0) = \frac{2}{T}\int_{-T/2}^{T/2} f(t+0)\, \frac{\sin\{(N+\frac{1}{2})2\pi\tau/T\}}{2\sin(\tau\pi/T)}\, d\tau,$$

or, observing that the integrand is even,

$$\tfrac{1}{2}f(t+0) = \frac{2}{T}\int_{0}^{T/2} f(t+0)\, \frac{\sin\{(N+\frac{1}{2})2\pi\tau/T\}}{2\sin(\tau\pi/T)}\, d\tau,$$

and, similarly,

$$\tfrac{1}{2}f(t-0) = \frac{2}{T}\int_{-T/2}^{0} f(t-0)\, \frac{\sin\{(N+\frac{1}{2})2\pi\tau/T\}}{2\sin(\tau\pi/T)}\, d\tau.$$

Consequently, (9) becomes

$$S_N(t) - \tfrac{1}{2}\{f(t+0) + f(t-0)\}$$

$$= \frac{2}{T}\left\{\int_{-T/2}^{0} [f(t+\tau) - f(t-0)]\, \frac{\sin\{(N+\frac{1}{2})2\pi\tau/T\}}{2\sin(\pi\tau/T)}\, d\tau.\right.$$

$$\left. + \int_{0}^{T/2} [f(t+\tau) - f(t+0)]\, \frac{\sin\{(N+\frac{1}{2})2\pi\tau/T\}}{2\sin(\pi\tau/T)}\, d\tau\right\}.$$

Each of these two integrals now satisfies the conditions of the Riemann-Lebesgue Theorem. Indeed,

$$\frac{f(t+\tau) - f(t+0)}{\sin(\pi\tau/T)} = \frac{f(t+\tau) - f(t+0)}{\tau}\, \frac{\tau}{\sin(\pi\tau/T)}$$

is piecewise continuous and bounded for $\tau \neq 0$, while

$$\lim_{\tau\to 0^+} \frac{f(t+\tau) - f(t+0)}{\tau}\, \frac{\tau}{\sin\dfrac{\pi\tau}{T}} = \frac{T}{\pi} f'(t+0),$$

is also bounded (even if t is a point of discontinuity for $f(t)$ or $f'(t)$, the right-hand derivative $f'(t + 0)$ and the left-hand derivative $f'(t - 0)$ exist, $f(t)$ being piecewise continuous). The same reasoning applies also to the first integrand. It now follows by the Riemann-Lebesgue theorem that $\lim_{N \to \infty} \{S_N(t) - \frac{1}{2}(f(t + 0) + f(t - 0))\} = 0$, or that the Fourier series of a piecewise smooth function $f(t)$ converges even at a point of discontinuity and that the sum of the series equals $\frac{1}{2}\{f(t + 0) + f(t - 0)\}$. This contains, in particular, the statement that if t is a point of continuity, so that $f(t + 0) = f(t - 0) = f(t)$, then $\lim_{N \to \infty} S_N(t) = f(t)$, the Fourier series converges to the value of the function.

11. TWO APPLICATIONS

(a) Let $y = x - \frac{1}{2}$ for $0 < x < 1$ and be defined by periodicity $(T = 1)$ for other values of x; then $y = ((x))$ (see Chapter 6) and is piecewise smooth. By (7), $\alpha_n = 0$ (this follows also directly, by observing that $y(x)$ is an odd function) and

$$\beta_n = 2 \int_0^1 (x - \tfrac{1}{2})\sin 2\pi nx \, dx = -\frac{1}{\pi n} \, (n = 1, 2, \ldots),$$

so that

$$y = ((x)) = -\frac{1}{\pi} \sum_{n=1}^{\infty} \frac{\sin 2\pi nt}{n}.$$

(b) The function defined by $y = x^2$ for $|x| \leq \pi$ and by periodicity $(T = 2\pi)$ for $|x| > \pi$ is continuous and piecewise differentiable. It is an even function, so that $\beta_n = 0$ (as follows also from (7)),

$$\alpha_0 = \frac{1}{\pi} \int_{-\pi}^{\pi} x^2 \, dx = \frac{2\pi^2}{3}, \, \alpha_n = \frac{1}{\pi} \int_{-\pi}^{\pi} x^2 \cos nx \, dx = (-1)^n \frac{4}{n^2} \, (n \neq 0),$$

so that, by Section 10, one has for $|x| \leq \pi$ the identity

$$x^2 = \frac{\pi^2}{3} - 4\left(\cos x - \frac{\cos 2x}{2^2} + \frac{\cos 3x}{3^2} - \cdots + (-1)^{n-1} \frac{\cos nx}{n^2} + \cdots\right).$$

Setting, in particular, $x = \pi$, one obtains

$$\pi^2 = \frac{\pi^2}{3} + 4\left(1 + \frac{1}{2^2} + \frac{1}{3^2} + \cdots + \frac{1}{n^2} + \cdots\right) \quad \text{or} \quad \sum_{n=1}^{\infty} \frac{1}{n^2} = \frac{2\pi^2}{3} \frac{1}{4} = \frac{\pi^2}{6}.$$

12. THE MELLIN TRANSFORM

(a) Let $f(x)$ be defined and piecewise continuous for $0 < x < \infty$, and assume that $f(x) = O(x^{\alpha-1})$ for $x \to \infty$, $f(x) = O(x^{\beta-1})$ for $x \to 0$, with $\alpha < \beta$. Let $s = \sigma + it$ be a complex number, whose real part σ satisfies $\alpha < \sigma < \beta$. Then there exist positive constants A_1, A_2, X, and η such that $|f(x)| < A_1 x^{\alpha-1}$ for $x \geq X$ and $|f(x)| < A_2 x^{\beta-1}$ for $0 < x \leq \eta$. Consequently, if $0 < \eta' < \eta < X < X' < \infty$, then

$$\int_{\eta'}^{X'} f(x)x^{-s}\, dx = \int_{\eta'}^{\eta} + \int_{\eta}^{X} + \int_{X}^{X'} f(x)x^{-s}\, dx.$$

The second integral exists, for instance, as a Riemann integral, for every complex s, because $f(x)$ is piecewise continuous. Estimating the first,

$$\left| \int_{\eta'}^{\eta} f(x)x^{-s}\, dx \right| \leq \int_{\eta'}^{\eta} |f(x)| x^{-\sigma}\, dx \leq A_2 \int_{\eta'}^{\eta} x^{\beta-1-\sigma}\, dx = A_2 \left. \frac{x^{\beta-\sigma}}{\beta - \sigma} \right|_{\eta'}^{\eta}.$$

If $\eta' \to 0$, the corresponding limit exists, because $\sigma < \beta$. Similarly, for the last integral,

$$\left| \int_{X}^{X'} f(x)x^{-s}\, dx \right| \leq \int_{X}^{X'} |f(x)| x^{-\sigma}\, dx \leq A_1 \int_{X}^{X'} x^{\alpha-\sigma-1}\, dx = A_1 \left. \frac{x^{\alpha-\sigma}}{\alpha - \sigma} \right|_{X}^{X'}$$

and, if $X' \to \infty$, the limit exists, because $\alpha - \sigma > 0$. Consequently, the improper integral converges and $F(s) = \int_0^\infty f(x)x^{-s}\, dx$ is a well-defined function of s, provided $\alpha < \sigma < \beta$. It is called the *Mellin transform of $f(x)$*. If, furthermore, $\varepsilon > 0$ and $\alpha + \varepsilon \leq \sigma \leq \beta - \varepsilon$, then $\sigma - \alpha \geq \varepsilon$, $\beta - \sigma \geq \varepsilon$, so that

$$\left| \int_{\eta'}^{\eta} f(x)x^{-s}\, dx \right| \leq A_2 \frac{\eta^\varepsilon}{\varepsilon}, \qquad \left| \int_{X}^{X'} f(x)x^{-s}\, dx \right| \leq A_1 \frac{X^{-\varepsilon}}{\varepsilon};$$

both these quantities can be made arbitrarily small, by taking X sufficiently large and η sufficiently small, regardless of s, η', and X'. This proves the uniform convergence of the integral; consequently, one may differentiate the function $F(s) = \int_0^\infty f(x)x^{-s}\, dx$, by differentiating under the integral sign, so that $F(s)$ is actually analytic for $\alpha < \sigma < \beta$.

(b) With $f(x)$ and $F(s)$ defined as before, let $\alpha < \gamma < \beta$ and consider the function

$$g(x) = \frac{1}{2\pi i} \lim_{T \to \infty} \int_{\gamma-iT}^{\gamma+iT} F(s)x^{s-1}\, dx.$$

We shall not prove here in detail that the limit exists, although this is not difficult (but lengthy), by using the representation

$$F(s) = \int_0^\infty f(x)x^{-s}\,dx = \int_0^\infty f(x)x^{-\gamma-it}\,dx = \int_0^\infty f(x)e^{-\gamma\log x}e^{-it\log x}\,dx,$$

setting $y = \log x$ and applying the Riemann-Lebesgue lemma; but by a sequence of transformations we shall obtain an integral whose convergence will be much easier to verify. We want to show that in general, $g(x) = \frac{1}{2}\{f(x+0)+f(x-0)\}$ and that, in particular, if x is a point of continuity of $f(x)$, then $g(x) = f(x)$. Substituting for $F(s)$ its value and $\gamma + it$ for s we obtain, successively,

$$g(x) = \frac{1}{2\pi}\lim_{T\to\infty}\int_{-T}^{T}\left\{\lim_{M\to\infty}\int_0^M f(y)y^{-\gamma-it}\,dy\right\}x^{\gamma-1+it}\,dt$$

$$= \frac{1}{2\pi}\lim_{T\to\infty}\int_{-T}^{T}\left\{\lim_{M\to\infty}\int_0^M \frac{f(y)}{y}\left(\frac{x}{y}\right)^{\gamma-1+it}\,dy\right\}dt.$$

The order of the operations $\int_{-T}^T \cdots dt$ and $\lim\limits_{M\to\infty}$ may be interchanged; indeed,

$$\left|\int_{-T}^{T}\left\{\int_{M_1}^{M_2}\frac{f(y)}{y}\left(\frac{x}{y}\right)^{\gamma-1+it}\,dy\right\}dt\right| = \left|\int_{M_1}^{M_2}\frac{f(y)}{y}\left(\frac{x}{y}\right)^{\gamma-1}\left\{\int_{-T}^{T}\left(\frac{x}{y}\right)^{it}\,dt\right\}dy\right|$$

$$= \left|\int_{M_1}^{M_2}\frac{f(y)}{y}\left(\frac{x}{y}\right)^{\gamma-1}\frac{2}{\log\dfrac{x}{y}}\sin\left(T\log\frac{x}{y}\right)\,dy\right|$$

$$\le 2\int_{M_1}^{M_2}\frac{|f(y)|}{y\left|\log\dfrac{x}{y}\right|}\left(\frac{x}{y}\right)^{\gamma-1}\,dy$$

$$\le 2\int_{M_1}^{M_2}\frac{A_1 y^{\alpha-1}}{y\log\dfrac{y}{x}}\left(\frac{y}{x}\right)^{1-\gamma}\,dy$$

$$= 2A_1 x^{\gamma-1}\int_{M_1}^{M_2}\frac{y^{\alpha-\gamma-1}}{\log\dfrac{y}{x}}\,dy$$

$$< 2A_1 x^{\gamma-1}\int_{M_1}^{M_2}y^{\alpha-\gamma-1}\,dy$$

$$= 2A_1 x^{\gamma-1}\left.\frac{y^{\alpha-\gamma}}{\alpha-\gamma}\right|_{M_1}^{M_2} < \frac{2A_1 x^{\gamma-1}}{\gamma-\alpha}M_1^{\alpha-\gamma}$$

and is arbitrarily small (uniformly in M_2), provided that M_1 is sufficiently large, because $\alpha - \gamma < 0$. We may, therefore, conclude that

$$g(x) = \frac{1}{2\pi} \lim_{T \to \infty} \lim_{M \to \infty} \int_{-T}^{T} \left\{ \int_0^M \frac{f(y)}{y} \left(\frac{x}{y} \right)^{\gamma - 1 + it} dy \right\} dt.$$

The repeated integral has finite limits and a bounded, piecewise continuous integrand; therefore, one may interchange the order of integrations, obtaining

$$\int_0^M \left\{ \int_{-T}^{T} \frac{f(y)}{y} \left(\frac{x}{y} \right)^{\gamma - 1 + it} dt \right\} dy = \int_0^M \frac{f(y)}{y} \left(\frac{x}{y} \right)^{\gamma - 1} \left\{ \int_{-T}^{T} \left(\frac{x}{y} \right)^{it} dt \right\} dy.$$

The inner integral is

$$\int_{-T}^{T} e^{it \log (x/y)} \, dt = \frac{e^{it \log (x/y)}}{i \log \dfrac{x}{y}} \bigg|_{-T}^{T}$$

$$= \frac{2}{\log \dfrac{x}{y}} \frac{e^{iT \log (x/y)} - e^{-iT \log (x/y)}}{2i}$$

$$= \frac{2}{\log \dfrac{x}{y}} \sin \left(T \log \frac{x}{y} \right).$$

Hence, setting $u = T \log (x/y)$, and $Y = T \log (x/M)$, so that $\log(x/y) = u/T$, $x/y = e^{u/T}$, $y = xe^{-u/T}$, $dy = -(x/T)e^{-u/T} \, du$, one obtains

$$g(x) = \frac{1}{\pi} \lim_{T \to \infty} \lim_{Y \to -\infty} \int_Y^{\infty} \frac{f(xe^{-u/T})}{xe^{-u/T}} e^{u(\gamma - 1)/T} \frac{\sin u}{u/T} \frac{x}{T} e^{-u/T} \, du$$

$$= \frac{1}{\pi} \lim_{T \to \infty} \lim_{Y \to -\infty} \int_Y^{\infty} f(xe^{-u/T}) e^{u(\gamma - 1)/T} \frac{\sin u}{u} \, du.$$

It is now relatively easy to show that one may replace the lower limit Y by $-\infty$ and that the improper integral obtained converges, that is, that

$$\lim_{Y \to -\infty} \lim_{Z \to \infty} \int_Y^{Z} f(xe^{-u/T}) e^{u(\gamma - 1)/T} \frac{\sin u}{u} \, du$$

exists for every T. Indeed, if $u \to \infty$,

$$xe^{-u/T} \to 0, \; |f(xe^{-u/T})| \le A_2 (xe^{-u/T})^{\beta - 1},$$

so that

$$\left| f(xe^{-u/T})e^{u(\gamma-1)/T}\frac{\sin u}{u} \right| \le A_2 x^{\beta-1}u^{-1}e^{-(\beta-\gamma)u/T}.$$

and the integral converges for $Z \to \infty$ because $\beta - \gamma > 0$; similarly, for $u \to -\infty$, $xe^{-u/T} \to \infty$,

$$|f(xe^{-u/T})| \le A_1(xe^{-u/T})^{\alpha-1}, \left| f(xe^{-u/T})e^{u(\gamma-1)/T}\frac{\sin u}{u} \right| \le A_1 x^{\alpha-1}u^{-1}e^{u(\gamma-\alpha)/T}$$

and the integral converges for $Y \to -\infty$, because $\gamma - \alpha > 0$. Having obtained

$$g(x) = \frac{1}{\pi} \lim_{T\to\infty} \int_{-\infty}^{\infty} f(xe^{-u/T})e^{u(\gamma-1)/T}\frac{\sin u}{u}\,du,$$

it is easy to finish the proof heuristically, in case $f(t)$ is continuous at $t = x$. Indeed, if we take $\lim_{T\to\infty}$ under the integral sign,

$$g(x) = \frac{1}{\pi} \int_{-\infty}^{\infty} f(x)\frac{\sin u}{u}\,du = f(x) \cdot \frac{1}{\pi} \int_{-\infty}^{\infty} \frac{\sin u}{u}\,du = f(x),$$

on account of Section 7. In what follows, the justification of this procedure will be sketched for the general case when $f(x + 0)$ and $f(x - 0)$ are not necessarily equal.

By Section 7,

$$\tfrac{1}{2} = \frac{1}{\pi} \int_0^{\infty} \frac{\sin y}{y}\,dy,$$

so that

$$\tfrac{1}{2}f(x + 0) = \frac{1}{\pi} \int_0^{\infty} f(x + 0)\frac{\sin y}{y}\,dy \quad \text{and}$$

$$\tfrac{1}{2}f(x - 0) = \frac{1}{\pi} \int_0^{\infty} f(x - 0)\frac{\sin y}{y}\,dy.$$

Also,

$$\int_{-\infty}^{\infty} f(xe^{-u/T})e^{u(\gamma-1)/T}\frac{\sin u}{u}\,du = \int_{-\infty}^{0} + \int_{0}^{\infty};$$

changing in the first integral u into $-u$, this becomes

$$\int_\infty^0 f(xe^{u/T})e^{-u(\gamma-1)/T}\frac{\sin u}{u}\,d(-u) = \int_0^\infty f(xe^{u/T})e^{-u(\gamma-1)/T}\frac{\sin u}{u}\,du,$$

so that

$$g(x) = \frac{1}{\pi}\lim_{T\to\infty}\int_0^\infty [f(xe^{u/T})e^{-u(\gamma-1)/T} + f(xe^{-u/T})e^{u(\gamma-1)/T}]\frac{\sin u}{u}\,du.$$

Subtracting from $g(x)$ the sum $\frac{1}{2}\{f(x+0)+f(x-0)\}$ expressed by integrals, we obtain

$$g(x) - \tfrac{1}{2}\{f(x+0)+f(x-0)\}$$

$$= \frac{1}{\pi}\lim_{T\to\infty}\Big\{ \int_0^\infty [f(xe^{u/T})e^{-u(\gamma-1)/T} - f(x+0)]\frac{\sin u}{u}\,du$$

$$+ \int_0^\infty [f(xe^{-u/T})e^{u(\gamma-1)/T} - f(x-0)]\frac{\sin u}{u}\,du.$$

We shall see that each of these two integrals approaches zero as $T \to \infty$, and this will finish the proof that $g(x) = \frac{1}{2}\{f(x+0)+f(x-0)\}$. It is, of course, sufficient to consider only one of the integrals, say, the first. Setting $u/T = v$, it reads

$$\int_0^\infty h(x,v)\sin Tv\ dv\quad\text{with}\quad h(x,v) = \frac{f(xe^v)e^{-v(\gamma-1)} - f(x+0)}{v}.$$

The result now follows from the Riemann-Lebesgue theorem, by observing that

$$h(x,v) \sim -\frac{f(x+0)}{v}\qquad\text{for } v\to\infty$$

and (by l'Hospital's rule)

$$\lim_{v\to0} h(x,v) = xf'(x+0) - (\gamma-1)f(x+0)$$

exists and is bounded, because $f(x)$ is piecewise continuous.

   This finishes the proof of

Mellin's Theorem.   *If $f(x)$ satisfies the stated growth conditions and is piecewise continuous, then $F(s) = \int_0^\infty f(x)x^{-s}\,dx$ is an analytic function of s, provided $\alpha < \sigma < \beta$; and, conversely, if $\alpha < \gamma < \beta$, then*

$$\lim_{T\to\infty}\frac{1}{2\pi i}\int_{\gamma-iT}^{\gamma+iT} F(s)x^{s-1}\,ds = \tfrac{1}{2}\{f(x+0)+f(x-0)\}.$$

BIBLIOGRAPHY

1. L. V. Ahlfors, *Complex Analysis*. New York: McGraw-Hill Book Co., Inc., 1953.
2. T. M. Apostol, *Mathematical Analysis*. Reading, Mass.: Addison-Wesley Publishing Co., Inc., 1957.
3. E. C. Titchmarsh, *The Theory of Functions*, 2nd edition. Oxford: The Clarendon Press, 1939.
4. E. C. Titchmarsh, *Theory of Fourier Integrals*, 2nd edition. Oxford: The Clarendon Press, 1962.

Selected Topics from Algebra

1. GROUPS AND SUBGROUPS

(a)   Let **G** be a set of elements (numbers, for instance), closed under a binary operation denoted by $\circ$; this means that to each ordered couple of elements of **G** is assigned some element of **G**, often called their product, in symbols: $\alpha, \beta \in \mathbf{G} \Rightarrow \alpha \circ \beta = \gamma \in \mathbf{G}$. The ordinary addition is such a binary operation on the set **Z**; to 3, 4 $\in$ **Z** corresponds $3 \circ 4 = 7 \in$ **Z**, if $\circ$ is interpreted as the ordinary addition symbol $+$. **G** is said to be a *group*, provided that

(i)   the operation is *associative* (that is, $\alpha \circ (\beta \circ \gamma) = (\alpha \circ \beta) \circ \gamma$ for all $\alpha, \beta, \gamma \in \mathbf{G}$);

(ii)   there exists a *neutral element* ε, also called *identity*, with the property that $\alpha \in \mathbf{G} \Rightarrow \alpha \circ \varepsilon = \varepsilon \circ \alpha = \alpha$; and finally,

(iii)   each element $\alpha \in \mathbf{G}$ has an *inverse*, that is, $\alpha \in \mathbf{G} \Rightarrow \exists \, \alpha' \in \mathbf{G} \ni \alpha \circ \alpha' = \alpha' \circ \alpha = \varepsilon$.

It may be shown that it actually is sufficient to assume somewhat less (for instance, only the existence of, say, a left identity and a left inverse) and one may then prove that all required properties hold. If $\alpha, \beta \in \mathbf{G} \Rightarrow \alpha \circ \beta = \beta \circ \alpha$, then the group is called *abelian*, or *commutative*.

If the number of distinct elements of **G** is finite, one speaks of a *finite* group and the number of elements is called the *order* of the group; otherwise the group is said to be infinite. When no confusion can arise, the symbol $\circ$ is suppressed and one writes simply $\alpha\beta$ rather than $\alpha \circ \beta$. In abelian groups the operation is often denoted by $+$ and the identity by 0. One may observe the following:

(i)   The composition of an element with itself is usually written as a power: $\alpha\alpha\alpha = \alpha^3$ (or, in abelian groups written additively, as a multiple, $\alpha + \alpha + \alpha = 3\alpha$);

(ii) for $n \in \mathbf{Z}$, $\varepsilon^n = \varepsilon$;

(iii) the inverse α' of α is usually denoted by α^{-1}, so that $\alpha\alpha^{-1} = \alpha^{-1}\alpha = \varepsilon$ (in additively written groups, $\alpha' = -\alpha$ so that $\alpha - \alpha = 0$);

(iv) the inverse of a product is the product of the inverses in reversed order, that is, $(\alpha\beta)^{-1} = \beta^{-1}\alpha^{-1}$ (*Proof.* $\alpha\beta(\beta^{-1}\alpha^{-1}) = \alpha(\beta\beta^{-1})\alpha^{-1} = \alpha\varepsilon\alpha^{-1} = \alpha\alpha^{-1} = \varepsilon$, where we used successively the associativity, the definition of an inverse, the definition of the identity and again the definition of the inverse; by the definition of the inverse it now follows that $\beta^{-1}\alpha^{-1} = (\alpha\beta)^{-1}$);

(v)   the equations $\alpha\xi = \beta$ and $\eta\alpha = \beta$ have unique solutions in $\mathbf{G}$ (*Proof.* $\xi = \alpha^{-1}\beta, \eta = \beta\alpha^{-1}$ will do, belong to $\mathbf{G}$ and are unique, as follows, e.g. for the first by left multiplication with α^{-1});

(vi) the cancellation law holds: $\alpha\beta = \gamma\beta \Rightarrow \alpha = \gamma$ (proof by right multiplication with β^{-1});

(vii) the identity and the inverse are unique (proofs follow from (v), when applied to the equations $\alpha\xi = \alpha$ and $\alpha\xi = \varepsilon$, respectively).

(b)   A nonempty subset $\mathbf{G}_1$ of $\mathbf{G}$, which is itself a group under the group operation of $\mathbf{G}$ is called a subgroup of $\mathbf{G}$.

EXAMPLE

$\alpha \in \mathbf{G} \Rightarrow \mathbf{G}_1 = \{\alpha^n \mid n \in \mathbf{Z}\}$ is a subgroup, if one interprets (as will be done consistently) $\alpha^0 = \varepsilon$. If a group consists of the powers of a single element (like $\mathbf{G}_1$ above), it is called *cyclic*. Cyclic groups (finite or not) are abelian (*Proof.* $\alpha^n \cdot \alpha^m = \alpha^{n+m} = \alpha^{m+n} = \alpha^m \cdot \alpha^n$). The subgroups of a cyclic group are cyclic (*Proof.* Let $\mathbf{G}_1 \subset \mathbf{G} = \{\alpha^n \mid n \in \mathbf{Z}\}$; $\mathbf{G}_1$ group $\Rightarrow \alpha^0 = \varepsilon \in \mathbf{G}_1$ and let m be the smallest positive integer so that $\alpha^m \in \mathbf{G}_1$;

$$\beta \in \mathbf{G}_1 \Rightarrow \beta = \alpha^k = \alpha^{lm+r}(0 \leq r < m) \Rightarrow \gamma = \beta(\alpha^m)^{-l} \in \mathbf{G}_1;$$

but $\gamma = \alpha^r \in \mathbf{G}_1, 0 \leq r < m \Rightarrow r = 0$ by the definition of m, so that

$$\beta \in \mathbf{G}_1 \Rightarrow \beta = (\alpha^m)^l = \alpha_1{}^l, (\alpha_1 = \alpha^m), \text{cyclic}).$$

If $\mathbf{G}$ is a finite group, $\alpha \in \mathbf{G} \Rightarrow \exists\, h \in \mathbf{Z}^+ \ni \alpha^h = \varepsilon$; the smallest such h is called the *order* of α. (*Proof*. If order of $\mathbf{G} = g$, then the set $\{\alpha^n \mid n \in \mathbf{Z}\}$ can contain at most g distinct elements; hence, $\alpha^n = \alpha^m$ or $\alpha^{n-m} = \varepsilon$ holds for some m, n with $0 \leq m < n \leq g$. The set $\{k \mid \alpha^k = \varepsilon, \ k > 0\}$ is therefore not empty and the result follows from the well ordering of the natural integers.)

If $\mathbf{G}_1 \subset \mathbf{G}$ is a subgroup of $\mathbf{G}$ and $\alpha \in \mathbf{G}$, the set $\{\alpha\gamma \mid \gamma \in \mathbf{G}_1\}$ denoted $\alpha\mathbf{G}_1$, is called a *left coset of* $\mathbf{G}_1$. Clearly, $\alpha \in \mathbf{G}_1 \Rightarrow \alpha\mathbf{G}_1 = \mathbf{G}_1$; also $\alpha, \beta \in \mathbf{G} \Rightarrow$ either $\alpha\mathbf{G}_1 = \beta\mathbf{G}_1$ or else $\alpha\mathbf{G}_1 \cap \beta\mathbf{G}_1 = \mathbf{O}$† (that is, two cosets either are identical, or else have no elements in common). Indeed, if $\alpha, \beta \in \mathbf{G}$, and $\gamma_i \in \mathbf{G}_1(i = 1, 2, \ldots)$, then $\alpha\gamma_1 = \beta\gamma_2 \Rightarrow \alpha = \beta\gamma_2\gamma_1^{-1} = \beta\gamma_3 \Rightarrow \alpha\gamma_4 = \beta\gamma_3\gamma_4 = \beta\gamma_5 \in \beta\mathbf{G}_1 \Rightarrow \alpha\mathbf{G}_1 \subset \beta\mathbf{G}_1$ and similarly $\beta\mathbf{G}_1 \subset \alpha\mathbf{G}_1$; these two inclusions prove the assertion $\alpha\mathbf{G}_1 = \beta\mathbf{G}_1$.

From this immediately follows

Lagrange's Theorem. *Let $\mathbf{G}$ be a finite group of order g and $\mathbf{G}_1 \subset \mathbf{G}$ be a subgroup of order g_1; then $g_1 \mid g$.*

PROOF. Each coset has exactly g_1 elements and there is no overlap of elements belonging to distinct cosets; there exist, however, only finitely many, say j distinct cosets, because $\mathbf{G}$ is finite; hence, $jg_1 = g$, $g_1 \mid g$ as claimed. The number j of distinct cosets is called *the index* of $\mathbf{G}_1$ in $\mathbf{G}$.

Corollary. *If $\mathbf{G}$ is a group of order g, then the order h of every element $\alpha \in \mathbf{G}$ divides g.*

PROOF. h is the order of the cyclic subgroup $\mathbf{G}_1 = \{\alpha^n \mid n \in \mathbf{Z}\}$.

2. RINGS, FIELDS, AND IDEALS

(a) Let $\mathbf{S}$ be a set of elements on which are defined two binary operations, say $\oplus$ and $\circ$, such that:

(i) $\mathbf{S}$ is an abelian group under $\oplus$; its identity element will be denoted by 0 (zero);

(ii) the operation $\circ$ is associative; and

(iii) the two *distributive laws*

$$(\alpha \oplus \beta) \circ \gamma = \alpha \circ \gamma \oplus \beta \circ \gamma \quad \text{and} \quad \alpha \circ (\beta \oplus \gamma) = \alpha \circ \beta \oplus \alpha \circ \gamma$$

hold. Then we say that $\mathbf{S}$ is a *ring*.

(b) If $\alpha, \beta \in \mathbf{S} \Rightarrow \alpha \circ \beta = \beta \circ \alpha$, the ring is said to be *commutative*. From the distributive law follows for all rings that $\alpha \circ 0 = \alpha \circ (\alpha - \alpha) = \alpha \circ \alpha - \alpha \circ \alpha = 0$, so that the product with zero is zero. The converse,

† $\mathbf{O}$ stands for the empty set.

however, need not be true, and we may have $\alpha \neq 0$, $\beta \neq 0$, $\alpha \circ \beta = 0$ (see the example of residue classes mod 6 in Chapter 3); then α and β are called *divisors of zero*. A commutative ring without divisors of zero is called an *integral domain*. A ring **S** may, or may not have an element ε with the property that for all $\alpha \in$ **S**, $\alpha \circ \varepsilon = \varepsilon \circ \alpha = \alpha$. If there is such an ε in **S**, ε is called a unit or an identity element, and **S** is said to be a *ring with identity* or *with unit element*. In general, even if **S** has a unit element, not every $\alpha \in$ **S** has an inverse α^{-1} such that $\alpha \circ \alpha^{-1} = \varepsilon$; those elements that have inverses are called *units* of **S**, in symbols **U** $= \{\alpha \mid \alpha \in$ **S**, $\alpha^{-1} \in$ **S**$\}$. The set consisting of zero alone, and having as operations the ordinary addition and multiplication is a ring, but a trivial one; we shall, as a rule, disregard it. If **S** is a ring, such that $0 \neq \alpha \in$ **S** and $\beta \in$ **S** $\Rightarrow \alpha \circ \xi = \beta$ and $\eta \circ \alpha = \beta$ have both solutions, then one may prove that **S** has a unit element, that it has no divisors of zero and that every non-zero element has a unique inverse; such a ring is called a *non-commutative* (or a *skew*) *field*. If **S** is also commutative, then it is called a *commutative field*, or simply a *field*. Alternatively, a field can also be defined as a set **K** with two binary operations, say $\oplus$ and $\circ$, such that **K** is an abelian group under $\oplus$, **K** $- \{0\}$ is an abelian group under $\circ$ and the distributive law $\alpha \circ (\beta \oplus \gamma) = \alpha \circ \beta \oplus \alpha \circ \gamma$ holds. In what follows we shall be concerned mainly with commutative rings and fields.

(c)　A subset $\mathfrak{a}$ of a commutative ring S is called an *ideal* if $\alpha, \beta \in \mathfrak{a}$, $\lambda \in$ **S** $\Rightarrow \alpha - \beta \in \mathfrak{a}$, $\alpha\lambda \in \mathfrak{a}$.

If **S** is not commutative, one has to make the obvious distinctions between right, left and two-sided ideals, but we shall ignore these here. **S** itself is an ideal; whenever viewed as such, we shall denote it, for uniformity, by $\mathfrak{i}$. Also the set consisting only of zero is an ideal, denoted by $\mathfrak{o}$. Unless we specifically state $\mathfrak{a} = \mathfrak{o}$, we shall tacitly assume that every ideal $\mathfrak{a} \subset$ **S** under consideration is not $\mathfrak{o}$. Clearly, for every ideal $\mathfrak{a} \subset$ **S**, $0 \in \mathfrak{a}$, because with $0 \neq a \in \mathfrak{o}$, also $0 = a - a \in \mathfrak{a}$.

If $\alpha, \beta \in$ **S** and $\alpha - \beta \in \mathfrak{a}$ we say that α and β are *congruent* to each other modulo the ideal $\mathfrak{a}$, or, in symbols, $\alpha \equiv \beta \,(\mathrm{mod}\ \mathfrak{a})$. One easily checks that this congruence is an equivalence relation; the corresponding classes of elements of **S** are called *residue classes*. If $\alpha \in \mathfrak{a}$, then $\alpha - 0 \in \mathfrak{a}$, and conversely, so that $\alpha \equiv 0 \,(\mathrm{mod}\ \mathfrak{a}) \Leftrightarrow \alpha \in \mathfrak{a}$. One may verify (we shall neither do it here, nor use the result) that these residue classes form a ring with the following property: For $\alpha, \beta \in$ **S**, and the ideal $\mathfrak{a} \subset$ **S** let $\alpha \oplus \beta = \gamma$, $\alpha \circ \beta = \delta$, and denote by **A**, **B**, **C**, **D** the residue classes mod $\mathfrak{a}$ of α, β, γ, and δ, respectively; then one can show that **C** and **D** are independent of the elements α, β to **S** and depend only on their residue classes **A** and **B**. This permits one to define operations among residue classes, by writing **A** + **B** = **C** and

$\mathbf{A} \cdot \mathbf{B} = \mathbf{D}$. This leads to a mapping $\alpha \to \mathbf{A}$ of the elements of $\mathbf{S}$ into the corresponding residue classes, with preservation of the ring operations. Such a mapping is called a *ring homomorphism*; under it the ideal $\mathfrak{a}$ is mapped into the zero element of the ring of residue classes and is called the *kernel* of the homomorphism. Also the converse is true: if a ring homomorphism $\mathbf{S}_1 \to \mathbf{S}_2$ is given, then the kernel (that is, the set of elements of $\mathbf{S}_1$ mapped into the zero of $\mathbf{S}_2$) is an ideal of $\mathbf{S}_1$.

3. POLYNOMIAL RINGS

(a) The integers $\mathbf{Z}$ form a commutative ring with unit element and without divisors of zero (that is, they form an integral domain with unity) under ordinary addition and multiplication; the rationals $\mathbf{Q}$ form a field and so do the reals $\mathbf{R}$ as well as the complex numbers $\mathbf{C}$, all under addition and multiplication.

(b) Given a ring $\mathbf{S}$, we denote by $\mathbf{S}[x]$ the set of polynomials in x (an indeterminate symbol), with coefficients in $\mathbf{S}$, that is, the set of formal "sums" $p(x) = \alpha_0 \oplus \alpha_1 x \oplus \cdots \oplus \alpha_n x^n$. No special meaning should be, attached to either the symbol x, or to the sign $\oplus$ (which, clearly, does *not* stand for addition in $\mathbf{S}$; the latter will be denoted from here on simply by $+$); both are used mainly for convenience and the "sum" could equally well be represented by a symbol like $(\alpha_0, \alpha_1, ..., \alpha_n)$.

The following rules govern the operations with polynomials:

(i)   if $m \geq n$, then

$$\alpha_0 \oplus \alpha_1 x \oplus \cdots \oplus \alpha_n x^n = \beta_0 \oplus \beta_1 x \oplus \cdots \oplus \beta_m x^m \Leftrightarrow$$

$$\alpha_0 = \beta_0, \quad \alpha_1 = \beta_1, ..., \alpha_n = \beta_n, \quad \text{and} \quad \beta_j = 0 \quad \text{for } j > n;$$

(ii) $\left(\sum_{j=0}^{n} \alpha_j x^j \right) \oplus \left(\sum_{j=0}^{n} \beta_j x^j \right) = \sum_{j=0}^{n} (\alpha_j + \beta_j) x^j$

(if the polynomials are not of the same degrees, any missing coefficients may be replaced by zero and $\alpha_j + \beta_j$ means addition in the ring $\mathbf{S}$);

(iii) $\left(\sum_{j=0}^{n} \alpha_j x^j \right) \otimes \left(\sum_{k=0}^{m} \beta_k x^k \right) = \sum_{i=0}^{m+n} \gamma_i x^i$ with $\gamma_i = \sum_{\substack{j+k=i \\ j,k \geq 0}} \alpha_j \beta_k$.

If $\alpha_n = \varepsilon$, the unity element in $\mathbf{S}$ (if such exists), the polynomial $p(x) = \sum_{j=0}^{n} \alpha_j x^j$ is said to be *monic*. If $\alpha_k = 0$ for $k > n$, $\alpha_n \neq 0$, then $p(x)$ is said to be of degree n, in symbols $\partial^0 p = n$. The polynomials form a ring under the operations $\oplus$ and $\otimes$. All verifications are trivial, except, perhaps, that the operation, $\otimes$ is associative; this proof is still easy enough to be suppressed here. Whenever possible without confusion, we shall replace from here on $\oplus$ and $\otimes$ by $+$ and $\cdot$; the reader should have no trouble in deciding from the context, whether the operations refer to $\oplus$ and $\otimes$, or to operations in the ring S.

If, in particular, S is a field K, all previous statements remain valid. In this case it becomes interesting to consider besides polynomials also rational fractions, that is, expressions of the form $p(x)/q(x)$, $p, q \in K[x]$, $q \neq 0$ with the obvious rules of operations

$$\left(\frac{p_1}{q_1} = \frac{p_2}{q_2} \Leftrightarrow p_1 q_2 = p_2 q_1, \frac{p_1}{q_1} \cdot \frac{p_2}{q_2} = \frac{p_1 p_2}{q_1 q_2}, \frac{p_1}{q_1} + \frac{p_2}{q_2} = \frac{p_1 q_2 + p_2 q_1}{q_1 q_2} \right).$$

Here and in what follows, we shall use the simpler notation p or q instead of $p(x)$, $q(x)$, whenever we are interested in the corresponding polynomials as elements of $S[x]$ (or $K[x]$), rather than in their dependence on x.

(c) If $p(x) \in S[x]$ and x is replaced by an element $\alpha \in S$, then $p(\alpha)$ itself becomes an element of S, provided that $\oplus$ and $\otimes$ are now interpreted as operations in S.

If $p = q_1 q_2$, $p, q_1, q_2 \in S[x]$, with neither q_1 nor q_2 a unit of $S[x]$ then p is said *to factor* or to *split* into q_1 and q_2 over S. If $q_1 \in K[x]$, in general $(1/q_1) \notin K[x]$; an exception occurs if and only if $q_1 \in K$. In that case $q_1 \in K[x]$, $q_1^{-1} \in K[x]$ and, consistent with previous terminology, we say that q_1 is a *unit* of $K[x]$. Consequently, the units of $K[x]$ are the elements ($\neq 0$) of K, also called *constants*.

Given $p, q \in K[x]$, one may show as in elementary algebra that $\exists\, q_1$, $r_1 \in K[x]$, $\partial^0 r_1 < \partial^0 q \ni p = q q_1 + r_1$. From this follows the existence of a Euclidean algorithm, with

$$r_{n-1}(x) = r_n(x) q_{n+1}(x) + r_{n+1}(x), \qquad 0 \leq \partial^0 r_{n+1} < \partial^0 r_n, \quad \text{or} \quad r_{n+1} = 0.$$

This breaks off after a finite number of steps because the integers $\partial^0 r_n$ are decreasing and non-negative. If $r_{m+1} = 0$, so that $r_{m-1} = r_m q_{m+1}$, then $r_m \mid r_{m-1}$; consequently, from $r_{m-2} = r_{m-1} q_m + r_m$, it follows that $r_m \mid r_{m-2}$ and, by a finite induction, $r_m \mid q$, $r_m \mid p$, so that r_m is a common divisor of p and q. Also, replacing in $r_m = r_{m-2} - r_{m-1} q_m$ the polynomial r_{m-1} by $r_{m-3} - r_{m-2} q_{m-1}$, and, in general, r_n by $r_{n-2} - r_{n-1} q_n$, one ends up with $r_m = ap + bq$, $a, b \in K[x]$. Hence, if $c(x) \in K[x]$, $c \mid p$, $c \mid q$, then $c \mid r_m$; this justifies calling r_m a greatest common divisor of p and q. If $d(x)$ is another g.c.d. of p and q, then $d \mid r_m$, $r_m \mid d$; hence, $d/r_m \in K[x]$, $r_m/d \in K[x]$, so that

$d/r_m = \alpha$ is a unit of $K[x]$, that is, $\alpha \in K$, and $d(x) = \alpha r_m(x)$. Requiring $d(x)$ to be monic, it follows that any two polynomials of $K[x]$ have a unic monic greatest common divisor. From here on one may proceed as in Chapter 3, obtaining the following results: Let $K[x]$ be the ring of polynomials over the field K; if $p = q_1 q_2$, $p, q_1, q_2 \in K[x]$, $p \notin K \Rightarrow q_1 \in K$ or $q_2 \in K$ (that is, q_1 or q_2 a unit of $K[x]$) then p is said to be *irreducible* over K. The factorization in $K[x]$ into irreducible polynomials is unique, except for order and units (that is, elements of K).

4. RINGS OF POLYNOMIALS OVER Z AND Q

(a) Let $p \in Q[x]$; then the Fundamental Theorem of algebra guarantees the existence of a $\theta \in C \ni p(\theta) = 0$. One may normalize p either by requiring it to be monic, with coefficients in Q, or by multiplying it by the least common multiple of the denominators, so that $p \in Z[x]$, and in either case $p(\theta) = 0$ will still hold. Any complex number θ, that satisfies an equation $p(x) = 0$ with $p \in Q[x]$, is said to be an *algebraic number*. If $p = p_1 p_2 \cdots p_r$ with $p_j \in Q[x]$ $(1 \le j \le r)$ and with the polynomials $p_j(x)$ irreducible over Q, then for at least one j, $p_j(\theta) = 0$ (because the $p_j(\theta)$ are complex numbers and C is a field, so that C has no divisors of zero); hence, every algebraic number θ is the root of some irreducible polynomial in $Q[x]$. This irreducible polynomial which we may denote by $p(x)$ (rather than $p_j(x)$) may also be defined as the polynomial over Q of lowest degree such that $p(\theta) = 0$. Indeed, if $f \in Q[x]$, $f(\theta) = 0$, and f is of minimal degree, then $\partial^0 f \le \partial^0 p$; by Section 3, $\exists\, q, r \in Q(x)$, $\partial^0 r < \partial^0 f$ or $r = 0$, $\ni p = f \cdot q + r$. Substituting θ for x, $r(\theta) = 0$; hence, $r = 0$, because of the minimal property of f. We obtain, therefore, $p = f \cdot q$; but p, being irreducible, $q \in Q$, $\partial^0 p = \partial^0 f$, and if we normalize p and f by requiring them to be monic, $p = f$.

(b) If $p \in Z[x]$ the g.c.d. of the coefficients of p is called the *content* of p; if the content of p is one, then p is said to be *primitive*. If $f \in Q[x]$, then $f = C\tilde{f}$, where $C \in Q$, $\tilde{f}$ is primitive and, if we also require $C > 0$, then C and $\tilde{f}$ are uniquely determined by f.

PROOF. Let $m = $ l.c.m. of the denominators of the coefficients of f; then $mf = f_1 \in Z[x]$. If c is the content of f_1, then $(c, m) = 1$ and $f_1 = c\tilde{f}$, with $\tilde{f}$ primitive; hence, $f = C\tilde{f}_1$, with $C = c/m \in Q$. For the uniqueness of the decomposition observe that

$$\frac{c_1}{m_1} \tilde{f}_1 = \frac{c_2}{m_2} \tilde{f}_2, \quad \frac{c_1}{m_1} > 0, \quad \frac{c_2}{m_2} > 0,$$

$$(c_1, m_1) = (c_2, m_2) = 1 \Rightarrow m_1 = m_2,$$

because $\tilde{f}_1$ and $\tilde{f}_2$ are primitive. Then c_1 and c_2 are both the content of f_1; hence they are equal.

(c) **Gauss' Lemma.**   *The product of primitive polynomials is primitive.*

PROOF. Let

$$f(x) = \sum_{j=0}^{n} a_j x^j, \quad g(x) = \sum_{k=0}^{m} b_k x^k, \quad h(x) = f(x)g(x) = \sum_{t=0}^{m+n} c_t x^t, \quad f, g, h \in \mathbf{Z}[x].$$

If h is not primitive then there exists some rational prime $p \ni p \mid c_t (0 \le t \le m+n)$. If f and g are primitive, then $\exists j, k \ni p \nmid a_j, p \nmid b_k$ and let j_1, k_1 be the lowest subscripts for which $p \nmid a_{j_1} b_{k_1}$ holds. Then

$$c_{j_1+k_1} = (a_0 b_{j_1+k_1} + a_1 b_{j_1+k_1-1} + \cdots + a_{j_1-1} b_{k_1+1}) + a_{j_1} b_{k_1}$$

$$+ (a_{j_1+1} b_{k_1-1} + \cdots + a_{j_1+k_1} b_0).$$

By the definitions of j_1 and k_1, the two brackets are divisible by p, because in the first bracket $p \mid a_j$ and in the second $p \mid b_k$, while $p \nmid a_{j_1} b_{k_1}$; hence $p \nmid c_{j_1+k_1}$, contrary to our assumption, h is also primitive and the Lemma is proven.

Corollary.   *If $f \in \mathbf{Z}[x]$ and splits over $\mathbf{Q}$, then it already splits over $\mathbf{Z}$.*

PROOF. Assuming (as we may) that f is primitive, let $f = f_1 f_2, f_1, f_2 \in \mathbf{Q}[x]$. Then $f_1 = C_1 \tilde{f}_1, f_2 = C_2 \tilde{f}_2$ with $\tilde{f}_1, \tilde{f}_2$ primitive, $0 < C_1 \in \mathbf{Q}, 0 < C_2 \in \mathbf{Q}$, so that $f = C_1 C_2 \tilde{f}_1 \tilde{f}_2$. By Gauss' Lemma $\tilde{f}_1 \cdot \tilde{f}_2 = \tilde{f}_3$ is primitive; therefore on account of the uniqueness of the representation $f = C\tilde{f}, C_1 C_2 = 1$, $\tilde{f}_3 = f, \ f = \tilde{f}_1 \tilde{f}_2$, and $\tilde{f}_1, \tilde{f}_2$ being primitive are both in $\mathbf{Z}[x]$.

(d) **Corollary.**   (Eisenstein's criterion of irreducibility). *Let $f(x) = \sum_{j=0}^{n} a_j x^{n-j} \in \mathbf{Z}[x]$; if there exists a rational prime $p \ni p \mid a_j, 0 < j \le n$, $p \nmid a_0, p^2 \nmid a_n$, then $f(x)$ is irreducible over $\mathbf{Q}$.*

PROOF. Assume $f = f_1 \cdot f_2$ over $\mathbf{Q}$; then, by previous corollary, such a factorization exists also with $f_1, f_2 \in \mathbf{Z}[x]$, and we may assume from the start that f_1, f_2 have so been selected. If

$$f_1 = \sum_{j=0}^{h} b_j x^{h-j}, \quad f_2 = \sum_{m=0}^{k} c_m x^{k-m},$$

then

$$p \mid b_h c_k = a_n, \quad p^2 \nmid b_h c_k;$$

therefore, p divides exactly one of b_h, c_k; say, $p \mid c_k, p \nmid b_h$. From $p \nmid a_0 = b_0 c_0$ follows $p \nmid b_0, p \nmid c_0$. Hence, there exists a subscript r such that $p \mid c_m$

for $r + 1 \leq m \leq k$, $p \nmid c_r$. Consider now $a_{h+r} = b_h c_r + (b_{h-1}c_{r+1} + \cdots + b_{h+r-k}c_k)$, $h + r > 0$; the bracket is divisible by p, because there $p \mid c_m$; but $p \nmid b_h$, $p \nmid c_r \Rightarrow p \nmid b_h c_r \Rightarrow p \nmid a_{h+r}$, contrary to our assumption, and the conclusion follows.

(e) **Corollary.** *The cyclotomic polynomials*

$$f_p(x) = \frac{x^p - 1}{x - 1} = x^{p-1} + x^{p-2} + \cdots + x + 1$$

are irreducible over **Q**.

PROOF. $f_p(x)$ and $f_p(x + 1)$ are simultaneously factorable or irreducible. One has

$$f_p(x + 1) = \frac{(x + 1)^p - 1}{(x + 1) - 1} = \frac{1}{x}\left\{ x^p + \binom{p}{1}x^{p-1} + \cdots + \binom{p}{p-1}x + 1 - 1\right\}$$

$$= x^{p-1} + pxg(x) + p, \quad \text{with} \quad g(x) \in \mathbf{Z}[x] \text{ (why?)}.$$

Eisenstein's criterion is now applicable and proves that $f_p(x + 1)$ (hence, also $f_p(x)$) is irreducible over **Q**.

5. FIELDS OF ALGEBRAIC NUMBERS, RINGS OF ALGEBRAIC INTEGERS

(a) Let $p(x) = \sum_{j=0}^{n} B_j x^j \in \mathbf{Q}[x]$, $p(x)$ irreducible over **Q**, monic, $p(\theta) = 0$. From $\theta^n = -(B_0 + B_1\theta + \cdots + B_{n-1}\theta^{n-1})$ it follows that every polynomial in θ can be reduced to a polynomial of degree at most $n - 1$. The set $\{A_0 + A_1\theta + \cdots + A_{n-1}\theta^{n-1} \mid A_j \in \mathbf{Q}\}$ forms a field **K**, denoted usually by $\mathbf{Q}(\theta)$. All verifications are trivial, except the existence of an inverse. Given $\alpha = \sum_{j=0}^{n-1} A_j \theta^j = g(\theta) \in \mathbf{K}$, one has to show that $\alpha^{-1} \in \mathbf{K}$. From $\partial^0 g \leq n - 1$, $\partial^0 p = n$ and the irreducibility of p follows that g and p are coprime, $(g, p) = 1$. Hence, $\exists s, t \in \mathbf{Q}[x] \ni sp + tg = 1$; replacing here x by θ, $p(\theta) = 0$, $t(\theta)g(\theta) = 1$, or $\alpha^{-1} = (1/g(\theta)) = t(\theta) \in \mathbf{K}$, as claimed.

The representation $\alpha = g(\theta)$ is unique. Otherwise, $\alpha = g_1(\theta) = g_2(\theta) \Rightarrow h(\theta) = g_1(\theta) - g_2(\theta) = 0$; but if $h(x)$ is not identically zero, then $\partial^0 h \leq n - 1$, and this leads to a contradiction because, as seen, $p(x)$ of degree n has the smallest degree among all polynomials having θ as a root.

The equation $p(x) = 0$ has n distinct roots (a polynomial with repeated roots cannot be irreducible); these may be labeled $\theta = \theta^{(1)}$, $\theta^{(2)}$, ..., $\theta^{(n)}$ and are called the *conjugates* of θ. If we replace in $\alpha = g(\theta)$, θ by any of its conjugates, we obtain the n (*field*) *conjugates* of α; these need not all be distinct, but if they are not, then they fall into k sets of m distinct ones and $km = n$.

(b)   Indeed, consider $u(x) = \prod_{i=1}^{n} (x - g(\theta^{(i)}))$. The coefficients of $u(x)$ are symmetric polynomials in the $\theta^{(i)}$; hence (see [1], pp. 78–82) in the coefficients of $p(x)$, so that they are rational numbers and $u \in \mathbf{Q}[x]$. If $h(x) \in \mathbf{Q}[x]$ vanishes for any conjugate of α, that is, for at least one value $x = g(\theta^{(i)})$, then $h(g(y))$ has a root in common with $p(y)$ so that, (see section 4(a), $p \mid h$ and $h(x)$ vanishes for all values $x = g(\theta^{(i)})$ $(i = 1, 2, ..., n)$. Now let $q(x) \in \mathbf{Q}[x]$ be the monic irreducible polynomial such that $q(x) = 0$ has α, as a root (we know that such a polynomial exists, because $u(\alpha) = 0$); then by section 4(a), $q \mid u$. Let $\partial^0 q = m$, let k be the highest power of q that divides u and set $(u/q^k) = v(x) \in \mathbf{Q}[x]$. We claim that actually $v(x) \in \mathbf{Q}$, so that $(u/q^k) = 1$, because u and q^k are both monic. Indeed, if $v(x) \notin \mathbf{Q}$, $v(x) \in \mathbf{Q}[x]$, then $v(x)$ shares a zero with $u(x)$; this is necessarily of the form $g(\theta^{(i)})$, so that, as seen, $v(x)$ vanishes for all values of $g(\theta^{(i)})$, $q \mid (u/q^k)$, contradicting the definition of k. This finishes the proof that $u(x) = q(x)^k$, so that $m \mid n$ and $mk = n$. Furthermore, if we define as *conjugates* of α the m (distinct) roots $\alpha = \alpha^{(1)}, \alpha^{(2)}, ..., \alpha^{(m)}$ of $q(x) = 0$, then the roots of $u(x) = 0$ which are the values of $g(\theta^{(i)})$ for $i = 1, 2, ..., n$, consist precisely of these m distinct values, each repeated k times. To distinguish between the irreducible polynomial $q(x)$ of degree m and the polynomial $u(x)$ of degree n (equal to the degree of the field), both of which vanish precisely for

$$x = \alpha^{(1)}, \alpha^{(2)}, ..., \alpha^{(m)},$$

we shall call $q(x)$ the *minimal* polynomial of α and $u(x)$ the *field* polynomial of α.

(c)   Elements $\phi_1, \phi_2, ..., \phi_r$ of $\mathbf{K}$, with the property that $A_1\phi_1 + \cdots + A_r\phi_r = 0$, $A_j \in \mathbf{Q}(1 \leq j \leq r)$ cannot hold, unless $A_1 = A_2 = \cdots = A_r = 0$, are said to be *linearly independent over* $\mathbf{Q}$. Such are, for instance, the distinct powers of θ with exponents less than n. If $\phi_1, \phi_2, ..., \phi_r$ are linearly independent over $\mathbf{Q}$ and have the property that $\alpha \in \mathbf{K} \Rightarrow \alpha = A_1\phi_1 + \cdots + A_r\phi_r$, $A_j \in \mathbf{Q}(1 \leq j \leq r)$, then the set $\{\phi_j, j = 1, 2, ..., r\}$ is said to form a *basis* for $\mathbf{K}$ over $\mathbf{Q}$. If such a representation exists, it is clearly unique; indeed,

$$A_1\phi_1 + \cdots + A_r\phi_r = B_1\phi_1 + \cdots + B_r\phi_r$$

$$\Rightarrow \sum_{j=1}^{r} (A_j - B_j)\phi_j = 0, \quad A_j - B_j = 0, \quad \text{or} \quad A_j = B_j(1 \leq j \leq r),$$

because the ϕ_j's are independent. We already saw that $\{1, \theta, ..., \theta^{n-1}\}$ form a basis.

(d) Let $\{\phi_1, ..., \phi_r\}$ be any basis; then

$$\theta^i = \sum_{j=1}^{r} D_{ij}\phi_j \quad (D_{ij} \in \mathbf{Q}; 0 \le i \le n - 1).$$

Also $\{1, \theta, ..., \theta^{n-1}\}$ form a basis; hence,

$$\phi_j = \sum_{i=0}^{n-1} C_{ji}\theta^i \quad (C_{ji} \in \mathbf{Q}, 1 \le j \le r).$$

Clearly, $r \ge n$; otherwise, eliminating the ϕ_j's, one obtains a nontrivial, linear relation among the $\theta^i(0 \le i \le n - 1)$, contrary to their independence. Similarly, $n \ge r$ so that the number of elements in *any* basis is n. If we define for any n algebraic numbers $\psi_1, ..., \psi_n \in \mathbf{K}$, their *discriminant* $\Delta(\psi_1, \psi_2, ..., \psi_n)$ by

$$\begin{vmatrix} \psi_1 & \psi_2 & \cdots & \psi_n \\ \psi_1^{(2)} & \psi_2^{(2)} & \cdots & \psi_n^{(2)} \\ \cdots\cdots\cdots\cdots\cdots\cdots \\ \psi_1^{(n)} & \psi_2^{(n)} & \cdots & \psi_n^{(n)} \end{vmatrix}^2 ,$$

then

$$\Delta(1, \theta, ..., \theta^{n-1}) = \begin{vmatrix} 1 & \theta & \cdots & \theta^{n-1} \\ 1 & \theta^{(2)} & \cdots & (\theta^{(2)})^{n-1} \\ \cdots\cdots\cdots\cdots\cdots\cdots \\ 1 & \theta^{(n)} & \cdots & (\theta^{(n)})^{n-1} \end{vmatrix}^2 = \prod_{1 \le i < j \le n} (\theta^{(i)} - \theta^{(j)})^2 \ne 0,$$

the determinant being of the well-known Vandermond type. Also, by the rules for the multiplication of determinants,

$$\phi_j = \sum_{i=0}^{n-1} C_{ji}\theta^i (1 \le j \le n) \Rightarrow \Delta(\phi_1, \phi_2, ..., \phi_n) = \|C_{ji}\|^2 \Delta(1, \theta, ..., \theta^{n-1}),$$

where $\| C_{ji} \|$ stands for the $n \times n$ determinant formed with the C_{ji}'s. Also, for arbitrary $\psi_1, ..., \psi_n \in \mathbf{K}$, $\Delta(\psi_1, ..., \psi_n)$ is rational, being symmetric in all conjugates.

(e) If $p \in \mathbf{Z}[x]$ and is monic, then the roots $\theta = \theta^{(1)}, \theta^{(2)}, ..., \theta^{(n)}$ of $p(x) = 0$ are called *algebraic integers*. It is sufficient to restrict our attention to irreducible $p(x)$. Indeed if $p = p_1 p_2$, $p_1, p_2 \in \mathbf{Q}[x]$, we already know from Section 4(c), that p_1, p_2 may be selected in $\mathbf{Z}[x]$; in that case p_1, p_2 have to be monic, because their product is monic. In a finite number of steps, $p = p_1 \cdots p_r$, with each $p_j(1 \le j \le r)$ a monic irreducible polynomial in $\mathbf{Z}[x]$, and if $p(\theta) = 0$, then also $p_j(\theta) = 0$ for some $j(1 \le j \le r)$ with monic, irreducible $p_j \in \mathbf{Z}[x]$. There is no loss of generality in assuming that θ, *the generator* of the field $\mathbf{K} = \mathbf{Q}(\theta)$, is itself an algebraic integer. Indeed, in general, if α is the root of

$$f(x) = a_0 x^n + a x^{n-1} + \cdots + a_n = 0,$$

it is also the root of

$$a_0^{n-1} f(x) = (a_0 x)^n + a_1 (a_0 x)^{n-1} + \cdots + a_{n-1} a_0^{n-2}(a_0 x) + a_0^{n-1} a_n = 0$$

and $\beta = a_0 \alpha$ is the zero of the monic polynomial

$$x^n + a_1 x^{n-1} + \cdots + a_0^{n-1} a_n \in \mathbf{Z}[x];$$

hence β is an algebraic integer. In particular, if θ is the root of $p(x) = a_0 x^n + \cdots + a_n = 0$, then $\tau = a_0 \theta$ is an algebraic integer and clearly,

$$\mathbf{K} = \mathbf{Q}(\theta) = \mathbf{Q}(\tau).$$

(f) **Theorem.** *The algebraic integers of* $\mathbf{K}$ *form a ring* $\mathbf{I} = \mathbf{I}(\theta)$.

PROOF. Let α and β be algebraic integers whose (field) conjugates are $\alpha^{(1)}$, ..., $\alpha^{(n)}$ and $\beta^{(1)}$, ..., $\beta^{(n)}$, respectively, and consider the polynomials $f(x) = \prod_{j=1}^{n} (x - (\alpha^{(j)} + \beta^{(j)}))$ and $g(x) = \prod_{j=1}^{n} (x - \alpha^{(j)} \beta^{(j)})$. The coefficients of both, f and g, are symmetric polynomials with integral coefficients in the conjugates of both, α and β; hence, by the theorem on symmetric functions (see [1], pp. 78–82), in the coefficients of the field polynomials for α and β. They are, consequently, rational, and, being also integers, are rational integers, so that $f, g \in \mathbf{Z}[x]$. Also, f and g are both monic, so that $\alpha + \beta$ (and its conjugates) and $\alpha \beta$ (and its conjugates) are algebraic integers.

Recalling that the sum of the conjugates is called the *trace* $(S(\alpha) = \sum \alpha^{(j)})$ and the product of conjugates is called the *norm* $(N\alpha = \alpha^{(1)} \cdots \alpha^{(n)})$ we also obtain now the

Corollary. $S(\alpha + \beta) = S(\alpha) + S(\beta)$ *and* $N(\alpha \beta) = N(\alpha) \cdot N(\beta)$.

PROOF. Consideration of $f(x)$ in previous proof shows that $\alpha^{(j)} + \beta^{(j)}$ $(j = 1, 2, \ldots, n)$ are the (field) conjugates of $\alpha + \beta$; hence,

$$S(\alpha + \beta) = (\alpha^{(1)} + \beta^{(1)}) + (\alpha^{(2)} + \beta^{(2)}) + \cdots + (\alpha^{(n)} + \beta^{(n)})$$

$$= (\alpha^{(1)} + \cdots + \alpha^{(n)}) + (\beta^{(1)} + \cdots + \beta^{(n)}) = S(\alpha) + S(\beta).$$

Similarly, consideration of $g(x)$ shows that

$$N(\alpha \cdot \beta) = \alpha^{(1)} \beta^{(1)} \cdot \alpha^{(2)} \beta^{(2)} \cdot \ldots \cdot \alpha^{(n)} \beta^{(n)}$$

$$= \alpha^{(1)} \alpha^{(2)} \cdots \alpha^{(n)} \cdot \beta^{(1)} \beta^{(2)} \cdots \beta^{(n)}$$

$$= N(\alpha) \cdot N(\beta).$$

(g) $\alpha \in I$ is a unit if and only if $N\alpha = \pm 1$. Indeed, let $p(x) = x^m + ax^{m-1}$ $+ a_2 x^{m-2} + \cdots + a_m \in \mathbf{Z}[x]$ and suppose that α is a root of $p(x) = 0$; then α^{-1} is a root of $a_m x^m + a_{m-1} x^{m-1} + \cdots + a_1 x + 1 = 0$ and $\alpha^{-1} \in I$ if and only if this polynomial is monic, that is, if and only if $a_m = 1$. But $a_m = \pm N\alpha$; hence, $N\alpha = \pm 1$, as claimed.

If $\gamma \in I$ and $N\gamma = p$, a rational prime, then γ is a prime, or irreducible element of I. Indeed, if $\gamma = \alpha \cdot \beta$, then

$$p = N\gamma = N\alpha \cdot N\beta \Rightarrow N\alpha \,|\, p \quad \text{and} \quad N\beta \,|\, p,$$

so that either $N\alpha = \pm 1$ or $N\beta = \pm 1$ in each factorization of γ. Hence, either α or β is a unit and γ is a prime in I.

(h)   An *integral basis* of K is a set of algebraic integers $\phi_1, ..., \phi_r$, such that every algebraic integer α of I has a (unique) representation of the form $\alpha = \sum_{j=1}^{r} a_j \phi_j$, $a_j \in \mathbf{Z}$. It is clear that every integral basis is also a basis according to the earlier definition (see part (c)). Indeed, as already observed, $\alpha \in K \Rightarrow \exists\, a_0 \in \mathbf{Z} \ni a_0 \alpha = \beta \in I$. Then, if

$$\beta = a_1 \phi_1 + \cdots + a_r \phi_r, \quad \alpha = \frac{a_1}{a_0} \phi_1 + \cdots + \frac{a_r}{a_0} \phi_r, \quad \frac{a_j}{a_0} \in \mathbf{Q} (1 \le j \le r),$$

so that $\{\phi_1, ..., \phi_r\}$ is a basis. It now follows from the properties of a basis that $r = n$ and that the ϕ_j's are linearly independent over $\mathbf{Q}$. It also follows that

$$\Delta(\phi_1, ..., \phi_n) = \begin{vmatrix} \phi_1^{(1)} & \cdots & \phi_n^{(1)} \\ \vdots & & \vdots \\ \phi_1^{(n)} & \cdots & \phi_n^{(n)} \end{vmatrix}^2$$

is rational, and having as entries algebraic integers, is a rational integer. It still remains to show that an integral basis always exists. For that, let us consider the set of bases formed by integers $\{\phi_1, ..., \phi_n\}$; such always exist, because $\{1, \theta, ..., \theta^{n-1}\}$ is one and θ may be chosen to be an algebraic integer. Form the discriminant $\Delta(\phi_1, ..., \phi_n)$ and select one among the bases for which the positive integer $|\,\Delta(\phi_1, ..., \phi_n)\,|$ takes on a minimal value. We claim that $\{\phi_1, ..., \phi_n)$ is actually an integral basis. This may be seen as follows. If $\{\phi_1, ..., \phi_n\}$ is not an integral basis, then there exists $\alpha \in I \ni \alpha = \sum_{j=1}^{m} a_j \phi_j$, $a_j \in \mathbf{Q}$ and where at least one $a_j \notin \mathbf{Z}$. Writing $a_j = a + r$, $a \in \mathbf{Z}$, $0 < r < 1$, set $\phi_1' = \alpha - a\phi_1$ and consider the set $\{\phi_1', \phi_2, ..., \phi_n\}$. One easily verifies that this is again a basis formed with integers and that

$$\Delta(\phi_1', \phi_2, ..., \phi_n) = r^2 \Delta(\phi_1, ..., \phi_n),$$

so that

$$|\Delta(\phi_1', ..., \phi_n)| < |\Delta(\phi_1, ..., \phi_n)|,$$

contradicting the minimality of $|\,\Delta(\phi_1, ..., \phi_n)\,|$.

Let $\{\psi_1, ..., \psi_n\}$ be another integral basis; then

$$\phi_i = \sum_{j=1}^{n} a_{ij}\psi_j \quad (i = 1, 2, ..., n) \qquad \text{with} \quad a_{ij} \in \mathbf{Z}$$

and

$$\Delta(\phi_1, ..., \phi_n) = \|a_{ij}\|^2 \Delta(\psi_1, ..., \psi_n).$$

From

$$|\Delta(\phi_1, ..., \phi_n)| = |\Delta(\psi_1, ..., \psi_n)|$$

follows that $\|a_{ij}\|^2 = 1$ so that $\Delta(\phi_1, ..., \phi_n) = \Delta(\psi_1, ..., \psi_n)$ for every integral basis. This common value d of the discriminant of all integral bases of the field is called the *discriminant of the field* $\mathbf{K}$. It is clear from the proof that every basis of integers $\{\psi_1, ..., \psi_n\}$ such that $\Delta(\psi_1, ..., \psi_n) = d$, is an integral basis.

6. CYCLOTOMIC FIELDS

(a) If $\omega = e^{2\pi i/p}$, $\mathbf{K} = \mathbf{Q}(\omega)$ is called a cyclotomic field. As already seen, ω is the root of the irreducible equation of degree $p - 1$: $x^{p-1} + x^{p-2} + \cdots + x + 1 = 0$. Its conjugates are the other p-th roots of unity, that is, $\omega^k = e^{2\pi i k/p}$ $(k = 2, 3, ..., p - 1)$. Also, $\omega^p = 1$, $\omega^{-j} = \omega^{p-j}$, and ω^{-j} is the complex conjugate of ω^j. Consequently, in the determinant formed with the conjugates of ω, one may replace $\omega^{(k)}$ simply by the power ω^k and the corresponding Vandermond determinant is easily computed, leading to

$$\Delta(\omega, \omega^2, ..., \omega^{p-1})$$

$$= \prod_{1 \le i < j \le p-1} (\omega^i - \omega^j)^2$$

$$= \{\omega^{((p-1)(p-2)/2)+((p-2)(p-3)/2)+\cdots+2\cdot 1/2} \cdot (\omega - 1)^{(p-2)+(p-3)+\cdots+1}$$

$$\cdot (\omega + 1)^a (\omega^2 + \omega + 1)^b \cdots\}^2 = \varepsilon \lambda^{(p-1)(p-2)}$$

$$(\lambda = 1 - \omega, \varepsilon, \text{unit of } \mathbf{I}),$$

or, using $\lambda^{p-1} = \varepsilon_1 p$ (see Corollary 9.2.1), $\Delta(\omega, \omega^2, ..., \omega^{p-1}) = \eta p^{p-2}$ (η a unit; it may be shown that actually $\eta = (-1)^{(p-1)/2}$). Passing from $\Delta(\omega, ..., \omega^{p-1})$ to $\Delta(1, \omega, ..., \omega^{p-2})$ one has to factor out $\omega^{1+2+\cdots+(p-1)} = (\omega^p)^{(p-1)/2} = 1$; hence, also the discriminant $\Delta(1, \omega, ..., \omega^{p-2}) = \eta p^{p-2}$.

(b) The set $\{1, \omega, ..., \omega^{p-2}\}$ forms an integral basis for $\mathbf{Q}(\omega)$.

PROOF. From $\omega + \lambda = 1$, $\omega^k = (1 - \lambda)^k$, $\lambda^k = (1 - \omega)^k$ it is easily seen that $\Delta(1, \omega, ..., \omega^{p-2}) = \Delta(1, \lambda, ..., \lambda^{p-2})$ (the determinant of the transformation

$\{\omega^k\} \leftrightarrow \{\lambda^k\}$ is triangular, with ± 1 on the main diagonal); hence, either both sets are integral bases, or neither is. If $\{\phi_1, ..., \phi_n\}$ is some integral basis (we know that such exists), then $\lambda^k = \sum_{j=1}^{n} c_{kj}\phi_j (c_{kj} \in \mathbf{Z}, 0 \le k \le p - 2)$; consequently,

$$\eta p^{p-2} = \Delta(1, \omega, ..., \omega^{p-2}) = \Delta(1, \lambda, ..., \lambda^{p-2}) = ||c_{kj}||^2 \Delta(\phi_1, ..., \phi_n).$$

It follows that $\| c_{kj} \|^2 = p^r (0 \le r \in \mathbf{Z})$. Solving $\lambda^k = \sum_{j=1}^{n} c_{kj}\phi_j (0 \le k \le p - 2)$ for the ϕ_j's,

$$\phi_j = \frac{1}{p^r} \sum_{k=0}^{p-2} b_{jk}\lambda^k, \qquad b_{jk} \in \mathbf{Z}.$$

By assumption, $\{\phi_j\}$ form a basis; hence,

$$\alpha \in \mathbf{I} \Rightarrow \alpha = \frac{1}{p^r} \sum_{k=0}^{p-2} c_k\lambda^k,$$

where the c_k depend, of course, on α. The claim is that $p^r \mid c_k$, so that the $\{\lambda_k, 0 \le k \le p - 2\}$ form an integral basis. If we deny this, then there exists some α such that $p^r \nmid c_k$ for some $r > 0$ and $k \le p - 2$. This means that at most the $(r - 1)$-st power of p divides all c_k and that, after all reductions have been made, at least a factor p is left in the denominator, while at least some of the new coefficients, $c_k/p^{r-1} = c_k'$, say, is not divisible by p. Let f be the smallest subscript such that $p \nmid c_f'$. From the fact that $(1/p) \sum_{k=f}^{p-2} c_k'\lambda^k$ is an algebraic integer and $p = \varepsilon\lambda^{p-1}$, it follows that $(1/\lambda^{f+1}) \sum_{k=f}^{p-2} c_k'\lambda^k$ is an integer (because $f \le p - 2 \Rightarrow f + 1 \le p - 1$); hence, c_f'/λ is an integer. This, however, is false; otherwise, $N\lambda \mid Nc_f'$ so that (see Lemma 9.2) $p \mid (c_f')^{p-2}$ $\Leftrightarrow p \mid c_f'$, while in fact $p \nmid c_f'$. This contradiction proves that $\{1, \lambda, ..., \lambda^{p-2}\}$, hence, also $\{1, \omega, ..., \omega^{p-2}\}$, are integral bases.

7. DOMAINS OF UNIQUE FACTORIZATION

Let $\mathbf{I}$ be a domain of unique factorization, let $\alpha, \beta \in \mathbf{I}$, $(\alpha, \beta) = 1$ and assume that $\alpha \cdot \beta = \gamma^n$, $\gamma \in \mathbf{I}$; then $\alpha = \varepsilon_1\phi^n$, $\beta = \varepsilon_2\psi^n$, with $\varepsilon_1, \varepsilon_2$ units, $\phi, \psi \in \mathbf{I}$, $(\phi, \psi) = 1$.

PROOF. If $\gamma = \pi^m (m \ge 1)$, then $\alpha \cdot \beta = \pi^{mn}$; hence, $\alpha = \varepsilon_1\pi^a$, $\beta = \varepsilon_2\pi^b$, $a + b = mn$. However, $(\alpha, \beta) = 1$, so that either $a = 0$, $b = mn$ or $b = 0$, $a = mn$. In the first alternative $\alpha = \varepsilon_1$, $\beta = \varepsilon_2\pi^{mn} = \varepsilon_2(\pi^m)^n$ and the statement is proven with $\phi = 1$, $\psi = \pi^m$; similarly, the second alternative leads to $\phi = \pi^m$, $\psi = 1$. Let us assume that the statement has already been proven for γ containing $k - 1$ distinct primes $\pi_j(1 \leq j \leq k - 1)$; then we shall see that it holds also for γ containing k distinct primes and the proof by induction will be complete. If

$$\gamma = \pi_1^{m_1} \cdots \pi_{k-1}^{m_{k-1}} \pi_k^{m_k} = \gamma_1 \pi_k^{m_k},$$

then

$$\alpha \cdot \beta = \gamma^n \Leftrightarrow \alpha \cdot \beta = \gamma_1^n \pi_k^{nm_k} ;$$

hence, $\pi_k^{nm_k} \mid \alpha \cdot \beta$. But $(\alpha, \beta) = 1$, so that π_k may divide only one of α and β. Let, for instance $\pi_k \nmid \beta$; then $\alpha = \alpha_1 \pi_k^{nm_k}$, $\alpha_1 \cdot \beta = \gamma_1^n$ and, by the induction hypothesis, $\alpha_1 = \varepsilon_1 \phi_1^n$, $\beta = \varepsilon_2 \psi^n$, $(\phi_1, \psi) = 1$. Consequently, $\alpha = \alpha_1 \pi_k^{nm_k} = \varepsilon_1(\phi_1 \pi_k^{m_k})^n = \pi_1 \phi^n$, with $\phi = \phi_1 \pi_k^{m_k}$ and $\beta = \varepsilon_2 \psi^n$. Also, $\pi_k \nmid \beta$, and $(\phi_1, \psi) = 1 \Rightarrow (\phi, \psi) = 1$ and the proof is complete.

BIBLIOGRAPHY

1. B. L. Van der Waerden, *Modern Algebra*, Vol. 1. New York: F. Ungar Publishing Co., 1953.

INDEX

Index

Abelian group, *see* Group, abelian
Addition of residue classes, *see* Residue classes, addition of
Ahlfors, ix, 274
Ahmes papyrus, 3, 13
Algebra, fundamental theorem of, 281
Algorithm, Euclidean, 33, 48, 65, 172, 182
Alter, x
Amitsur, 157
Analytic continuation, 118, 119, 126, 132, 263
Apostol, 139, 274
Archimedes, 71
Archimedes', axiom of, 26, 27
Argument of a complex number, 98, 251
Argument of a Ramanujan sum, 98
Arithmetic, fundamental theorem of, 21-27
Artin, 215
Associates, 169, 173, 178, 179, 187, 205
Associativity, 187, 275
Asymptotic equality, 100, 236
Asymptotic formula, 236

Bachet, 159
Bachmann, 71
Backlund, 138, 139
Baker, 13
Barban, 139
Basis, 168, 188
  integral, 169, 196, 287, 288, 289
Bateman, ix, x, 247
Bernoulli numbers, 161, 212
Binary relation, *see* Relation, binary
Bohr, 10
Borel, 10
Brahmegupta, 50, 51
Branch (of a function), 119, 123, 150
  principal, 132
  single valued, 119, 123, 131, 142
Brun, 32, 34, 114, 139

Cancellation law (or rule), 40, 190, 276
Cauchy, 117, 119, 161, 180, 183, 237, 258
  theorem of, 118, 145, 151, 152, 254
Chinese remainder theorem, 49-51
Chowla, 159
Class number, 193, 197, 213, 244

293

Arithmetical Functions